The LIFE AND WORKS *of*

THE HONOURABLE ROBERT BOYLE

ON THE HISTORY AND PHILOSOPHY OF SCIENCE

Limitations of Science

Dogma of Evolution

Isaac Newton: a Biography

Life and Works of Robert Boyle

THE
Life and Works of The Honourable
ROBERT BOYLE

LOUIS TRENCHARD MORE
FELLOW OF THE GRADUATE SCHOOL
UNIVERSITY OF CINCINNATI

OXFORD UNIVERSITY PRESS
LONDON   NEW YORK   TORONTO
1944

PRINTED IN THE UNITED STATES OF AMERICA

To Dr. Frank D. Conroy

My dear Dr. Conroy:

When I entertained the idea of writing a life of Robert Boyle some seven years ago, it seemed to be a rather presumptuous resolve for a man of my age. Now the task is finished; and I like to recall that you advised me to ignore my years. It is even pleasanter to remember the skill and devotion you lavished on me during a time of serious illness when they were sorely needed.

I can think of no place more appropriate than this for such an acknowledgement. Boyle tells us that, from his own hard experience, he had learned to 'apprehend more from the physician than the disease,' and that it was this fear which interested him first in medicine. It would be difficult to exaggerate his influence on the great advance in the art since then —an advance which has given to you the knowledge and ability to allay that dismal dread. I remain

Cordially and gratefully yours,

LOUIS TRENCHARD MORE

Contents

Preface

I HAVE OFTEN directed attention to the unfortunate practice of discussing the history and philosophy of science as if it could be isolated from all other activities. There may be scientists so restricted in interests and so independent in ideas that a mere chronicle of their achievements is useful. Robert Boyle was certainly not such a man: his biographer, to do him justice, must have a broad knowledge of the mediæval and modern sciences, and be conversant with the general history of the seventeenth century. Whatever the cause, the fact remains that there is no satisfactory account of Boyle's life, and no comprehensive criticism of his work, although he was one of the really great pioneers of science.

Mr. Basil Willey, in his *Seventeenth Century Background,* likened that great creative period to a two-faced Janus—looking back with sympathy to the credulous spirit of the Middle Ages, and forward confidently to a new world dominated by rational knowledge. He selected Sir Thomas Browne to illustrate how a passion for observation and reason could live harmoniously with a 'marvelling temper.' But Boyle might serve even better as an example of that 'amphibious age'; his ideas were creative as well as reflective.

Not only in his ideas, but also in his diction, Boyle provides a conspicuous link in the rapid transition from the involved style and exuberant fancy of the Elizabethan writers to the terse expression and prosaic attitude of the Augustan Age. By birth, he was a Cavalier; but by temperament, he was sympathetic with the new aspirations of the Commonalty. In religion, he was a leader of the Anglican Church, which opened a *via media* between Romanism and Protestantism. Most strikingly of all, he was a professed alchemist and at the same time was devoted to the new experimental science; nor could he see any essential conflict between the tenets of the Christian religion and the mechanistic philosophy which he instituted.

ix

We have abundant material from which to form a just estimate
of Boyle's character and work. For this, we have his prolific 'tracts,'
his autobiographic sketch, his incomplete correspondence, and
Thomas Birch's biography. From contemporary sources, there are
accessible his father's *Diary* and reminiscences, and many references
in diaries and in collections of anecdotes about distinguished men.
In spite of this seeming wealth, there is a serious lack of data on
the facts and incidents of his daily life.

Shortly before his death, Boyle appointed his friend, Evelyn, as
one of his literary trustees, and gave to Bishop Burnet material for
his biography. We know that Evelyn advised the other trustees,
Bishop Burnet and the Archbishop of Canterbury, to choose William Wotton, F.R.S., as their authorized biographer. Apparently,
Wotton received such encouragement that he accepted the offer,
and promised to use speed. But, vexatious delays occurred, and he
wrote a year later that Lord Burlington, Boyle's oldest brother, in-
sisted on a personal bond, although the trustees had promised him
free use of all the documents, and he had executed a note pledging
their return. He refused to satisfy this new demand, and left town.
Then Burlington relented and also returned the pledge note. However, the biography was not written, and his material was dispersed.

Boyle's works, written hastily and carelessly published, had suffered from pirated editions issued during his life, and they were, at
his death, in great confusion. After Wotton's failure, nothing further was done until Thomas Birch published in 1744 *The Works
of the Honourable Robert Boyle* in five volumes, folio. This edition
of his 'tracts' was fairly complete, and titles of most of the omitted
works were listed.

As a preface, Birch wrote a life of Boyle in which were included
the autobiographic sketch, some correspondence, and the Earl of
Cork's *True Remembrances;* but, the biography is a dull thing. We
have no other account of his life, except one by Miss Masson, which
does not pretend to be more than a pleasing narrative. Birch was an
industrious and plodding writer, from whom we have also a *History
of the Royal Society.* No other opinion of his qualifications as a
biographer need be given than Dr. Johnson's half-humorous comment: 'Tom is a lively rogue; he remembers a great deal, and can
tell many pleasant stories: but a pen is to Tom a torpedo [electric
fish], the touch of it numbs his hand and his brain. Tom can talk,
but cannot write.'

The reputation of Boyle was then so high that a second edition of the *Works* was published by Birch in 1772 in six volumes, quarto. Of new material, the most important was: 'A large collection of letters of Mr. Boyle and his friends upon various subjects, selected from about fifteen hundred written by most of the great men of the last age both at home and abroad, with whom he corresponded. These additions the public owes to the reverend and learned Mr. Henry Miles of Tooting in Surrey, and F.R.S.; who is possessed of those manuscripts of Mr. Boyle, which were put into his hands, with leave to make use of them for the public good, by the late worthy Mr. Thomas Smith, apothecary in the Strand, who lived seventeen years with Mr. Boyle, and was with him at his death; and which have been lately increased by a part of the original collection, that had been communicated to Dr. William Wotton, author of *The Reflections upon Ancient and Modern Learning,* and were restored by his son-in-law, the reverend Mr. William Clarke, canon residentiary of Chichester.' Unfortunately, only a very few of these letters were written by Boyle.

Although Boyle was a popular author and several editions of many of his 'tracts' had been issued, Birch states that the only complete set was then to be found in the vast library of Sir Hans Sloane. This is probably an exaggeration; the British Museum inherited that collection, and there is now no complete set in existence. Fortunately, students of Boyle have now the great help of Dr. Fulton's elaborate *Bibliography.* Besides listing his own remarkable collection of Boyliana, he has located each known copy, in all editions, with full bibliographic details, and a comment on its history and contents.

The question, however, has not been answered in regard to the whereabouts of the material available to Dr. Wotton, the letters in the possession of Mr. Smith, and a very large number of personal letters which Boyle undoubtedly wrote to his family, his friends, and to his great circle of acquaintances. In my desire to locate these missing documents, I naturally turned to Dr. Fulton; next to Mr. Geoffrey Keynes, the bibliographer of Sir Thomas Browne, but without success; finally, to Mr. Francis Thompson, Librarian to the Duke of Devonshire, whose ancestors inherited much of the Irish estates of the Boyles. At first, I was encouraged by his statement that all the letters of all the Boyles were at Chatsworth; afterwards, I received the disappointing qualification—except those of

Robert Boyle. So the matter rests at present; probably this and other lost material will unexpectedly come to light.

Only two portraits of Boyle are known: a drawing, depicting him at the age of thirty-eight, was made by Faithorne. A reproduction was used by Birch to embellish the title page of each volume of his work.

There is also a portrait of Boyle, in the later part of his life, painted by Kersseboom. The original belonged to Dr. Mead, and is now in the collection of the Royal Society. A copy, engraved by Baron, was reproduced for a frontispiece by Birch, and is again copied for this *Life of Boyle*.

Besides these portraits, a posthumous bust was made, about 1734, by the sculptor, J. M. Rysbrack, on the order of Queen Caroline, as one of a number of illustrious men, for her Grotto at Richmond. The original, apparently forgotten, was found in the greenhouses at Windsor by Dr. Fulton, and was removed to Kensington Palace. He has used it for the frontispiece to his *Bibliography*.

Quotations from Boyle's works are taken from the second edition of Birch, unless otherwise noted. In this form, they are more accessible for verification, and they agree with the originals except for an occasional misprint. Spelling and capitals have been modernized. It would have served no good purpose to retain the original form; also, Birch had previously altered them.

There remains only the pleasant acknowledgement of assistance: to Yale University Library for the loan of the rare *Lismore Papers;* to Morehouse-Gorham Co. for permission to include my brother's essay on the *Spirit of Anglicanism;* to Mr. Basil Willey, whose *Seventeenth Century Background* was a frequent source of information. My obligation to Dr. Fulton is in a class by itself. It can best be appreciated by his statement that he had the material necessary for a *Life of Boyle,* and that he desired me to write it—in his generous assistance and encouragement, he has never relaxed.

L. T. M.

Cincinnati, November 1943.

The LIFE AND WORKS *of*

THE HONOURABLE ROBERT BOYLE

I

A CAPTAIN OF INDUSTRY

THE Hon. Robert Boyle once expressed the opinion that, to understand best the character of a man, attention should be directed chiefly to his youth and to his old age; in this spirit, that others might know the springs of his life, he wrote a short autobiography with the title: *An Account of Philaretus during his Minority.** He undoubtedly adopted the pseudonym of Philaretus to signify that the love of truth was the fundamental trait of his character and the chosen ideal of his principles. In this sketch, he cited two influences which had had an enduring effect on his life and fortunes; following his example, his biographer may well introduce his life by quoting them.

The greatest disaster in its effect on his life Philaretus believed to be the death of his mother when he was four years old:

> . . . Whose death would questionless have excessively afflicted him, had but his age permitted him to know the value of his loss; for he would ever reckon it amongst the chief misfortunes of his life, that he did never know her that gave it him, her free and noble spirit (which had a handsome mansion to reside in) added to her kindness and sweet carriage to her own, making her so hugely regretted by her children, and so lamented by her husband, that not only he annually dedicated the day of her death to solemn mourning for it, but burying in her grave all thoughts of after marriage, he rejected all motions of any other match, continuing a constant widower till his death.

In this tribute Boyle idealized his mother's memory and her influence on her family. In the first place, of all her children, he was by far the best-bred in manners and principles, with the possible exception of his sister Katherine, some twelve years his elder. Nor can we attribute excessive grief to her husband for his remaining a widower; he was sixty-four years old at the time of her death,

---

* *Works*, Vol. I, pp. xii-xxvi. Derivation of Philaretus: The Greek word is used by Aristotle (*Eth. Nic.*, I, ch. viii) in the general sense of 'fond of virtue.' If Boyle deemed virtue and truth to be synonymous, as he apparently did, the translation is his and not mine.

3

and had all his life observed solemnly the anniversaries of the births
and deaths of members of his family.

We know but little of the life and character of Catherine Fenton,
Lady Boyle; at best she was a shadowy figure cast by the vivid life
of her husband. Apparently, she was a lady of some beauty and of a
gentle and amiable disposition; but she was almost illiterate, judging from a few letters, and wholly dominated by her lord and
master, whom she addressed as 'My owne good selfe.' However
much she may have loved her children, she made no objection to
their removal from her care; shortly after birth they were sent
away to be nourished by peasant foster-nurses, and then to school
and college, or abroad with tutors; as for her daughters, they were
early contracted in marriage and usually lived in the houses of their
future husbands.

If we remember that Lady Boyle was married at the age of seventeen, that she bore fifteen children in twenty-three years, and that
she died of consumption the year following the birth of her last
child, when she was only forty-four years old, we can little wonder
that she had no time or strength for self-education or for much influence over her household. Her chief occupation was to produce a
rapid succession of babies, and in this she was eminently successful;
but her influence on them was limited principally to such qualities
as they might inherit from her.

The feeling of disaster which Robert Boyle attributed to her death
was rather the result of the loneliness of his youth, passed mostly
away from home, and his inevitable isolation when he was at home,
of which a studious and serious boy in such a house of bustling
activity and worldliness must have been acutely conscious.

If his mother's early death was regarded by Boyle as his greatest
loss, so also he believed his father's influence and career to have
been his greatest asset. Of his father, Robert wrote: 'He, by God's
blessing on his prosperous industry, from very inconsiderable begin-
nings, built so plentiful and so eminent a fortune, that his prosperity has found many admirers, but few parallels.'

Of his own fortunate station in life, Boyle says:

To be such parents' son, and not their eldest, was a happiness, that our
Philaretus would mention with great expressions of gratitude; his birth
so suiting his inclinations and designs, that, had he been permitted an
election, his choice would scarce have altered God's assignment . . . But

now our Philaretus was born in a condition, that neither was high enough to prove a temptation to laziness, nor low enough to discourage him from aspiring. And certainly to a person, that affected so much an universal knowledge, and arbitrary vicissitudes of quiet and employments, it could not be unwelcome to be of a quality, that was a handsome stirrup to preferment, without an obligation to court it, and which might at once both protect his higher pretensions from the guilt of ambition, and secure his retiredness from contempt.

What most impressed Boyle about his father was the prodigious ability and industry which, 'by God's blessing,' had made him the richest man in Great Britain and the most influential man in Ireland. Robert had had many proofs that he was his father's favourite son, and the family considered the two to be closely alike in character and ability. On the surface, no two persons seemed to be more diverse in their ambitions and ways of life; yet, if we make a proper allowance for external facts and motives—the one to dominate in worldly affairs as a man of action, the other to impose a new philosophy as a scholar—they both did manifest the same traits of indomitable persistence, insatiable curiosity, broad generosity, and conspicuous piety.

Boyle was also correct in his estimate of his fortunate social position: to be rich and, at the same time, as a younger son, to be free from the responsibilities, the distractions, and the temptations inherent in the management of a great estate during a period of such social unrest permitted him to follow his chosen work without the constant worry which was the lot of most of his contemporaries. He also saw clearly that a man like himself, allied to many families of the nobility and eligible to the highest positions in church and state, could exert a unique influence in raising the dignity of scientific work by showing its value in the arts, industry, and health. If he himself thus gave such emphasis to his parentage and family background, it will be well for us to devote some attention to the life and character of his father, the Great Earl of Cork.*

* In addition to the frequent references to Richard Boyle, Earl of Cork, in the State Papers of his time, we have a great mass of his papers—documents on Irish affairs, correspondence, a diary, and a short account of his life entitled *His True Remembrances*. These original manuscripts have long been in the possession of the Dukes of Devonshire, who inherited Lismore Castle and much of the property of the Earls of Cork. Towards the close of the nineteenth century, they were entrusted to the Rev. Alexander B. Grosart to edit and publish. They were finally published as the '*Lismore Papers* of Sir Richard Boyle, First and Great Earl of Cork. Edited by the Rev. Alexander B. Grosart. Printed for Private Circulation only

The family name of the Boyles before the Conquest is said to have been Biuvile; it probably was, as there is a record of a Humphrey de Biuvile, Lord of Pixely Court, near Ledbury, Herefordshire. He is commonly assumed to be the ancestor of the family, whose authentic genealogy begins with Lodowick Boyle, a gentleman of Herefordshire, living in the thirteenth century. The family continued as prosperous county gentlemen for several generations, keeping close to Herefordshire until a Roger Boyle, being a younger son, moved to Kent. He married Joan, daughter of John Naylor, and their second son, Richard, afterwards the Great Earl of Cork, was born in Canterbury on 3 October 1566.

Since his father died when Richard Boyle was ten years old, his mother had a difficult task to maintain her family of five children; but she seems to have succeeded well, as she sent both her two older sons to Cambridge. Richard, who left a short autobiography, *His True Remembrances,* tells us that he was a scholar at Benet College, now Corpus Christi, and after leaving Cambridge he studied law in the Middle Temple; soon finding his money would not permit him to continue in the Inns of Court, he became one of the clerks of Sir Richard Manwood, Chief Baron of the Exchequer. The young man not only found this dull work, but also saw no future in it; and he was not of a nature to submit tamely to the routine of a clerk's life. His mother had died in 1586 and he was freed from any ties; so in the spirit of the Elizabethan age he 'resolved to travel into foreign Kingdoms, and to gain learning, and knowledge, and experience abroad in the world.'

The foreign country Richard Boyle chose or rather to which, as he declared, God's providence led him by hand, was Ireland; and, on Midsummer Eve, 23 June 1588, he landed in Dublin. So strongly was this fateful adventure impressed on his memory, and so complacent was he in the belief that his great fortune was the direct outcome of God's guidance, that nearly fifty years later he recorded in his *Remembrances* of having arrived with £27. 3s. in money, two pieces of jewellery, and a fair stock of clothes; and this extraordinary man actually remembered and described his fine garments piece by piece.

by the Duke of Devonshire, 1886.' My sincere thanks are due to the Yale University Library for the generous loan of these valuable books.

Mr. Grosart intended also to write a life of Lord Cork, but failed to do so. For his biography, we are mainly indebted to the excellent *Life and Letters of the Great Earl of Cork,* by Dorothea Townshend, London, 1904.

These were stirring times; all England was tense with excitement, as the dreaded Spanish Armada was sighted just at the time Boyle reached Dublin. Ireland was as foreign a country and as full of adventure as were the new lands across the ocean. Twenty-five years earlier, Shan O'Neil had made his submission at the Court of Elizabeth, and since then the country was supposed to be at peace; but it was a peace in name only, for not only the rivalry of the Fitzgerald and Butler clans kept up a perpetual guerrilla war, but vast tracts of land had been assigned for English colonization, and there was incessant fighting between the colonists and the dispossessed natives, embittered by religious intolerance. When no other cause for trouble could be found there was always the Spanish question, since Ireland was the gate through which Spain could harass the English. A young man who chose that country in which to seek his fortune need walk warily if he would escape disaster; and it is an epitome of Boyle's character that, in spite of his turbulent life and the powerful enemies he made, he could achieve an astonishingly great fortune where almost all other men failed; and he could always win friends who were so powerful and devoted to him that they circumvented the machinations of his enemies.

Ireland, when he landed in 1588, was enjoying a period of relative peace; Sir John Perrot, the reputed son of Mary Berkley and Henry VIII, had, first as Lord President of Munster and later as Lord Deputy of Ireland, relentlessly hunted down James Fitzmaurice Fitzgerald, Earl of Desmond, and had brought him to abject submission. His chief instructions had been to parcel out the 600,000 acres in Munster confiscated from the Desmonds and to assign them to English landlords at a nominal rent, if they would agree to colonize them with English farmers and labourers. To carry out this plan, vast tracts of wilderness had been given to men such as the courtier, Sir Walter Raleigh, and the poet, Spenser, who either remained absentee landlords or, if resident, were unfitted to guide or to protect their unfortunate colonists. The same sort of situation developed between the English and the Irish as between the American colonists and the Indians. Stragglers caught by the Irish were tortured and murdered, and the English retaliated by racking, hanging in chains, and executing their prisoners in Dublin Castle. Of all the Crown officers, Sir Geoffrey Fenton, Secretary of State for Ireland, alone questioned this policy; and yet his bigoted Protestantism made him long to use the rack and wheel against 'the diabolical secte of Rome'; also, his practice of keeping Elizabeth secretly informed about the character of her other officials, and his hostility to the Lord Deputy Perrot did not conduce to harmony. Although Perrot deserved well of Elizabeth, his ungovernable temper and his criticism and even abuse of his associates caused his removal from office the year Boyle arrived in Dublin. Four years later he was convicted of high treason, Fenton being one of the commissioners on impeachment; but he died in the Tower before the sentence could be carried out.

Young Richard Boyle, when he reached Dublin, was far from being an impecunious and friendless adventurer. He had a fair amount of ready money and a fashionable wardrobe to last him till he could obtain employment. Nor was he, even at the beginning, without influential friends ready to introduce him into society and to advance his interests. Although he was a younger son of a younger son, his family was long established and well known in Herefordshire; and in Dublin he also found two Kentish gentlemen who were friends of his immediate family, Sir Anthony St. Leger, a descendant of a former Lord Deputy, and Sir Edward Moore, owner of a splendid mansion, earlier the Abbey of Mellifont, in County Meath. It was Sir Edward who had advised the youth to quit law business in London and to try his fortunes in Ireland.

We may assume that Boyle immediately paid a visit to Mellifont to obtain advice and introductions,* and it is certain that he found favour at once, for the two families became intimate friends and later intermarried. But above all in determining his rapid advancement were Boyle's own attractive personality, great mental gifts, and indomitable ambition. A man of such character necessarily made many enemies; but he had the supreme gift of making friends, and, once made, they were attached to him for life. Amongst his other early friends were the poet Spenser, who married Boyle's cousin Elizabeth, and Sir Geoffrey Fenton, then Secretary for Ireland and later to be Boyle's father-in-law. However treacherous to others Fenton may have been, he never failed to promote the interests of Boyle and to guide him wisely during his many difficulties in England and in Ireland. With such friends and his own ability, Boyle's advancement was certain.

* It was even rumoured that the young man forged letters of introduction to prominent persons. *Dict. Natl. Biog.*, art. 'Cork.'

At first Boyle engaged in such legal business as he could find, but within two years he obtained the post of Deputy to the Escheator General, John Crofton. No employment could have offered greater opportunities to a young man who had a passion to develop the resources of a naturally rich but unexploited country, and who was destined to become the greatest landowner and the richest man of his day.

As Deputy Escheator, Boyle had to examine the titles to all the Irish estates which came into the possession of the Crown by confiscation, lack of heirs, or through heirs in ward. If we recall that immense estates had been confiscated from the Irish and bestowed on English favourites of the Crown; that the original titles themselves were complicated and frequently dubious; and that the transfers were often carelessly drawn, we can readily understand the difficulties and opportunities of the inexperienced Deputy. His investigations must have required frequent journeys to all parts of the country; so keen an observer inevitably became thoroughly acquainted at first hand with its resources and most advantageous tracts, and he would also learn on these surveys what Irish estates were so heavily mortgaged as to be obtainable at a ridiculously small cost.

An escheator was engaged in a dangerous business: each decision in establishing a title made an enemy of the loser, usually more bitter in feeling than the winner of the title was grateful. Apparently, no disputed title was settled without open accusations of bribery by the disappointed parties. Bribery and corruption in office were even more rampant in Ireland than in Elizabethan and Stuart England; nothing is more astonishing to our modern standards of propriety than the unblushing favouritism in appointments; and no honours or positions were conferred without at least what were euphemistically called 'presents' to influential friends. Boyle states emphatically that his hands were clean: although bitter charges were made of his corrupt practices, it is very probable that they were legally false and were often made by those whose own peculations had been discovered and noted by the inquisitive Deputy. But it is also probable that he received presents and other benefits from grateful beneficiaries—if we can judge by his own later habit of giving costly presents to Court favourites for their influence in securing him honours and positions or in circumventing his enemies; the *Lismore Diary* contains frequent references to such gifts, carefully recording the exact sums given and who received them.

Although the exact cause is in doubt, Boyle as Deputy Escheator aroused the implacable enmity of a group of high officials, chief of whom was Sir Henry Wallop, Vice-Treasurer of Ireland.* Whatever specific acts of Boyle may have aroused the fear and enmity of Wallop, it is sufficient to know the Deputy Escheator had become so dangerous that he must be driven from Ireland. He was thrown into prison on the charge of embezzling records, and while there his private papers were rummaged by a disreputable agent; when this move did not accomplish his enemies' purpose, he was released on bail and successively rearrested four or five times in order to blacken his reputation and to exhaust his patience. Finally Wallop sent charges against him to Elizabeth, accusing him of being in league with Spain, of protecting Roman Catholics, of accepting bribes, of stealing a horse, and of other malfeasance in office.

Boyle's pluck and determination were shown by his sticking uncomplainingly to his duties, and, in spite of his troubles, by his finding time, in 1595, to woo and to marry Joan Apsley. She and her sister were daughters and co-heiresses of a Mr. Apsley, a wealthy landowner of Limerick, who, being an indulgent father, permitted the marriage with a young and obscure man of no fortune. But he may have been shrewd enough to foresee the future. Boyle notes that, by the providence of God, this marriage was the beginning of his great fortune, as his wife not only brought to him, as her portion, the estate of Galbally with an income of £500 a year; but also by her social position made him a county magnate allied to the prominent families of Munster. However, his married life was brief, as his wife died within a year in child-birth, bequeathing to him all her property.

Broken by the shock of her death and discouraged by the unremitting persecutions of Wallop and his other enemies, Boyle real-

---

* Sir Henry Wallop (c. 1540-1599) of Farleigh-Wallop, Hants, was appointed Vice-Treasurer of Ireland in 1579. In 1582, he and Adam Loftus, Archbishop of Dublin, governed Ireland for two years as Lords Justices, until they were replaced by Sir John Perrot. Wallop continued as Treasurer until 1599 when he resigned, or, according to Boyle's statement, was dismissed by Elizabeth because of his unjust charges preferred against Boyle. The biographer of Newton and Robert Boyle finds an accidental connection in their lives. A descendant of Wallop, whose enmity to Boyle is recorded in the *Lismore Papers* by the Earl of Cork, married Catherine Barton, the favourite niece of Newton, and their son was created Earl of Portsmouth. Thus the *Portsmouth Collection* of Newton's papers came into the possession of that family, where it remained until the summer of 1937, when it was sold and scattered.

ised that there would be no peace or safety unless he could clear himself at headquarters. While preparing himself to go to England, his plans were knocked awry when, in October 1598, the general rebellion of Munster broke out, and, as he mournfully noted, 'all my lands were wasted as I could say I had not one penny of certain revenue left me, to the unspeakable danger and hazard of my life, yet God preserved me, as I recovered Dingle and got shipping there which transported me to Bristol.[1]

So sudden and so complete was this renewal of the old rebellions of the Desmonds that Boyle, like most of the English colonists who were able to flee, arrived in London practically penniless. In these desperate circumstances, he decided to abandon his Irish adventure and to return to his law practice; but fate intervened in the chance renewal of his friendship with Anthony Bacon, a companion of his Cambridge University days. All England was enraged by this new rebellion, and the volatile Earl of Essex had been appointed general of the army to avenge the insult. Anthony Bacon, who with his brother Francis was devotedly engaged in the service of Essex, at once realized the value of the information to be got from such a man as Boyle, and succeeded in attaching him to the service of the inexperienced general.

Wallop, who also had fled to London, was alarmed by the prospect of Boyle's return to Ireland under such powerful protection as that of Essex, and again struck at his enemy by renewing at Court his charges of malfeasance: convicted by the Court of the Star Chamber, Boyle was closely confined, by explicit order of the Queen, in the Gate-House Prison, and kept there till two months after Essex and his army had sailed on their disastrous expedition.*

By some means, Boyle finally succeeded in his plea to present his case in person to the Queen and her Privy Council. Although he appeared before the Council without documents and without influence, the evidence he presented of the unjust persecutions he had suffered was given so conclusively that Elizabeth in a hot anger gave her decision:

[1] Numbered notes will be found on pp. 299-303.

* 'Boyle was examined not on the charge of favouring Spain and Catholicism, but on the causes of his previous imprisonments and trafficking in forfeited estates. His reputation was sullied and he owed his escape to the information he gave of Wallop's peculations.' *Dict. Natl. Biog.*, art. 'Cork.' The Spanish and Catholic charge was certainly ridiculous. I can find no other record proving traffic in estates, but I am convinced from many entries in his Diary that he seized every advantage. Under the conditions of Ireland downright dishonesty was unnecessary.

By God's death, these are but inventions against this young man; and all his sufferings are for being able to do us service, and those complaints urged to forestall him therein. But we find him to be a man fit to be employed by ourselves; and we will employ him in our service; and Wallop and his adherents shall know, that it shall not be in the power of any of them to wrong him; neither shall Wallop be our Treasurer any longer.[2]

With singular restraint and almost as if such unfounded charges were to be expected, Boyle's only explanation of his successful plea was the dry comment, as if the information of a greater wrong should balance a less one, that Sir Henry Wallop was 'conscious in his own heart, that I had sundry papers and collections of Michael Kettlewell's, his late under-Treasurer, which might discover a great deal of wrong and abuse done to the Queen in his late accounts; and suspecting, if I were countenanced by the Earl of Essex, that I would bring those things to light, which might much prejudice or ruin his reputation or estate, although I vow to God, until I was provoked, I had no thought of it.'[3]

The final results of Wallop's persecution were that he himself was utterly discredited, and that Sir George Carew was appointed to the new post of Lord President of Munster and later advanced to be Lord Deputy of Ireland, while Boyle became Clerk to his Council. By Carew's appointment, Elizabeth secured the services of one of her ablest subjects and most faithful friends to repair the failure of Essex and to pacify rebellious Ireland. In his *Pacata Hibernia,* Carew gave a detailed account of his success and of the distinguished aid of his clerk; the confidence shown by such a man as Carew is the best evidence of Boyle's essential integrity of character. The two men became sworn friends. Carew took the young man with him on all his expeditions and selected him as messenger to the Court for his dispatches.

In gratitude and friendship, Carew set about to advance the interests of Boyle. As a first step, he allayed the suspicions of Cecil in regard to his young clerk, which, for some reason, still lurked at Court; he then proposed to him that Cecil should persuade Sir Walter Raleigh to sell his great Irish estate to Boyle. Raleigh had received from Elizabeth a grant of three and a half seigniories, or about 42,000 acres, on the Blackwater River in Munster, which he was to colonize and improve. But, owing to his many other activities, he had remained an absentee landlord, and had so utterly neglected this estate that it was merely a serious burden to him. As a result of Carew's suggestion, Boyle stated in *True Remembrances:* 'There was a meeting between Sir Robert Cecil, Sir Walter Raleigh, and myself; where Sir Robert Cecil mediated and concluded the purchase between us. Accordingly my assurances were perfected; and this was the third addition and rise to my estate.' *

Carew was not content merely to assure the fortune of Boyle, but just before he retired as Lord Deputy from Ireland: 'He also,' as Boyle proudly noted, 'dealt very nobly and fatherlike by me, in persuading me, it was high time for me to take a wife, in hopes of posterity to inherit my lands; advising me to make choice of Sir Geoffrey Fenton's [only] daughter.' Aided by this powerful support, Boyle married Catherine Fenton, 25 July 1603, and his hope of posterity was amply fulfilled to the number of fifteen children, twelve of whom lived to maturity. On the day of his wedding he was knighted for distinguished service by the departing Lord Deputy. From this time on, his advancement in fortune and power was the marvel of the age. In 1616, he was created Baron of Youghal, and four years later was advanced to the title of Viscount Dungarvan and Earl of Cork.

As a landowner, Boyle added to his already immense estates every parcel of land he could acquire till they reached from Youghal on St. George's Channel to Dingle on the west coast, and covered most of the southern counties. Over this miniature kingdom, he ruled as a generous and autocratic feudal lord, fighting ruthlessly all contests over his doubtful and disputed titles; after he won, he generally recompensed the disappointed claimants with more than they had asked for, but he kept the land. He built model towns, equipping them with churches and schools; and, at strategic points, he erected fifteen defensive castles, or peel towers, where he organized and drilled his retainers and colonists into an effective little army. During the course of years, forests, agriculture, mines, fisheries, linen manufactures, harbours, and shipping were so developed under his incessant supervision that, for the first and only time, England

---

* There is much confusion about the size of this estate. The *Dict. Natl. Biog.*, art. 'Cork,' states that Boyle bought 12,000 acres from Raleigh for £1000. The *Encyc. Brit.* contradicts itself. In art. 'Cork,' it agrees with the above; but in the art. 'Raleigh,' it correctly states that Raleigh's grant was 42,000 acres.

But Lord Cork explicitly states in *True Remembrances* that he bought the whole of Raleigh's estate. Townshend, *Life of Cork*, proves what can easily be verified, that the price was in three payments of £500, each, or about 9d. an acre for 42,000 acres.

marvelled at a prosperous and quiet southern Ireland. So strongly
governed was the Province of Munster that later, when Cromwell
finished his bloody Irish campaign, 'he declared that had there been
an Earl of Cork in every Irish Province, the rebellion he had just
crushed would never have broken out.'[4]

For his own use, Boyle built, and constantly enlarged and adorned,
two great mansions at Youghal and at Lismore, in addition to his
town house in Dublin, and other manor houses in Ireland and England; and in them he extended a lavish and ostentatious hospitality
to his numerous family, friends, and acquaintances. To each of his
sons he gave generous estates, and for all but one of them he obtained by purchase or influence courtesy titles of nobility, and
married them into noble families; his daughters, when they were
scarcely out of the nursery, he contracted to young noblemen and
sent to live in the houses of their future husbands; when they
married, he gave them lavish portions, and usually supported their
husbands. He may have grumbled about the extravagance and dissipation of his sons and sons-in-law; but he was secretly proud of
his ability to pay their debts, and was lenient to excesses considered
proper to young gentlemen of fashion.

Such was Lord Cork's life, led with an activity which would exhaust a half-dozen ordinary men; yet he found time to jot down a
daily record of his life so fully that it fills five large quarto volumes
of the *Lismore Papers*. From 3 January 1611/12 to 13 August 1643,
just a month before his death, he scarcely missed a day in making
at least a brief note of what happened.

There is hardly a day during the long stretch of thirty-one years
and seven months in which a money transaction is not carefully
recorded in the diary, and frequently it is the sole event of the day
deemed worthy of notice. No discrimination is shown: transactions
involving thousands of pounds and large increases to his estates;
bribes for patronage and honours; loans to and from an incredible
number of people; generous and insignificant gifts to his immediate family and a multitude of hungry relatives; and every tip of
a few shillings to servants, messengers, and beggars; all are equally
important and all are noted, because the acquisition of a landed
estate and wealth was the consuming passion of his life.

Only second to the Earl of Cork's ambition for wealth and power
was his pride in the glory of his family and its noble alliances. One
can hardly separate the two interests, for the perpetuation of the

power of his clan was hardly distinguishable in his mind from the perpetuation of his own power. He was genuinely lavish and affectionate by nature, but his judgement was so warped by self-interest that he could rarely exercise those virtues without ulterior purposes. The births, the christenings, the acquisition of property for his many children are carefully recorded; but his absorbing interest in his children was to contract them in marriage to the wealthiest and most powerful families he could find complacent to an alliance. He made exhaustive enquiries into marriage portions and rank, but few regarding character and habits. The result was that, with the exception of Lord Digby, his sons-in-law were dissolute leeches, exerting every wile to extract money from him; and his daughters-in-law, while better, were often a source of anxiety and worry. His daughters he could for the most part keep restrained; but his sons, with the exception of Robert and probably of Francis, were in their youth wild and dissolute, and not until they had been subjected to the trials of a perilous age did their better qualities show themselves. Every relative of Lord Cork came under his influence and protection, and was sooner or later aided by gifts and loans, and advanced to a position of responsibility in church or state. The only return he exacted was unswerving loyalty to him as head of the clan; he expected, and tolerated, hostility and treachery from the world at large, but the least opposition from an ungrateful relative was unpardonable.

If Lord Cork's public and administrative work in Ireland be examined, we must take serious exception to his complacent declaration that he found Munster a desert and made it a prosperous and peaceful province. The advantages which he and his contemporaries cited were limited to himself and his family, to his English colonists, and to his Protestant Irish tenants; for the welfare of the Catholic landowners and peasantry there was no regard; they had been dispossessed, overawed by force, and driven into the wilderness. Although he was constantly suspected of corrupt practices, we can assume that, hated and feared as he was by the Irish, he obtained his vast estates legally, since he cleared his titles after many contests; but Papists and the Irish received little consideration in the Dublin or English courts of law. His bigotry towards papistry and his horror of the Irish peasants, whom he and the English regarded as savages, left his whole administration a foreign and hated imposition, to be attacked and swept away whenever the power of Government relaxed. While his development of agricultural, manufacturing, and marine industry was an extraordinary accomplishment, the benefits accrued much too largely to himself; and he relentlessly exhausted the mineral resources and destroyed the forests so that, in the end, the province was probably impoverished for temporary wealth.

Cork's influence and power extended to the whole of Ireland, since he occupied a succession of high government positions. As Lord Treasurer, his genius for affairs stood him in good stead and he directed the finances of the country ably and with exceptional probity. As one of two Lords Justices, his short rule was thwarted by the jealousy existing between him and his colleague. His greatest service to the nation was his vigorous and successful resistance to the rebellions which swept over Ireland. There is no doubt that he and his sons deserved the high praise of Cromwell.

In English politics, Cork took but little part; although he was a consistent royalist, his assistance to the Stuart cause was limited to keeping the Irish rebellions in check, and to advancing great sums voluntarily by gifts and loans, or involuntarily by assessments and extortion. In his mind, the King could do no wrong and, in spite of frequently harsh and unjust treatment, there is not a single complaint or criticism of the King in all his diary, however often he might inveigh against the acts of the ministers and judges. He did nothing to oppose the scandalous venality of the time and, as a matter of course, paved the way for, and obtained, many honours of office and rank by lavish gifts of money and plate to the King and court favourites, to judges and lawyers, to secretaries and servants. And all these bribes were accepted equally as a matter of course, except one striking instance which he noted in his diary: 'August 5, 1629. His Majesty's Secretary, Sir John Cook, refused my present of gold.' We cannot know how much he spent in such ways, but we do know that in 1640 Charles I, in desperate need, begged a 'loan' of £5,000 but was grudgingly satisfied with a gift of 1,000 pieces, on Cork's plea that he had in the past enriched the Crown by more than £26,000; and we can guess, with a considerable degree of accuracy, that he expended an equal sum in the purchase of titles and offices.

Lord Cork's religion can be stated as a blind acceptance of the state rule of worship and an uncompromising hostility to Roman Catholicism and Sectarianism. He was notorious for his nepotism and for his expropriation of church property and the income of the parishes in his domains, and he exacted subservience from his parish priests. Personally, he regarded his whole life and his every act as especially directed by God's providence, and as a compact with his Overlord he chose as his life's motto, 'God's Providence is my Inheritance.' No Jewish patriarch was more certain of worldly fellowship with God, or that riches, many children, and a flourishing posterity were the surest signs of grace. Two quotations from many entries in the diary will be sufficient to show his gratitude for God's bounty. On 5 January 1631/2, on his return to Ireland after a visit of two and a quarter years in England, he records the capital sum he had paid out during that time in addition to all his unusually lavish and unrecorded current expenses; and he adds this pious comment: 'And therefore to that bountiful, and all giving good God, that hath so plentifully enabled me with an estate to make these great payments, in so short a time, let me and all mine (as we have just cause and reason) offer to his divine Majesty all possible praise and thanks from henceforth for everymore: Amen, Amen. £43,415 ster.'

And on 1 March 1636/7: 'This day I did examine and cast up that fair and large revenue wherewith my good and gracious God hath without any merit or desert of mine, so bountifully (with his all giving hand) blessed me, which I have in, and by my half year's rental book, for our Lady Day 1637, apportioned and distributed amongst those my five sons.' This distribution of a half year's rentals amounted to the respectable sum of £8,460. 16s. 11d. What must have been the man's whole income? In references to his Divine and his temporal Majesty there is but a slight difference in his language to express the difference in their rank, and in the homage due to them.

Of books, there is in Cork's diary no mention of one having been read in all his life. It is certain that he must have read during his college and Temple days, and we may assume that he read somewhat in later life. There are a few records of rare volumes given as acceptable presents to his friends, or by them to him, and mention of the loan of one of his two presentation copies of Carew's *Pacata Hibernia*—but this book was treasured by him because it contained a generous acknowledgement of his own services to the Crown. In all the dry chronicle of his life, there is but this one gleam of homely humour, and it owes its point to the ability of his son-in-law, Lord Kildare, to outwit him in a bet:

My Lord of Kildare for discovering who it was that had battered and abused my silver trencher plates, was by me promised £5, for which, when he had my promise, he said that it was himself with knocking marrow bones upon them; whereupon in discharge of my promise, I commanded my servant William Barber to fetch him £5 in gold, which his lordship without making any bones thereat accepted, and [I] presently pocketed that wrong.

One more entry in Lord Cork's diary, which was of prime importance to the history of thought, should be quoted. The entry for 25 January 1626/7, when the Great Earl of Cork was sixty years old and his wife forty-seven, runs: 'My wife, God ever be praised, was about 3 of the clock in thafternoon of this day, the sign in gemini, libra, Safely delivered of her seaventh son at Lismoor: God bless him, for his name is Robert Boyle.'[5]

II

CHILDHOOD

1627-1638

A FORTNIGHT after Robert Boyle's auspicious birth under the influence of Libra, the child was formally christened in the private chapel of Lismore Castle and named in honour of Lord Digby, his godfather and the Earl's favourite son-in-law.

The child was early removed from his mother's care and put out to nurse in a peasant's house. Boyle gave as the reason for this removal that:

> When once Philaretus was able, without danger, to support the incommodities of a remove, his father, who had a perfect aversion for their fondness, who used to breed their children so nicely and tenderly, that a hot sun, or a good shower of rain, as much endangers them, as if they were made of butter, or of sugar, sends him away from home, and commits him to the care of a country nurse, who by early inuring him, by slow degrees, to a coarse but cleanly diet, and to the usual passions of the air, gave him so vigorous a complexion, that both hardships were made easy to him by custom, and the delights of conveniences and ease were endeared to him by their rarity.[1]

This plan of his father's was continued only till it was time for his children to begin their education. It was a general custom with the Munster gentry, who often prolonged the exile of their children till their sons were so imbued with native speech and manners as to be incapable of taking their place in refined society.

During Robert's infancy the Earl was a sexagenarian, hale in health, and at the very apex of his fortunes. His ambition was pushing him to seek high public office and by so doing he made himself vulnerable to the attacks of enmity and jealousy. With the unforeseen tide of social upheaval so rapidly approaching, it was no time for so rich a man, whose phenomenal success, rightly or wrongly, had always been regarded with suspicion, to venture from the comparative security of a private life.

The year after Robert's birth Lord Cork decided to spend a season in England, with all the pomp and circumstance of a great nobleman and the richest subject of Great Britain. His affairs were prosperous; his older sons were at Oxford or with a tutor making the grand tour; his older daughters were married or contracted; and his younger children were safe at home; it was, he thought, a proper time for him to show himself at Court on the great stage of affairs. On 21 April 1628, with his wife, his two marriageable daughters, Lettice and Joan, a large retinue, and a lavish wardrobe and purse, he left Lismore and arrived in London, 15 May.

Although the journey was ostensibly to find a wife for his oldest son, Viscount Dungarvan, and husbands for his two daughters, during a year of entertaining and of being entertained by society, there were serious dangers threatening him, and much business to be done. King James had died three years earlier, and envious tongues were insinuating to the young Charles I that there was no more vulnerable man in the kingdom than the opulent Earl from whom to squeeze ill-got gains and so to fill an embarrassed treasury.

The one sure way to obtain favour with Charles was through the goodwill of the Duke of Buckingham and, on the day of his arrival in London, Lord Cork hastened to pay his respects to the all-powerful favourite. He complacently notes that he was received cordially and kept to dinner, and was then taken to the King, 'whose gracious hands I had the honour to kiss, accompanied with gracious language full of comfort.' This comfort was expensive; Cork's diary mentions many costly gifts to influential persons, and contemporary rumour tells us that a present of several thousand pounds passed to Buckingham.

It is not difficult to surmise correctly what Lord Cork sought. Lord Deputy Falkland was about to resign, and as the two men were close friends, it is probable that the Earl wished to be his successor; if so, his desire was partly accomplished, since, before leaving England, he and Adam Loftus, Lord Chancellor of Ireland, were appointed Lords Justices to rule jointly till a successor to Falkland should be chosen. Lord Cork, having secured the favour of Buckingham and Falkland, might well feel that his journey and its lavish expense were justified; and that after a decent interval he would be established as Lord Deputy, and free to carry on his ambitious plans to benefit a sorely harassed country. If such were his hopes, they were shattered by the murder of Buckingham.

In addition to these personal ambitions, Lord Cork had two law-suits on his hands which demanded his attention. The first involved his title to the Raleigh estate. A certain Blacknoll, the trusted man-ager of his ironworks in the Blackwater Valley, started the trouble by writing to the King's lawyer that the Earl's title was defective in that the original grant to Raleigh was illegal. As a result, the rumour had spread that the Great Earl of Cork would be summoned to England to be tried as a criminal: the possibility of securing prop-erty worth at least £50,000 for the Crown was too tempting a bait for the King to let slip.

There is no doubt that Blacknoll was a treacherous rogue and that he and his associates had made a compact to pay to the King £8,000 a year for the use of the woods and mines, and another £4,000 a year for a concession to make iron ordnance: 'And if the King re-covered Sir Walter Raleigh's lands from the Earl of Cork on which lay the greatest part of the Earl's iron works—they to be made tenants at a rent of £4,000 as the same they were paying the Earl of Cork.'[2]

State papers of the time have many references to this celebrated case. The Crown lawyers argued that these estates, confiscated from the Earl of Desmond for treason, had not been forfeited to the Crown, since he had never been convicted of a rebellion by a Court, and rebellion without conviction was not treason; but Cork's lawyers proved that a bill of attainder against Desmond had been passed by the Irish Parliament. How doubtful the case was can be understood from the cynical advice of Sir William St. Leger, who also owned some of the forfeited lands: '. . . Lord Cork's best chance of security would be to give the Duke of Buckingham four thousand pounds, and another thousand to the King's servant, Endymion Porter.' * The case ended in favour of Lord Cork, who received in April 1629 an entirely new grant of the estates, signed and passed under the Great Seal of England; the fact that it was passed by such a man as Lord Coventry, Lord Keeper of England, is strong evidence of the legality of the decision, whatever the influences used may have been. One cannot help suspecting bribery from the fact that in the same month the case was decided, Lord Cork agreed to loan the

* For the interesting and sinister details of this case, see Townshend, op. cit. p. 166, et seq. There is good evidence for the rumours about Lord Cork's use of presents.

King the great sum of £14,000 on very dubious security. In his diary he disclosed the cause of his anxiety: 'He wrote letters of thanks to the lord chief justice, and to the lord chief baron, for preserving his iron works to him, otherwise the lord chancellor of Ireland would have ordered for Blacknoll and Wright. God forgive the chancellor this great injustice.'[3]

The second lawsuit, for which there were neither moral nor legal grounds, was instigated by Raleigh's widow, who claimed from the original sale of the estate to Lord Cork her dower right amounting to £500. Cork had treated Raleigh generously at the time of sale, and if, as the impoverished widow of his former friend and benefactor, she had asked for assistance as a favour, he would probably, judging from his practice, have more than satisfied her need. But, as was his habit when he thought he had been unjustly accused, he wrathfully and obstinately fought the case in court after court. How it ended has been forgotten.

Late in the autumn of 1629, Lord Cork, his business affairs satisfactorily finished, his purse deeply depleted, returned to Ireland with his retinue. Lady Cork had been in delicate health and had given birth in London to her fifteenth child; after her return, her health continued to fail. Her death the following February was a crushing blow to her husband, who with all his faults was devoted to his family. Believing it 'the first turning away of Providence,' he two years later wrote *His True Remembrances* as a vindication of his character. As if he felt his own life were precarious, he closed it with these solemn words:

My dear wife, the crown of all my happiness, and the mother of all my children, Catherine Countess of Cork, was translated at Dublin from this life into a better the 16th of February 1629/30, and was the 17th privately buried in the night in the upper end of the choir of St. Patrick's Church in Dublin . . . I have purchased from the dean and chapter of St. Patrick's Church the inheritance of the upper part of the chancel, wherein the cave or cellar under ground is made, and wherein the tomb is built, to be a burying place for me and my posterity, and their children.

If Lord Cork had succeeded in his ambition to govern Ireland with the full authority of Lord Deputy, it is probable that with his known and respected executive ability and his unequalled acquaintance with the people and conditions, he would have extended the peace and prosperity of Munster far beyond its borders. But, it was impossible to carry out any such ambitious plans under the joint rule of two men so different in temperament and so jealous of each other as were he and his colleague, Adam Loftus. The four years of office were a busy and anxious period, and his duties kept him constantly at his town house in Dublin. During all those years, he was buoyed up with the hope that he would finally be appointed Lord Deputy and be able to work unfettered by opposition. He must have been both disheartened and alarmed when the news reached him in January 1632 that the obdurate Thomas Wentworth had been appointed to the coveted office. On the day of July 1633 when the new Lord Deputy arrived in Dublin, Cork with prophetic insight wrote in his diary: 'A most cursed man to all Ireland, and to me in particular.'

At first, Lord Cork disguised his chagrin and welcomed the Lord Deputy with full honours and hospitality. He still had hopes of security at least in his own Munster, for his oldest son, Lord Dungarvan, was then engaged to Elizabeth Clifford—an alliance splendid enough to satisfy even Cork's ambitious desires, since she was the granddaughter and co-heiress of the Earl of Cumberland, and her mother was a sister of Cecil, the second Earl of Salisbury, and thus a relative of Wentworth. The marriage finally took place in 1634, but only after much trouble and bickering over settlements, which, as these negotiations were conducted by Wentworth, caused the first clash between them. Two months afterwards, Dungarvan and his wife visited his father in Dublin, and the Earl resolved to celebrate Christmas with a great festival at Lismore Castle, which had been deserted for almost seven years.

Sometime during the family's stay in Dublin, the infant and motherless Robert had been taken home from his country nurse, and he was a member of this journey to Lismore. On the road, he narrowly escaped drowning; while crossing a brook swollen with immoderate rain, he was carelessly left alone with only a foot-boy in the ponderous coach. A gentleman, well-horsed and seeing his predicament, pulled him out and carried him to safety in his arms; he was no sooner out of the coach when the rapid current carried it down-stream and overturned it. Robert, as we shall learn, carefully mentioned all his early accidents, and attributed his escape from death in each case as a warning of Providence to conduct his life in a manner to be worthy of such a special dispensation.

In addition to Robert's conviction that his life had been miraculously saved several times for some high purpose, he regarded a love of truth to be his guiding principle.* This sincerity of character impressed his family, and his father recorded in his diary that Robyn, as he affectionately nicknamed him, was never known to tell a lie. His favourite sister, Katherine, was fond of telling a story to illustrate his truthfulness, which, trifling as it may have been in itself, became a family tradition; Robert thought it worth preserving in his biographic sketch:

His sister, it seems, had given strict orders that the fruit of a certain plum tree should be reserved for her sister-in-law, Lady Dungarvan, but little Robert ignored the prohibition. On discovering this, his sister accused him of having eaten a half dozen of the plums. His answer and its solemn moral are taken from Robert's account:

Nay, truly, sister, (answers he to her) I have eaten half a score. So perfect an enemy was he to a lie, that he had rather accuse himself of another fault, than to be suspected of that. This trivial anecdote I have mentioned now, not that I think, that in itself it deserves a relation, but because as the sun is seen best at his rising and his setting, so men's native dispositions are clearliest perceived, whilst they are children, and when they are dying. And certainly these little sudden accidents are the greatest discoverers of men's true humours; for whilst the inconsiderateness of the thing affords no temptation to dissemble, and the suddenness of the time allows no leisure to put disguises on, men's dispositions do appear in their true genuine shape, whereas most of those actions, that are done before others, are so much done for others; I mean most solemn actions are so personated, that we may much more probably guess from thence, what men desire to seem, than what they are.[4]

Boyle's early education was directed at home by tutors. He learned to speak French from a Frenchman, Mr. François de Cary, and all the Latin he later forgot at Eton from his father's chaplain, Mr. Wilkins. But also as a child he learned a trick which he referred to as the second great disaster of his life. By mimicking too persistently the stuttering of some of his companions, he himself acquired the habit and, although by care he reduced the affliction, he was never able to overcome it. One may wonder why this so deeply

* He, Philaretus, the lover of truth, it will be remembered, was born in Libra. If we also knew that the sun was then in Libra and near Venus, then according to Vanini: 'By the rules of astrology, he could not lie.'

affected him but, as it evidently did, it must have reacted seriously on his sensitive nature. The coarse ridicule, common to that blunter age, may have discouraged his social life and increased his tendency to loneliness and a mild melancholy; his inability, because of slowness of speech, to take part in general conversation may partly explain why he eschewed the high offices in church and state which were later offered him.

Robert as a child was gentle and amiable in character and quite studious, and these traits together with his veracity endeared him to his father, to whom he was the Benjamin of his old age. The old man was puzzled to find himself the father of one so different in temperament from the others in that great brood which followed the dissipated and extravagant habits of court society, and yet who best exemplified his own character. He exerted himself especially to provide an estate in England for his Robyn where later he would be able to live in a quieter and more intellectual atmosphere than could be found in Ireland; he also decided to educate this son in England. Robert tells the story himself:

Philaretus had now attained, and somewhat past the eighth year of his age, when his father (who supplied what he wanted in scholarship himself, by being both a passionate affector, and eminent patron of it) ambitious to improve his early studiousness, and considering, that great men's children breeding up at home tempts them to nicety, to pride, and idleness, and contributes much more to give them a good opinion of themselves, than to make them deserve it, resolves to send over Philaretus in the company of Mr. F. B. his elder brother, to be bred up at Eton College near Windsor, whose provost at that time was Sir Henry Wotton, a person, that was not only a fine gentleman himself, but very well skilled in the art of making others so, betwixt whom and the Earl of Cork an ancient friendship had been constantly cultivated by reciprocal civilities.[5]

If we compare the future manners and morals of these two brothers with those of the Earl's four older sons, it was a wise decision; as for the statement, that his father was a 'passionate affector and patron of scholarship,' there is no other evidence that he was in the least interested in either.

In those days of small sailing vessels and of piracy, to cross the Irish Channel was a matter of time and danger. The two little boys, under the direction of Badnedge, the Earl's trusted business agent, and with their own tutor and valet, a wily rascal named Cary or

Carew, were delayed for a fortnight at Youghal; then with a favourable wind, and by good luck not meeting any Turkish pirates, they reached Bristol safely, having stopped at Ilfracombe and Minehead. From there, they arrived at Eton by coach on 2 October 1635. They entered this famous school under the most favourable conditions; they could expect the personal interest of the Provost; they had a liberal allowance and the attention of their own servant as befitted the state of two young lords.

While we do not know the exact course of study and life at Eton in the seventeenth century, it is probable that such a conservative school had changed but little from the time of Elizabeth. Then the boys rose at five o'clock and had prayers read in school by an usher at six. At seven, work began under the direction of the headmaster and lasted till nine. After an hour's recess, there was chapel at ten and dinner at eleven; work again and study from noon to three o'clock. This was followed by a play-hour, known now as 'after four.' After another hour of lessons, supper came at five; preparations for the next day from six to eight, with bread and beer at seven; and all were in bed at eight.

The regular students, as boarders, lived in Long Chamber and ate in hall; but the sons of the nobility had special privileges. They were known as 'commensals,' and while they dined in hall, they sat at the second table with the chaplain, an usher, and the upper clerks who were skilled in chant; they were waited on by lower clerks and thirteen poor students, or servitors. The commensals did not live with the collegers, but rented rooms in the houses of the Provost and Fellows: these they furnished and in them they ate their meals, except dinner, and were waited on by their own personal servants.

Sir Henry Wotton had been a successful Provost for ten years, after a long career as statesman, foreign ambassador, and envoy from the Court on several secret missions. While he was a resident in Florence, the Grand Duke of Tuscany informed him of a plot to murder James VI of Scotland, and sent him with letters to warn that King of this danger and also with Italian antidotes for poison. Wotton was well received at the Scottish Court and lived there for three months incognito, as Ottavio Baldi, an Italian. When James became King of England, Wotton was knighted and appointed ambassador to Venice, where he lived for the best part of twenty years. He is said to have aroused temporarily the King's anger by the famous pun which he indiscreetly wrote in a friend's album: An ambassador is an honest person sent to lie abroad for the good of his country.

Wotton was a good scholar and a lover of fine books. He had absorbed the new culture of Italy and was in love with what he fondly called that 'delicate piece of the world'; he knew personally, and corresponded with, the best scholars of the continent, dabbled in science, wrote pleasant verse, and intended to write, but never finished, biographies of Donne and Luther and a history of England. He had been in the service of the Earl of Essex, a friend of Raleigh, and was an early disciple of the new philosophy of his cousin, Francis Bacon, to whom he supplied facts. While at Eton, he and Izaak Walton became intimate friends and spent many a day smoking and fishing while their talk wandered in the paths of philosophy; and after death separated them, these pleasant days were recorded in Walton's biography of his friend.

Now, after an eventful life, Wotton had settled down to rule Eton and to exercise a gentle and sympathetic guidance over its young scholars. He made it a practice to have small groups of the more promising lads dine with him; and one can readily believe that his courtly manners and his reminiscences of the great world, in which he had lived and taken part, fascinated them and influenced their characters as deeply as their studies did their minds. To his table came also many other guests, in particular the young poet, Milton, who just before his Italian journey rode over from near-by Horton for advice and letters of recommendation. As a remembrance when he left, he sent the Provost a copy of *Comus,* then newly published. As the Boyles were frequent guests at his table, it is quite possible that the boy met Milton, whose life was later to be so curiously associated with his family. To the Provost must largely be given the credit not only of arousing in him an ardent appetite for reading, but also of developing, by example, the exquisite manners which so invariably impressed his contemporaries.

The Provost had also been fortunate in the selection of John Harrison as headmaster; also of the learned Mr. Hales * and an excellent corps of tutors. As the boys, Francis nicknamed 'α Boyle' and Robert 'Boyle 1,' naturally entered as commensals, they were as-

---

* The ever memorable John Hales, as he was called, 'In 1619 returned to Eton and spent his time among his books and in the company of literary men, among whom he was highly reputed for his common sense, his ambition and his genial charity.' *Encyc. Brit.*

signed to live in Harrison's house and to be taught by him. Besides the strictly classical course of study then in vogue, the boys had private tutors in French, dancing, and music, for whom they paid extra fees. Some trait in Robert's character made Harrison, who was especially fond of him, try the dangerous plan of relaxing discipline and indulging him with special favours. The boy was given extra holidays in order to encourage him to play games, and he was even given toys taken from other boys for breaking rules. He was also frequently excused from class recitations and instead was taught privately and familiarly in the master's chamber.

In the *Philaretus,* Boyle paid this affectionate tribute to Harrison:

He was careful to instruct him in such an affable, kind, and gentle way, that he easily prevailed with him to consider studying, not so much as a duty of obedience to his superiors, but as the way to purchase for himself a most delightsome and invaluable good. In effect, he soon created in Philaretus, so strong a passion to acquire knowledge, that what time he could spare from a scholar's talk, which his retentive memory made him find not uneasy, he would usually employ so greedily in reading, that his master would sometimes be necessitated to force him out to play, on which, and upon study, he looked, as if their natures were inverted.

In spite of such favouritism, the boy did not become a prig. It speaks wonders for his innate manliness that he could lecture his elder brother on his careless habits without arousing resentment, and was even more popular in the school than the more normal, pleasure-loving Francis.

Apparently Boyle imbibed fine manners and courteous habits from Wotton, and developed a disciplined mind and such a passion for reading that Mr. Harrison was obliged to force him to forsake books for play. Philaretus tells us it was Quintus Curtius who first made him love 'other than pedantic books.' And this love of reading became Boyle's most notable trait; he read while walking and at inns when he travelled, and during most of his waking hours.

Nor is it surprising that a boy of Boyle's contemplative temperament, a frequent guest of the Provost, who owned a choice collection of books and prints, should have had an appetite aroused for reading. What other books he read we do not know, except he tells us that when mentally languid from a persistent attack of tertian ague, or malaria, which he contracted in London while visiting his brother, Dungarvan, he was induced to read *Amadis de Gaule* and other romantic tales.

Boyle himself attributed to this reading of 'fabulous and wandering tales' a lasting and unfortunate influence: he thought they unsettled his mind so that he scarcely ever was able to master it or to keep it from 'gadding to unseasonable and impertinent objects.' Long afterwards he found the most effectual way 'to fetter, or at least to curb the roving wildness of his wandering thoughts,' was to extract square and cube roots of large numbers, and to do those other laborious processes of algebra which closely fix the attention. It is probably true that such reading did distract a mind inordinately curious rather than inwardly meditative and logical. We should remember that his future scientific work was diffuse and touched on every conceivable topic, that he wrote *belles lettres,* and that his style was florid and romantic. Later, when he was in Ireland, his friend and physician, Dr. Petty, thought he had embarrassed his mind with too much knowledge and warned him against reading too much—a habit, he quaintly said, which 'weakens the brain, causeth defluxions, and hurts the lungs.' But Boyle persisted till, in his old age, his eyes failed.

Some of our knowledge of Boyle's school years is gleaned from his father's diary; for example, the total cost of the two sons for the three years at Eton was £914. 3s. 9d. In recording these and other items of his expenses, charities, and gifts, he shows a tinge of the complacency of the self-made man, that he could lavishly meet such demands on his purse. Other knowledge of a gossipy nature is got from the long and frequent letters to the Earl from the valet Cary, who was a wily rascal, and knew how to flatter the old gentleman. According to Cary, no such amiable and youthful prodigies had ever been at the school.

Philaretus remembered his school days affectionately. Besides a modest account of his studious achievements, he narrates briefly the events of his life at Eton and particularly the dangers he survived. We get from him a picture of a studious boy mature beyond his years, caring little for exercise or games, and yet a great favourite with his schoolmates. During the vacations, as he was too distant from Dublin to go home, he, with his brother, visited in England. Once, at least, they stayed with their oldest brother, Lord Dungarvan, in London. And one of their long vacations was spent at Lewes in Sussex with their sister Lettice. She was the problem of the family—ill-natured and peevish from poor health and a weak intellect, her disposition had not been helped by her marriage to the fascinating Lord Goring, who was always begging and borrowing money, but whom his father-in-law could not even bribe into a decent behaviour to his wife. It must have been a weird experience for the two boys, if we can judge from the account of it given to Lord Cork by that elegant epistolary genius, Cary.

There was nothing wanting to afford a good and pleasant entertainment, if my honourable Lady had not been visited with her continual guest, grief and melancholy: which is incurable while she lives among those unhappy plants [sic] which yield her nothing but vexation of mind, yea, have already sucked from her all comfort . . . My masters did comfort as much as they could, but her languishing heart could not receive much comfort, so that it made them cry often to look upon her.[6]

Philaretus was careful to note and to record his deliverances from dangerous accidents at Eton. Twice he was almost killed by horses; and once, while he and his brother were talking with some companions in their room and he was lying in bed, the whole wall of the room fell in and they were saved with difficulty by a watchful Providence, by their own efforts, and by the aid of a lusty youth who accidentally happened to be present. But his even more vivid remembrance was of dangers from drugs and physicians. Once a physician sent to him, while he was sick with an ague, a purge 'to give (as he said) the fatal blow to the disease.' The boy's gorge revolted at the drug, which was even more nauseous than he expected, and a sympathetic maidservant slyly substituted a vial of syrup of stewed prunes. Not only did Philaretus recover but 'from that hour to this, agues and he have still been perfect strangers'; so, with his tongue in his cheek, he thanked and paid the doctor, who complacently attributed the cure to his skill.

Another experience of Philaretus was more serious. Being newly recovered of a flux, his physician prescribed a refreshing drink. The apothecary, however, carelessly gave him a strong vomit intended for another patient. By good luck some of his schoolmates gave him some sweetmeats at breakfast, and his squeamish stomach rebelling made him lose his breakfast and much of the drug. In spite of that relief, the remnant 'cast him into hideous torments,' and 'after a long struggling, at last the drug wrought with such violence, that they feared that his life would be disgorged with the potion.'

Attention has been called to the profound effect, for good or evil, that the Earl of Cork's conviction of 'Divine Guidance' had on his life, persuading him that all his acts were justified. By either heredity or example, the same conviction was startlingly present in his son's mind. This catalogue of accidents gives us a clue to his character and work which cannot be neglected. With him, this guidance fortunately took a less gross form than with his father, for it fixed him in his purpose to lead a virtuous and unselfish life.

This accident made him long after apprehend more from the physicians, than the disease, and was possibly the occasion, that made him afterwards so inquisitively apply himself to the study of physic, that he might have the less need of them, that profess it. But Philaretus would not ascribe any of these rescues unto chance, but would be still industrious to perceive the hand of heaven in all these accidents; and indeed he would profess, that in the passages of his life, he had observed so gracious and so peculiar a conduct of providence, that he should be equally blind and ungrateful, should he not both discern and acknowledge it.[7]

While the years were passing quietly and pleasantly for Francis and Robert Boyle at Eton, their father was involved in his great duel for supremacy with the Lord Deputy Wentworth.*

When Wentworth arrived in Dublin as Lord Deputy, in July 1633, he and Laud were fixed in their determination to advance, by every means in their power, the prerogative of the Crown over the opposition of the Commons, and to cleanse the Church by their policy of Thorough—which in essence was to strengthen their friends and to crush their enemies. To aid in the state policy, funds to make the King independent were to be collected from Ireland;

---

* Those interested in the lives of Wentworth and Cork can find abundant material to satisfy their curiosity. The chief sources are the diary of Cork, the correspondence of both men, and the state papers of the time. It is extraordinarily difficult to judge two such dominating and wilful characters, and their biographers are prone to partisanship. Thus Dorothea Townshend in her *Life of the Earl of Cork* relies too strongly on evidence in his diary, forgetting that so obstinate and ambitious a man is quite incapable of judging the motives of an opponent dispassionately. Cork's fixed idea that he was the instrument of providential guidance would convince him that his personal advancement was also the public benefit. On the other hand, Lord Birkenhead, in a series of articles in the Sunday *Times* for 1937 on Thomas Wentworth, Earl of Strafford, sees Cork only as 'the chief offender:—the Boss, as Americans would call him, of this [Irish] rascaldom was that "great" Earl of Cork who, as Lord Justice and Lord High Treasurer, had in honeyed words welcomed the new Lord Deputy on his appointment.' He is also the unscrupulous oppressor of the Irish and robber of the Church. In fact, both of these men were so dominated by their wills to carry out their purposes that their actions should not be judged without scrupulous investigation. Their bitter quarrel in Ireland was an impersonal contest for power. The battle over, Wentworth and Laud were friendly enough with Boyle; who, humiliated though he had been, took no prominent part at Wentworth's trial.

and no Laudian reform could be successful in the Anglican Church until its degraded condition in Ireland was raised. They both saw, also, that the Lord Deputy must either crush the powerful Earl of Cork, who would be bitterly hostile to their plan of diverting Irish subsidies to English uses, or else be subservient to him as had been previous deputies. Their correspondence makes it clear that their scheme to humiliate the Earl and extract all the money from him they could did not arise from personal hatred but simply from the fact that he was the richest man and easiest target: as one artifice after another succeeded, they referred to him with a curious mixture of pity and glee.

Bishop Bramhall accompanied Wentworth as Laud's emissary, and his report on the state of the Irish Church, and of the conduct and habits of its clergy from its archbishops down to its illiterate and half-starved parish priests, scandalized his superior. It also gave to Wentworth his best opportunity for attacking the Earl of Cork.

The first attack on Cork hit his pride in the tenderest spot, where he was helpless to defend himself. He had built an ostentatious monument in black marble to his wife in St. Patrick's Cathedral and had placed it conspicuously where the high altar should be. Laud, when informed of this sacrilege, wrote scathing letters in rebuke and ordered it removed. Two years later, Wentworth replied: 'The Earl of Cork's tomb is now quite removed: how he means to dispose of it I know not, but up it is put in boxes, as if it were marchpanes and banquetting stuffs going down to the christening of my young master [Lord Dungarvan's son] in the country.' [8]

All the other contests for power hinged on finance. In 1634, Wentworth assembled a hand-picked and submissive Irish Parliament, and easily succeeded in extracting from it an astonishing grant of six subsidies; when apportioning the levy, he boldly set Cork's share at £3,600, of which £600 was to be paid in cash and the balance within four years. When the Earl protested that he had been grossly over-rated, he was threatened with a huge fine for having been under-rated in previous grants. The contribution was finally paid four years later. Cork wrote: 'The whole £3,000 which the Lord Deputy (God never forgive his good Lordship) taxed me withal, is fully satisfied and paid.' [9]

With these victories won, and having found the rich man an easy prey, Wentworth next turned his attention to Cork's spiritual lordship. The Earl of Cork undoubtedly thought himself an exemplary churchman because he had restored and built churches and schools on his estates; but he had acted as a dictator in the parishes of Munster: in many where he held the patronage, vacancies were not filled, benefices were impropriated or held *in commendam,* or occupied by ill-paid curates; and the revenues were used for himself or for other secular purposes. Lord Cork was not singular in this misuse of church funds, as it was only too frequent even in England; his practice was more glaring only because of his greater opportunity.

During the first year of his rule, the Lord Deputy wrote to Laud: 'I did the other day make the Earl of Cork disgorge himself of two vicarages that his tenant and he had held from the poor incumbents these thirty years. And they, having reduced him to a stipend of 6 pounds a year, paid him not that neither . . . I am most confident this day's work will gain 100 livings to the Church thus sacrilegiously taken from it by fine, force, and rapine.' [10] He also wrote to his brother-in-law that the Earl had been a most notorious robber of the Church. To the bewildered Earl, who regarded himself as a pillar of the Church, no humiliation could be more devastating than thus to be charged publicly with sacrilege.

But the great blow to the Earl of Cork was to come from Michael Boyle, Bishop of Waterford and Lismore and Warden of Youghal College, who not only was a cousin of the Earl but had also been made a bishop by his influence. He first charged that the church property of Lismore had been alienated by Cork, for which he paid to the Bishop a rental of only 40s. a year. Hard upon the heels of this accusation, in May 1634, Wentworth informed Lord Cork that the Bishop had also petitioned the King to restore all the property formerly belonging to the College of Youghal, which was included in the grant to Raleigh and had been acquired by his cousin by fraud from the then Warden of the College. If the charge could be proved, then all the Youghal Estates bought from Raleigh could be confiscated by the Crown, in addition to what other penalties would be imposed, and the Earl would be practically ruined.

There is slight doubt that Wentworth's purpose in instituting this suit was to break the power of his rival and to extract from him a huge fine for the King, rather than to do justice and return the property to the Warden. It is on record that he wrote to Laud: 'That he never in all his life undertook any business so much against his private affections, and were it possible to conceal this business and yet preserve those duties he owed to God, and the faith and integrity which he must exercise towards his master, he would gladly have done so.' [11]

In spite of the pious sentiments of the letter to Laud, the true reason for the attack on Cork is clear from a letter of Wentworth to the King, May 1634:

In that other great business concerning the Earl of Cork, I have clearly set forth the state thereof in my letter to my Lord's Grace of Canterbury [Laud], only I shall crave leave with some assurance to deliver my opinion to your Majesty, that if in your wisdom you shall think it good to entrust it with me, I rest most confident out of his fine to discharge one-half of the debts which press so heavily upon this crown.

Without this letter one could scarcely believe an entry in Cork's diary:

I prayed him to consider whether in justice he could impose so great a fine upon me. Whereunto he replied, 'God's wounds, Sir! When the last Parliament in England brake up, you lent the King fifteen thousand pounds, and afterwards in a very uncivil, unmannerly manner you pressed his Majesty to repay it you. Whereupon I resolved, before I came out of England, to fetch it back again from you, by one means or other. And now I have gotten what I desired, you and I will be friends hereafter.' *

The case would have had little chance of success in the regular courts, where the decision would depend on evidence, because Lord Cork had ample documents attesting his full legal title to the property, as originally granted by Raleigh and later confirmed under the Great Seal. However, as no one could know what pressure had been brought to bear on the then Warden twenty-seven years earlier, the charge was boldly made that the original seals affixed to the deeds had been forged.

It was imperative for Wentworth to remain inflexible in his determination to keep the case in the Irish Court of the Castle Chamber, where he was all powerful, where there was no jury, where rumour was accepted as evidence and torture could be applied, and where any penalty except death could be inflicted. It was his policy to prolong the trial and so to worry and excite the fears of Lord Cork that he would accept any compromise lest worse should befall him. Yet

---

* *Lismore Papers,* Vol. II, 3, 257. We shall see later that this sum is what Wentworth finally extracted from Lord Cork; and that once it was paid, Wentworth's enmity ceased.

the Earl almost circumvented the scheme by getting letters from high officers of the Crown requiring that, when the examination of witnesses in the Castle Chamber was taken and Wentworth's opinion was given, then Lord Cork should carry and present the documents to the King and be censured by him. Knowing his rival's power of persuasion by word and by gift, the Lord Deputy was deeply offended by the trick, and with difficulty brought his vacillating Master back to his will. He then so harassed Cork in the Court, and so worked on the fears of his friends, that the Earl at last proposed a reconciliation, in which he would pay what fine Wentworth thought just. In reply, Wentworth refused to take the responsibility, and countered by proposing five arbitrators; knowing who they would be, Lord Cork declined.

In the meanwhile, the case dragged on, and Wentworth let it be known that he could and would exact the immense fine of £30,000 in the Court unless his obstinate opponent, of his own accord, would offer to pay half that sum. There followed a dramatic period when Lord Cork's friends and especially his son, Dungarvan, warned him that he was helpless in the power of the Lord Deputy, who would convict him on the charge of forgery. At last the old warrior, with rage in his heart, succumbed; on 2 May 1636 he entered in his diary: 'I am to pay to his Majesty for my redemption out of Court of Castle Chamber (though my innocence and integrity be as clear as the sun at high noon) £5000 cash, £5000 on midsummer 1637, and £5000 on midsummer 1638.'

In return, Wentworth secured the college property to Boyle, but all its rectories, vicarages, and tithes were detached from it and were retained by the Crown. What galled Lord Cork most was that his faithless and perfidious kinsman, whom he had raised from being a poor schoolmaster at Barnett, had played the trick on him.

That the case was purely a political and financial stratagem seems evident, because no stain rested on Cork's character as a forger during or after the trial. He kept up the ordinary civilities of hospitality with Wentworth, and accompanied him to say farewell when he sailed from Ireland. The only plausible excuse, if it be one, for this scandalous case was the desperate need of the King for money, which he could not get from Parliament.

Sympathizers of Lord Cork spoke of the magnitude of the fine as though it would ruin him. Yet, if we remember that he was able easily, a few years earlier, to discharge over £40,000 of debt for purposes of investment; that in January 1636/7 he apportioned £8,460 of half year's rental to his sons, we should not regard him as ruined. There is no evidence that he had even been crippled; his diary, in fact, shows quite the contrary, since he paid his fines promptly and continued to live on the same lavish scale. We may even guess that he feared the worse fate of conviction for forgery and confiscation of his estate. Such, apparently, was the reason he divided and entailed his property amongst his sons; and, fearing he might be forced to flee Ireland, he bought in the autumn of 1636, for £5,000, the manor of Stalbridge in Dorsetshire, as a refuge. This lovely estate, with a residence in Mallow and much land in Tipperary and in Kildare, became Robert's portion.

This protracted struggle, in which the Great Earl of Cork had been brought to his knees, had been such a terrible strain that it brought on a stroke of apoplexy. Characteristically, there is no reference in his diary to this affliction except a record of a paltry expense made in January 1637/8: 'To my German physician for plasters and prescriptions to stay the increase of the dead palsy which hath seized upon all the right side of my body (God help me) £5.' [12]

The victory won and the money exacted, Lord Deputy Wentworth, on 8 August 1637, graciously permitted the Earl of Cork, supposedly a broken and dying man, to leave Ireland with his family for an unlimited stay in England. The indomitable old man, to avoid any appearance of disgrace or compulsion, leisurely put his affairs in order and, in July 1638, set sail for England to hold a great reunion of his family. He was to have some pleasant and useful years before him; to regain favour with King Charles and to serve his cause valiantly; and to have the satisfaction of being vindicated at the trial of his great enemy.

III

YOUTH

1638-1644

WHEN the Earl of Cork landed at Bristol at the age of seventy-two, paralysed on his right side and defeated by a combination of the King, the Lord Deputy of Ireland, and the Archbishop of Canterbury, he was supposed to be seeking a shelter where in obscurity he could safely spend his remnant of days. What memories must have passed through the old man's mind of the crowded years in Ireland since he, a raw youth, had set sail from that port exactly a half century ago—memories of friends and enemies; of a phenomenal fortune acquired by prodigious effort and now trembling in the balance; of Munster, which he had found a desert and had made an example of prosperity; and of Ireland, which he had governed and from which he now was an outcast. If he could have foreseen the future, he would have known that his 'Divine Providence' permitted him three halcyon years of peace in England where he was to regain esteem, gather his family about him as a patriarch, and have a brief and happy intimacy with his beloved son Robert—that odd son who was to give a higher and more lasting honour to his name than all the long line of his noble descendants. After that, he and his family were to go back to Ireland and bravely try to stem the catastrophe of a Civil War, which to their minds was the end of England.

Those who regarded the Great Earl of Cork as a beaten man little understood him; after refreshing himself at Bristol, he mounted horse and rode the sixty miles to Stalbridge in one day; met his son Dungarvan on the way; and, in the evening, had his first sight of the beautiful estate in peaceful Dorset. No sooner was he settled than he found that the family he had gathered there was much too large to be accommodated, and he at once set about his favourite occupation of building and planting, until he had made the manor of Stalbridge one of the lovely Jacobean mansions in the

37

west of England. His family welcomed and the plans of his architect, Monsieur Decon, examined and approved, he went to London
to explore his relations with the Court; on the way, he stopped a
night at Eton to see his sons and the Provost. His stay at Court was
short but satisfactory; he had 'a most gracious conference with his
Majesty at Whitehall, who gave me a most comfortable acknowledgement of the many good services I had done his royal father and
himself, especially for my acceptable discharge of the government
of Ireland, which he would reward to me and my children.' Also,
this 'great robber of the Church' and the austere Archbishop of
Canterbury became friends, and Laud wrote to Wentworth, now
Earl of Strafford, 'how discreetly and nobly the old man spake';
Lord Cork, in his turn, wrote 'thankful letters to my Lord of Canterbury, and £100 to present to him for the re-edifying of Paul's
Church.'

In the family gathering at Stalbridge we must include the two
Etonians, Francis and Robert, who had been brought home by their
sister, Lady Kildare, to pass their long vacation. Lord Cork had for
some time past been suspicious of the influence of Cary, in spite of
his unctuous and elegant epistles and the excellent reports of his
conduct from the Provost. When, at his request, Wotton made an
investigation, he found to his amazement that there had been amorous passages between Cary and the pretty daughter of the school's
under-baker. Now that the two boys were with their father and
could be questioned, his fear that all was not well at the school was
confirmed. Cary not only had fallen to wenching, but had become
a confirmed dicer and gambler; and the Earl might well fear that,
with such an influence, his two youngest sons would follow into
their brothers' extravagance and dissipation. He also found that
Francis had been induced by Cary, or by an Italian servant of the
Provost, to back a bill. As for Robert, he had perhaps been spoiled
by Harrison until he had grown soft and unwilling to stick to the
hard grind of discipline; and now, at the beginning of his fourth
year, he had lost interest in his studies, as Harrison had retired and
had been replaced by a strict disciplinarian.

Robert Boyle, looking back, explained his change of attitude towards his studies and the school thus:

Philaretus had spent in that school (then very much thronged with
young nobility) not much beneath four years, in the last of which he

forgot much of that Latin he had got, for he was so addicted to more
solid parts of knowledge, that he hated the study of bare words naturally,
as something that relished too much of pedantry to consort with his disposition and designs; so that by the change of his old courteous schoolmaster for a new rigid fellow, losing those encouragements that had formerly subdued his aversion to verbal studies, he quickly quitted his
Terence and his grammar, to read in history their gallant acts, that were
the glory of their own, and the wonder of our times. And indeed it is a
much nobler ambition to learn to do things, that may deserve a room in
history, than only to learn, how congruously to write such actions in the
gown-men's language.[1]

With evidence that matters at Eton were no longer wholesome,
the Earl stopped there on his return to Stalbridge from London and,
with whatever excuses he gave to the Provost, took the boys, in November 1638, permanently away.

For a year, Robert Boyle lived with his father and, during that
period, the relations between the old man and his young son became
intimate and tender. The son long afterwards recalled this happy
time in the following account, all the more touching since he was
never to see his father again:

The good old Earl welcomed him very kindly, for whether it were to
the custom of old people (as Jacob doted most on Benjamin and Joseph)
to give their eldest children the largest proportions of their fortunes, but
the youngest the greatest share of their affections; to a likeness observed
in Philaretus, both to his father's body and mind; or, as it seems most
likely, to his never having lived with his father to an age that might
much tempt him to run into debt, and take such other courses to provoke
his dislike, as in his elder children he severely disrelished; to which of
these causes the effect is to be ascribed, it is not my task to resolve, but
certain it is, that from Philaretus's birth, until his father's death, he ever
continued very much his favourite.[2]

The boy's sincerity, high principles, and precocious mind were so
clearly recognized by his father that Cork not only made a companion of his son but also took pains to shield him from the temptations of a dissipated and idle household. With this in mind, Philaretus was put under the tutelage of Mr. W. Douch, the parson of
the village and one of the Earl's private chaplains, and was sent to
lodge and board with him although his house was not 'more than
twice a musket shot away.' Mr. Douch evidently returned to the
persuasive methods of the boy's former master, Harrison; under

this discipline, or perhaps lack of discipline, Robert took up again
his neglected Latin, and was soon able to read and write fluent prose
in that language, and to compose tolerably good verse. He tells us
that, because of the later distractions of his frequent travelling, he
again forgot much of his Latin, but certainly not to the extent of
not reading it fluently. As for reading English poetry, he makes the
odd criticism that it is not very profitable, because the living English tongue changes greatly and rapidly and thus even its noblest
poetry soon becomes obsolete. In looking back on this period, he
remembered best that it was a time when he let his thoughts wander in idle and romantic fields, spending much leisure in solitary
walks and letting his fancies have free reign. As a result, 'he at idle
hours wrote some few verses in French and Latin, and many copies
of amorous, merry, and devout ones in English.' All these youthful
essays he scrupulously and wisely burned on his twenty-first birth-
day. However precocious he may have been—and undoubtedly he
was remarkably so—as he was at that time only twelve years old
and his stay at Stalbridge lasted only for a year, it is likely he assigned to that period many romantic *belles lettres* which were
written later. The attraction to such a literary career lasted till he
was well along in his twenties, when he became permanently absorbed in theology and science. He even adventured in music, but
an indifferent voice quickly discouraged him.

With the evil distractions of the times and Lord Cork's impatient
schemes, such a period of peace could be but of the shortest. In
January 1638/9, the King, at a deadlock with the Commons, sent a
circular letter to all his gentlemen and peers, asking for money and
men-at-arms to accompany him on his Scottish Expedition—the ill-
fated First Bishops' War, which was to usher in years of civil and
religious strife and his own death on the scaffold.

Lord Dungarvan, enthusiastically and without his father's knowledge, pledged himself to raise and lead a troop of a hundred horse.
At first, the Earl was angered by such unprecedented independence
in one of his children; then, like an old war-horse at the sound of
the trumpets, he took over to himself the management of his son's
offer and enlarged it. He advanced £3,000 for the expenses of Dungarvan's troop, and as two other sons, Lord Kynalmeaky and Lord
Broghill, were newly returned to London with M. Marcombes, their
tutor and governor, from a Grand Tour of three years on the Continent, the Earl offered also the equipment and service of all five of

his sons. Philaretus tells us that he was greedy to go but was denied the excitement because Francis fell ill and he was required to stay with the invalid. One may marvel at the decision to send him to war, but in such a futile expedition, the boy of twelve years of age would have been as effective as a seasoned trooper. At Midsummer, Lord Broghill clattered back into the courtyard of Stalbridge with the news of the happy treaty of peace.

While the older sons were in the North, the household settled down to a routine of peace and quiet. Temptation being thus removed, Robert returned to live at home, where his whole education was assigned to M. Marcombes. During the summer, his father entrusted him with the keys of all his gardens and orchards, in order that in the midst of plenty he might learn to be temperate. Greediness was not one of his temptations and he restrained himself without the least regret; but he did give way to the temptation of often spending four or five hours a day wandering alone in the fields, not because he was melancholy, but to let his fancy rove in imaginary romances.

In August, Lord Cork's intimate friend, Sir Thomas Stafford, stepson of his early patron Carew, paid a visit to Stalbridge with his wife, who was the widow of Sir Robert Killigrew and the mother of several children, among them Tom Killigrew, afterwards the notorious wit and dissolute friend of Charles II, and a daughter Elizabeth, a young and beautiful maid of honour in the Court of Charles I. As a result of many interviews, a marriage was arranged between Francis Boyle and Elizabeth. Since they were both very young, only a binding contract was signed; the actual marriage was to be deferred for two or three years, until Francis, accompanied by Robert and Marcombes, should return from an extended trip on the Continent.

But the King interfered in the plan by flatly commanding that the Queen's little maid of honour must be married before the bridegroom departed on his travels. So in August, the Staffords took Francis and Robert with them for a visit to Sir Charles Berkeley at Brereton, and a month later to London to became acquainted with the bride-to-be. Stalbridge was dismantled, and the whole household followed to occupy the great Savoy House in the Strand, the property of Lady Stafford, which she loaned to them for the occasion. Even that immense palace was not large enough to accommodate the Boyle clan, and the overflow of family and servants was lodged in adjacent houses.

On 24 October 1639, there was a grand wedding in the Royal Chapel of Whitehall, at which the King gave away the bride. Lord Cork, uplifted with pride, noted in his diary for that glorious day: 'The King took the bride out to dance; and after the dancing was ended, the King led the bride by the hand to the bed-chamber, when the Queen herself with her own hand, did help to undress her. And his Majesty and the Queen both stayed in the bed-chamber till they saw my son and his wife in bed together.'

Four days later, the sixteen-year-old bridegroom was separated from his bride, and with Robert, a boy of twelve, was commanded to leave for France. After refreshing themselves at Dieppe, the travellers set out for Paris and passed some time 'visiting that vast chaos of a city'; they then journeyed by way of Lyons to Geneva, which had been fixed as their place of residence.

Their father's choice of Geneva was not unusual, as that city was a favoured place in which to educate youthful Englishmen. The purity of its French accent was accepted, and, as an asylum for both Protestants and Catholics, it had attracted a notable group of intellectual men and women. Although its own people had adopted Protestantism and the city, as the shelter of Calvin and Beza, was a focus of the Reformation, still safety was assured for all opinions. Evelyn wrote of it in 1646: 'The church government is severely Presbyterian, after the discipline of Calvin and Beza, who set it up; but nothing so rigid as either our Scots or English sectaries of that denomination.'[3] Much of the sectarian tolerance was due to the eloquent and scholarly preacher Dr. Giovanni Diodati, a distinguished member of a remarkable Italian family which had been converted to Presbyterianism; another member of this family, Diodato Diodati, was a prominent banker of Rome; and a second branch was settled in London. Milton was the intimate personal friend of the Diodatis of London and, with letters of introduction from them, had stayed as a guest at their relative's house in Geneva, whose hospitality so many other English travellers had enjoyed. In fact, it was well known to the Boyles, for Robert's two older brothers had lived there when they had been on the Continent.* With the

---

* It is often erroneously stated that Milton and the elder Boyles stayed at the Villa Diodati where later Byron lived. Dr. Diodati lived in the city, and the Villa was not built until the early part of the eighteenth century. Cf. *Dramatic Works of Roger Boyle* by W. S. Clark, p. 6, Harvard University Press.

certainty of such a religious influence, Lord Cork could feel sure that his sons were protected from the wiles of the Jesuits, who were suspected of lying in wait to entrap the souls of the English youth.

The two boys did not follow the example of their older brothers by living with Dr. Diodati, but were provided with lodgings and entertainment by their tutor, who now had a wife and children living in the town. Geneva was their home for twenty-one months, a period of steady mental discipline and of innocent amusement. M. Marcombes proved to be the treasure he had been recommended to be by Sir Henry Wotton; he was not only successful in his teaching, but his moral character had a lasting and wholesome effect on his charges. Later he was the steadfast friend and the only support of Robert in a time of sore distress. The character of this humble man, who had so profound an influence on his pupil's great career, is sketched by Philaretus:

[M. Marcombes, a French gentleman,] was a man, whose garb, his mien, and outside, had very much of his nation, having been divers years a traveller, and a soldier; he was well fashioned, and very well knew what belonged to a gentleman. His natural were much better than his acquired parts, though divers of the latter he possessed, though not in an eminent, yet in a very competent degree. Scholarship he wanted not, having in his greener years been a professed student in divinity; but he was much less read in books than men, and hated pedantry as much as any of the seven deadly sins. Thrifty he was extremely, and very skilful in the slights of thrift; but less out of avarice, than a just ambition, and not so much out of love to money, as a desire to live handsomely at last. His practical sentiments in divinity were most of them very sound; and if he were given to any vice himself, he was careful by sharply condemning it, to render it uninfectious, being industrious, whatsoever he were himself, to make his charges virtuous. Before company he was always very civil to his pupils, apt to eclipse their failings, and set off their good qualities to the best advantage; but in his private conversation he was cynically disposed, and a very nice critic both of words and men; which humour he used to exercise so freely with Philaretus, that at last he forced him to a very cautious and considerate way of expressing himself, which after turned to his no small advantage. The worst quality he had was his choler, to excesses of which he was excessively prone; and that being the only passion, to which Philaretus was much observed to be inclined, his desire to shun clashing with his governor, and his accustomedness to bear the sudden sallies of his impetuous humour, taught our youth so to subdue that passion in himself, that he was soon able to govern it habitually and with ease.[4]

M. Marcombes, in his frequent reports to his employer, gave a detailed account of their days, which were arranged systematically in study and play. In the mornings they studied Latin and rhetoric, the latter of which Philaretus thought was unseasonably given and on the whole rather hindered than improved the power of expression. After dinner they read two chapters of the Old Testament with a discussion of obscure points. Before supper, they read Roman history in French and repeated the Calvinistic catechism with, as the Earl was carefully assured, a thoroughly orthodox exposition. And after supper, two chapters of the New Testament were read and discussed. A portion of each afternoon was devoted to exercise and play, of which tennis and fencing were the favourites. The brisk and invigorating mountain air gave Philaretus a keen appetite, making him fat and his cheeks as red as vermilion.

Philaretus added to this account of his tutor his own recollections. After he had mastered those 'slighter studies,' he tackled mathematics and in a few months 'grew very well acquainted with the most useful part of arithmetic, geometry, with its subordinates, the doctrine of the sphere, that of the globe, and fortification.' He became enamoured of those delightful disciplines and practised so assiduously that he acquired a more than ordinary skill in them. This is the first intimation of his interest in science.

During his entire absence from England, Robert spoke and thought only in French, until he acquired such a mastery of the language that he often passed himself as a Frenchman. This subterfuge was, at times, a matter of convenience and perhaps of safety, since England and Englishmen were deeply out of favour in Roman Catholic countries. Although he read voraciously in the French romances, his favourite pastime was to read and discuss a voluminous history called *Le Monde,* in which was gathered a great collection of the known facts of the whole world, past and present. He also kept up his reading in the classics, both poetry and philosophy; in the latter he was much drawn to Stoicism, and boy-like determined to put its doctrines into practice; for the moment, the only way he could emulate the Stoic was to endure a severe toothache with silent fortitude.

In the summer of 1640, at the age of thirteen, Boyle experienced a religious crisis as significant and as lasting in its influence on his character as was that of St. Paul, St. Francis, or Pascal. Until then he had lived a virtuous and blameless life, but it had been that of an immature, thoughtless boy, endowed with an obedient and temperate character, to whom religion was more or less a matter of course. The causes of such religious crises are so unpredictable and so different in their effects that it is wise to give Boyle's experience exactly in his own vivid words:

For at a time, which (being the very heat of summer) promised nothing less, about the dead of night, that adds most terror to such accidents, Philaretus was suddenly waked in a fright by such loud claps of thunder (which are oftentimes very terrible in those hot climes and seasons) that he thought the earth would owe an ague to the air, and every clap was both preceded and attended with flashes of lightning so frequent and so dazzling, that Philaretus began to imagine them the sallies of that fire that must consume the world. The long continuance of that dismal tempest, when the winds were so loud, as almost drowned the noise of the very thunder, and the showers so hideous, as almost quenched the lightning, ere it could reach his eyes, confirmed Philaretus in his apprehensions of the day of judgement's being at hand. Whereupon the consideration of his unpreparedness to welcome it, and the hideousness of being surprised by it in an unfit condition, made him resolve and vow, that if his fears were that night disappointed, all his future additions to his life should be more religiously and watchfully employed. The morning came, and a serener cloudless sky returned, when he ratified his determination so solemnly, that from that day he dated his conversion, renewing, now he was past danger, the vow he had made whilst he believed himself to be in it; that though his fear was (and he blushed it was so) the occasion of his resolution of amendment, yet at least he might not owe his more deliberate consecration of himself to piety to any less noble motives than that of its own excellence.[5]

Even in later years Boyle felt this conversion to be the turning point of his life, and he rejoiced that the vows he had made under the influence of terror were renewed and persisted in as a result of his calmer judgement. But the religious serenity of his future life was not to be won without a struggle. His first feeling of exaltation, that he had received a proof of the immanence of God, was followed by a natural reaction of doubt and despair lest he should prove to be unworthy of such divine confidence. As in the first crisis, a second one was directly caused by a natural event—one that led to his life-work in science, which he regarded primarily as a means of discovering the nature and purpose of God. The spring following the great storm, Philaretus took a three weeks' trip in the neighbouring country, during which he visited Chambéry, Aix, and Grenoble. How closely he kept in his own heart the experience he was passing through can be judged from a letter of M. Marcombes to his patron, in which he mentioned the fine health and happy state of mind of his charges. And yet at this time the boy was secretly wrestling with despair:

His curiosity at last led him to those wild mountains, where the first and chiefest of the Carthusian Abbeys does stand seated; where the devil taking advantage of that deep raving melancholy, so sad a place, his humour, and the strange stories and pictures he found there of Bruno, the father of that order, suggested such strange and hideous thoughts, and such distracting doubts of some of the fundamentals of Christianity, that, though his looks did little betray his thoughts, nothing but the forbiddenness of self-dispatch hindered his acting it. But after a tedious languishment of many months in this tedious perplexity, at last it pleased God, one day he had received the sacrament, to restore unto him the withdrawn sense of his favour. But though since then Philaretus ever looked upon these impious suggestions, rather as temptations to be suppressed, than doubts to be resolved; yet never after that did these fleeting clouds cease now and then to darken the clearest serenity of his quiet, which made him often say, that injections of this nature were such a disease to his faith, as the tooth-ache is to the body; for though it be not mortal, it is very troublesome. And however, as all things work together to them that love God, Philaretus derived from this anxiety the advantage of groundedness in his religion: for the perplexity his doubts created obliged him, to remove them, to be seriously inquisitive of the truth of the very fundamentals of Christianity, and to hear what both Turks, and Jews, and the chief sects of Christians could allege for their several opinions.[6]

The testimony of Boyle's friends and the record of his own life are certain evidence that, from this time, he not only constantly lived a life of Christian humility and piety, but also that all his work and thought were saturated with the questions of religion. Although he was repeatedly offered the highest positions in the Church if he would take orders, he declined because he felt himself to be unworthy of so sacred an office; believing he could do more service if not so bound. He once summed up his reasons for not taking orders as follows: He had no interest in religion except to save his own soul; * he hoped to have more influence if he had no patrimony of the Church; he had so high a sense of the obligations, difficulties, and importance of pastoral care that he durst not attempt it and would thus pursue his philosophical studies in such a manner as would best support religion.

He made himself a profound Biblical scholar; in addition to acquiring a fluent knowledge of Latin and Greek, he learned Hebrew, Aramaic, and Syriac, that he might read all the sacred works in their original text, lest by translation the original meaning should be impaired. As regards the authority of the Bible, he was not in accord with the dogmatic authority of the religious teaching of his time, for he said: 'We should carefully distinguish betwixt what the Scripture itself says, and what is only said in the Scripture.' He found his satisfaction in the abiding sacraments of Christianity, and had little patience with squabbles on minor doctrines, or with the two hundred sectaries hurrying into England from Amsterdam, each eager to promote his own particular dogma and to add to the discord. At his death, he established the famous Boyle Lectures to combat atheism by an appeal to moderation and reason. Although his life was lived in an age of the fiercest contention and of acrimonious slander, there is not a slur on his character; he was universally regarded as a noble and upright man without malice or guile.

His religion not only guided his life, but it permeated all his work. He wrote voluminously on religious subjects, and selections from his essays will stand comparison with such great English divines as Barrow, Cudworth, and Hooker. Such was the profound and lasting effect of a common event of nature, which to most men would have been but a casual incident, but to him, just a boy, was the crisis of his life.

Both of the boys, and probably Marcombes also, were growing tired of their quiet life at Geneva and were begging their father for permission to travel extensively in Italy. Francis was influenced by the hope that it would shorten his absence from England and his bride, who was becoming rebellious over their long separation; and Robert was keen to see that country whose history and monuments of antiquity had fired his imagination when so enticingly

* In this day, when the chief purpose of one's religion seems to be to save and to serve others, such a confession will be regarded as selfish. But perhaps a greater consideration of one's own salvation may lead to a truer humility and piety and even, in the process, best serve others.

dwelt upon by the Provost of Eton. Their father was reluctant to give his approval; apparently, he feared for their safety because of the growing antagonism of the Italians towards the English. But at last he gave his reluctant consent to make a long visit in Italy, and then to return home; and he doubled their allowance of £500 a year, which was ample for their life in Geneva. The summer of 1641 was taken up with refitting their wardrobes to an elegance proper to their dignity, and in learning Italian. In September, well horsed and attended, they crossed the 'hideous mountains,' as they then were judged, and 'having passed through such a purgatory as the Alps to their Italian paradise,' they spent some time visiting Venice and the other delightful towns of the Lombardy plains. The winter was passed in Florence, where Philaretus acquired a native accent in Italian by conversing with his tutor, who spoke it perfectly; and in his spare hours he read much modern history in that tongue.

While Philaretus was in Florence, Galileo died in his exile at his villa in near-by Arcetri, and the boy eagerly read that author's great works on the new mechanics and the Copernican system. This year, 1642, in which occurred the death of Galileo, the birth of Newton, and the beginning of Boyle's study of the new mechanics, was a memorable one in the Renaissance of science, which finally developed the mechanistic hypothesis, proposed by Democritus and revived after a neglect of twenty centuries. In spite of his youth and lack of preparation in science, the 'paradoxes of the great star-gazer,' as he calls them, deeply impressed him and very probably influenced him to adopt a scientific career and to become a leader of the 'New Knowledge.' At least, it is certain that he became a convert to Galileo's philosophy, as is proved by his caustic comment:

[These] ingenious books, perhaps because they could not be so otherwise, were confuted by a decree from Rome; his highness the Pope, it seems, presuming, and that justly, that the infallibility of his chair extended equally to determine points in philosophy as in religion, and loth to have the stability of that earth questioned, in which he had established his kingdom.

Philaretus, with the ardor of the new-born convert in religion and burdened with the doubts which pestered his inquisitive mind, had long discussions with some Jewish Rabbis who lodged in the same house with him; and it is a remarkable evidence of the precocious maturity of this boy, then fifteen years old, that he argued with them on an equal footing. Another instance may be cited of his maturity, or else of a method of teaching continence which is not in paedogogical fashion today. His tutor took him, out of curiosity only, to visit the famous bordellos of Florence. Philaretus returned from them as chaste as he went into them, and found their naked exhibition of vice the most convincing sermon for an unblemished chastity.

The old Earl need have had no fear that an intimate acquaintance with Italian Romanism would shake the Protestantism of his impressionable son. In the following spring, the travellers went to Rome and stayed there until the heat drove them back to Florence. After mentioning his delight in viewing the memorable monuments of the Eternal City, Philaretus recorded that 'He never found the Pope less valued than in Rome, nor his religion fiercelier disputed than in Italy; and sometimes added, that he ceased to wonder, that the Pope should forbid the sight of Rome to Protestants, since nothing could more confirm them in their religion.'

It is a curious comment on the Italy of the time that Boyle, who spoke French like a native, passed himself off as a Frenchman in order to be able to move more freely in Rome. He maintained the habit also away from Rome, because of his fear and detestation of the Jesuits and friars. And incredible as such a fear might seem, an experience in Florence gave support to such an apprehension. He was at that time in the flower of youth and of a fresh and brilliant complexion. While sauntering alone in the suburbs of Florence, 'he was somewhat rudely pressed by the preposterous courtship of two friars, whose lust makes no distinction of sexes,' and the boy escaped from them with difficulty and with some danger to his life.

Their renewed stay in Florence was but short, for they soon began their journey home by descending the Arno in a boat. At Livorno, they hired a felucca and sailed north to Genoa, drawing their boat ashore each night; from there, they sailed leisurely along the Riviera till they reached the French border and then travelled overland to Marseilles.

Boyle mentions an incident on the way to Marseilles which is worth preserving, since it shows in him the proud obstinacy of his father.* During his residence in Italy, he adhered to his Protestant

---

* The manuscript of Philaretus is here defective and the particulars must be guessed.

habits, amongst which was to keep his head covered while the crucifix was borne past him in a procession, although it was the habit of English gentlemen to regard their safety by taking off their hats. Apparently, such a religious procession met them in France and the boy, refusing to recognize the crucifix, managed to escape with only the punishment of ill-words and some menace of bodily harm.

At Marseilles, the travellers expected to find directions and money from their father to enable them to return to England. In this expectation they were disappointed and they waited for days in great anxiety, and almost without money. At length, in May 1642, they did receive a long and despondent letter from the Earl. It told of the family's return to Ireland and the almost immediate outbreak of a general rebellion in Munster, so general and so unexpected that he and his sons were with the greatest difficulty defending themselves in their fortified castles of Youghal and Lismore. He himself was barely able to furnish funds for the war and the support of his family; but he had by selling some of his plate scraped together £250 and had sent bills of exchange to that amount to his tailor and financial agent in London, to be forwarded to them. But this was the last remittance they could expect. He begged Marcombes to use it to send his sons to Dublin, Cork, or Youghal, the only Irish ports not possessed by the enemy, or to send them at once to Holland to enter the service of the Prince of Orange. He then concluded his letter:

I know well you will be too generous to leave them till you see them shipped for Ireland, or well entered in the wars in Holland; but in any case I pray be very circumspect how you spend this last £250, and put all unnecessary servants and dependents from you . . . Into England I will not consent they shall come till Ireland be recovered, for I have neither money nor means to defray their expenses there; and for them that have been so well maintained, to appear there without money, would grieve and disgrace me, and draw contempt upon us all.[7]

As if such disastrous news were not a sufficient shock, there were no bills of exchange from Mr. Perkins (the odd combination tailor-financial agent) and they were never forwarded. When the Earl later demanded an explanation from him, the only answer was that the money was kept to pay for the young Lords' parliament robes and for Lord Kynalmeaky's debts; and, in addition he himself was in great trouble since he had been arrested twice on Lady Kildare's account, and once on Lady Lettice Goring's—a striking confirmation of the wanton extravagance, even in a time of the greatest distress, of the Earl's older children. But Robert Boyle was always convinced that, trusting in the confusion of the times, Perkins simply stole the money.

On the receipt of their father's astounding news, the boys and Marcombes held an anxious conference on what to do. Francis refused flatly to go to Holland or to do anything else but to rush to Ireland to the aid of his father and brothers. As for Robert, he had neither the temperament nor the years to be a soldier. By scraping together their reserve funds, enough was obtained to send Francis home and to carry Marcombes and Robert back to Geneva.

It was the only practicable decision, for Robert in his anxiety became seriously ill. He wrote to his father from Lyons that he would obey him if so directed. But, he added, 'I am already weary with a long journey of above eight hundred miles, I am as yet too weak to undertake a long voyage in a strange country, where when I arrive I know nobody and have little hope by reason of my youth to be received amongst the troops.'

We have little or no knowledge of the life of Boyle during his enforced stay at Geneva; his autobiography stops abruptly with the account of the catastrophe at Marseilles. We can guess that he renewed his quiet life of study and amusement. Marcombes proved to be a sincere and disinterested friend, supporting him entirely from his own funds. The Earl preserved one or two letters from the exile, but they give little information except his affection and anxiety, and that he was in good health.

The minor and personal troubles of the exile were overshadowed by the vague and intermittent news of the sinister events which were overwhelming England in this year, 1642, and which filtered but slowly into Geneva. Actual civil war had begun in the Eastern Counties; the Court had moved to Oxford; and London was left in the hands of the Parliamentarians. In Ireland, affairs were going from bad to worse. Lord Cork, aided gallantly by his sons and sons-in-law, was holding grimly to his castles and walled towns of Munster; but his estates were devastated, his industries ruined, and his income gone.

On 23 July 1643, the Irish forces besieged Lismore Castle, and the indomitable old man proudly related he had so strengthened its defences and trained his retainers that the enemy, attacking one side after another, were driven back in turn from each assault. Three days later the Earl's two oldest sons, Dungarvan and Broghill, landed at Youghal with letters from the King requesting a truce of six days while a treaty of peace was arranged with the Irish enemy.

To Lord Cork, who had for fifty years regarded the Irish with contempt, to have his King thus treat them as equals and recognize them as having suffered by injustice, was more than his proud heart could bear. For thirty and more years, he had kept a diary and had not once complained against his Sovereign. To avoid breaking that habit now, he closed his record forever, and turned his face to the wall to die.

Robert Boyle continued to live in exile until he had exhausted all funds of his own and also of Marcombes. At length, in the summer of 1644, by selling 'some slight jewels at a reasonable rate,' he contrived to reach England safely.

IV

APPRENTICESHIP

1644-1654

AS a forlorn stripling, seventeen years old, Boyle arrived in London with no acquaintances, little or no money, and no preparation to earn a living. His family was ignorant of his arrival and he, apparently, had no knowledge of their whereabouts and must have been apprehensive for their welfare and even safety. His long stay abroad had imbued him with foreign manners and speech, so that London would have been strange to him even under ordinary conditions; but London was now foreign to its own inhabitants: the King and Court had moved to Oxford, the Long Parliament obstinately refused to be dissolved, and the city was seething with radical ideas on religion and politics, which burst forth from a feverish and illicit press. All over England recruits were on the roads to join their forces, and the fate of England was on the eve of decision at the battle of Marston Moor.

Boyle made the surprising statement that, on his arrival in London, he met his sister Katherine, Viscountess Ranelagh, quite accidentally, and that he went immediately to her house where he continued to live for four and a half months. He thought this fortunate accident, or rather guidance by Providence, influenced all his future life: [1] This statement that he met his sister 'accidentally,' is very surprising. It is incredible that Marcombes should have let him go to London without a letter of introduction from Dr. Giovanni Diodati to his brother, Dr. Theodore, a well-known physician in London. With such an introduction, Boyle would certainly have learned that his sister was in town, for Milton was an intimate friend of the Diodatis and of Lady Ranelagh, and would undoubtedly have thought of her.

However, it was a fortunate accident that brought the forlorn youth to Katherine Boyle's protecting shelter, for she had had a special fondness for him. These two seemed to be the only children of the family who gave their father no trouble by extravagance and wilfulness, and were his favourites; it was Katherine who watched over Robert's welfare and nursed him during his frequent illnesses; and during his later years he made his home in her house.

Katherine Boyle, born in 1614 and nearly thirteen years older than her brother, was, with the possible exception of Mary, Countess of Warwick, the most beautiful and talented of the Earl of Cork's daughters. At about the age of sixteen, she was married to Arthur Jones, eldest son of Lord Cork's intimate and trusted friend, the Viscount Ranelagh; and her father must have bitterly repented the day when he sacrificed such a daughter to his inordinate ambition for power and place. Much of her early married life was passed in a dreary castle in Ireland, and they must have been years of humiliation and disgust, for her husband was a brute. Sir John Leeke, in a letter introducing her to the Verneys, calls her husband 'the foulest churl in Christendom, whose best point was that he was nightly dead drunk and so probably not quarrelsome.' He also says of her, 'that she was one of the most beautiful as well as the most talented of her time. A more brave wench, nor a braver spirit you have not often met withal; she hath a memory that will hear a sermon and go home and pen it after dinner verbatim.' Now her beauty was somewhat marred by sorrow, but, in spite of her troubles, she managed to make a useful and influential life for herself. Fortunately, her husband continued to stay mostly in Ireland and permitted her to live in London; he also had the grace to die young and to grant her twenty years of pleasant widowhood. In London, she had become an acknowledged leader of its best and most intellectual society; besides Milton, she was an intimate friend of 'the incomparable' Lucius Cary, Lord Falkland, and undoubtedly from them and their friends she had lost the partisanship of her family and had strong sympathy with the Parliamentarians; what was even more important for the future career of her brother, she was the honoured friend of the group of scholars who were later to create the Royal Society and to make England for a century the leader in the Renaissance of science.

During Robert Boyle's stay with his sister, he was introduced to many persons, and especially to a society of scientists, of whom he became later an honoured and life-long friend and leader. In addition to the mental and spiritual comfort which he received in his sister's house, he also reaped a great material advantage. A sister-in-law of Lady Ranelagh was also living with her, and she, who was the wife of one of the principal members of the Long Parliament, introduced him to some of the leaders of that party. By their influence, his Irish and English estates, including Stalbridge, were secured to him, and he was given a valuable safe-conduct which permitted him to travel with less danger. These business affairs having been arranged so satisfactorily, he determined to retire to Stalbridge; there, sick of fratricidal war and religious extravagance, and apprehensive of the fate of his family, who were in the thick of the Irish rebellion, he hoped to live quietly and to occupy himself in the life of a scholar till the issues were decided and peace should return.

There is considerable confusion regarding Boyle's movements between the time when he first arrived in London in the summer of 1644, and when he finally settled at Stalbridge in March 1645/6. His statement that he lived four months with his sister is confirmed in a letter to Tom Murray, steward of his estate: 'We got safe into England towards the middle of the year 1644, where we found things in such a confusion, that although the manor of Stalbridge were, by my father's decease, descended unto me, yet it was near four months before I could get thither.'[3] He evidently found not only confusion, but that his steward had been dishonest; apparently he had to wait almost two years before returning permanently.

From letters and casual statements, we can piece out Boyle's probable movements until he settled permanently at Stalbridge. After his first and discouraging inspection of his estate, he must have returned to London until order was restored to his affairs; while there he lived mostly with Lady Ranelagh; also he seems to have visited his sister Mary, who had married Charles Rich, the son of the Earl of Warwick, either at Warwick House in Holborn, or at Leeze, their country estate in Essex. During the summer of 1645, he made a short trip to the Continent, as we learn from a letter to Lord Broghill, dated London, 25 August, which begins: 'The necessities of my affairs calling me away (according to the leave the Parliament has given me) into France.'[4] We can assume that he made this trip in order to repay Marcombes the generous loans made by him; especially since we know that his former tutor, deprived of English pupils and without other resources, was in desperate circumstances. It also seems probable that he bought a chemical furnace and apparatus with which to equip a laboratory at Stalbridge.

In December 1645, he paid a visit to Cambridge. While there he became acquainted with a Mr. Francis Tallents, a Fellow of Magdalene College and a rigid non-conformist, who had tutored several sons of the Earl of Suffolk (one of whose daughters was married to Lord Broghill). A lasting friendship was cemented by the two young men, who had a common interest in religion.

At last, in March 1645/6, Boyle left London for Stalbridge, accompanied by his brother, Lord Broghill, who was desirous of visiting his estate at Marston Bigot in Somersetshire, and was escorted for safety by a parliamentary messenger. He describes this adventurous journey in one of his few long letters to Lady Ranelagh in a lighter vein:

Sister,

If the busy idleness of receiving senseless visits (whose continuance, if otherwise unavoidable, were capable, in my opinion, to justify the retiredness of an hermit) had not so totally taken up my leisure, you should not so long have had a reprieve from the importunity of my letters. But now at last, to make you amends for my fault (if at least the amends itself be not a fault) I will present you with a piece of a real romance in the story of my peregrination hither. The morning I had the unhappiness to take my leave of you and my lady Molkin [his sister Mary], I bid farewell to the city, and began my journey upon a courser. Him I rid to dinner to Egham; and at the end of the town, there it was my good fortune (as we are pleased to miscall it) to overtake an express sent from the parliament to the general [Lord Broghill], making ceremonies with his horse, whether of them two should lead the way . . . As we went along, we met divers little parties, with whom we exchanged fears, and found, that the malignant humours, that were then abroad, had frighted the country into a shaking ague, till we came to Farnham, which we found empty and unguarded, all the townsmen being gone out to oppose the king's party, and choosing rather to have their houses empty, than replenished with such guests, as otherwise they were necessarily to expect . . . I went to supper, and thence to bed, not without some little fear of having our quarters beaten up by the cavaliers that night; when lo! to second my apprehensions, about the dead of my sleep, and that night, I heard a thundering at the door, as if they meant to fright it out of the hinges, and us out of our wits. I presently leaped out of my bed, in my stockings and clothes (my usual night-posture, when I travel); and while Roger was lighting a candle, got my bilboa

and other instruments from under my pillow: whereupon Roger opening the door, saw it beset with musketeers, who no sooner saw us, but
said aloud, that we were not the men they looked for; and being in-
treated to come into the chamber, refused it, and he, that brought them
thither, excused their troubling us, with as transcendent compliments
as the brown bill could afford. I wondered at their courtesy, till I knew,
that it was the town-constable, that, making a search for some suspicious persons, and coming by my chamber, that wanted a lock, either
had a mind to make us take notice of so considerable an officer, or no
mind that we should sleep, whilst our betters watched . . . The next
day we dined at Winchester, and ever and anon, by the trembling pas-
sengers we met, were as nicely catechized concerning our ways, as if we
were to be elected in the number of the new lay elders. From thence we
reached Salisbury that night, though before we came thither, we were
fain to pass in the dark through a wood, where we had warning given
us, that about an hundred woodmen (we have got wild English too now)
lay leiger [resident], where these night-birds used to exercise their charity in easing weary travellers of such burthensome things as money and
portmanteaus . . . At Salisbury I overtook my trunks I had sent thither
before; and the next morning took them along with me over the plain;
where when we had gone about half the way, we were suddenly environed with a party of horse (beyond whom we might discover a body
of foot) who came powdering so furiously upon us, that they scarce
gave us leisure to draw; but coming nearer, and knowing the state's
messenger (as he called himself) they durst not meddle, neither with
us, nor with my trunks, which they eyed though very lovingly; and
had not we been there, would, I believe, have opened to search for
malignant letters, such as use to be about the king's picture in a yellow
boy [sovereign]. The foot we saw were poor pressed countrymen, whom
this party of horse were sent, not to convey, but to guard. Amongst them
I saw one poor rogue, lacqueyed by his wife, and carrying a child upon
his shoulders. A pretty device, methinks, to make those, who have no
goods, to fight for their wives and children! Good God! that reasonable
creatures, that call themselves Christians too, should delight in such an
unnatural thing as war, where cruelty at least becomes necessity, and
unprocured poverty becomes a crime; and a man with his whole family
must be subject to be unavoidably undone, because the violence perhaps
of those very soldiers that press him, had made him poor. At last on
Saturday night I arrived, God be praised, at Stalbridge, and found by
experience the truth of that senseless proverb, the longest way about is
the nearest way home. And here the fair weather, that had been my
constant companion from London hither, as soon as it saw me housed,
took leave of me; in whose absence winter weather has always so fully

and uninterruptedly domineered, that we all suspect the almanac-maker of a mistake, in setting down March instead of January. It confines me to my chamber, and is so drooping, that it dulls me to all kinds of useful study, and (which is worst of all) it renders me obnoxious to these country visits (or visitations rather) which, you know, use to supply with their length what they want in their goodness. As soon as the weather will give me leave, I intend to take Marston Bigot in my way to Bristol, to put some end or other to the business—I am loaded with civil language and fair promises, but I have always observed, that in the troopers dictionary the pages are so close and thick written with promises, that there is no room left for such a word as performance.

My Ethics go very slowly on; neither have I been possibly able to do any other business, save to make my brother's sixty trees bear him some golden fruit, of which (though I did my uttermost endeavour to ripen it) I must gather but one third at May-day next, the other at, etc.

My stay here, God willing, shall not be long, this country being generally infected with three epidemical diseases (besides that old leiger sickness, the troop-flux) namely the plague, which now begins to revive again at Bristol and Yeovil six miles off, fits of the committee, and consumption of the purse; to which so violent expulsives, if so potent an attractive, as a letter from you, were but added, it would both extremely sweeten the stay, and accelerate the departure of,

My dearest sister,

your most affectinate brother,

and humble servant,

Robert Boyle.[5]

Stalbridge, March 30,
                1646

When Boyle, at the age of nineteen, returned to his Manor of Stalbridge as its master and owner, he had good cause for melancholy reflections. He refers to it as half ruined, with its tenants gone, or sullen, and paying no rentals. Even if it had not been pillaged, it had been neglected and permitted to sink into decay. The last time he had lived there, his doughty old father had been busy building and decorating the house, and laying out gardens, orchards, and farms. The house had been full to overflowing with his sons and daughters and their children, and echoed with the cheerful sounds of laughter and entertainment; now its deserted halls and rooms echoed only to his own solitary footsteps.

There is no doubt that the manor-house was a noble building after its embellishment by the Earl of Cork, and it is unfortunate

that no contemporary description of it remains. The following note
of its condition in 1863 is worth recording:

Till within the last thirty years [1833], the present mansion in the
park was said to contain the room where he [Robert Boyle] studied and
where his first experiments were made. A stone wall five miles in circum-
ference surrounds the park. All the old dwelling has, however, disappeared. A pair of massive stone pillars, surmounted by lions, flank the
entrance to what was once a noble avenue of elms and form the chief
remains of a place once memorable for its magnificence.[6]

Boyle's first duty in setting his household to rights was to discharge Tom Murray, the steward left in charge of the estate, whose
'roguery gave me a great deal of trouble to discover and prevent.'
He found it fortunate to be thus suddenly thrown on his own resources, since it compelled him to give strict attention to his economy. In a letter to Marcombes is a comment curiously characteristic
of his father: 'I turned him [Murray] away last year, to let him
know, that I could do my business very well without him; but now,
having attained to a knowledge of my own small fortune beyond
the possibility of being cheated, I am likely to make use of him
again, to shew my father's servants, that I wish no harm to the
man, but to the knave.'
In spite of Boyle's wish to make his stay at Stalbridge brief, it
was his fate to live there continuously for the following six years
except for occasional absences. And, on the whole, it was a fortunate necessity: these years of loneliness encouraged him to make
his first essays in writing, to fill his mind with knowledge, and to
harden his character. By living in retirement, he avoided the necessity of taking sides in the clash of political parties and of being
drawn into active life. The facts of his life during this period have
not been preserved for us, but we do know, from two letters written by him at this time, what was his own state of mind, and what
were his opinions on the political and religious state of the nation.
The first letter was written from London, 22 October 1646, to Marcombes.

Monsieur,
Since discountenance of the practice of your language has robbed me
of that little readiness your converse had taught me in it, I shall take
the liberty to make use of mine, which I know you understand equally
with your own.
In my last I promised you a more full account of sundry particulars,

I had then the leisure but to touch at; and for my disengagement I shall tell you, that we are in a very doubtful condition for the present, though in all probability a few days will determine either our hopes or our fears. In England the great and uninterrupted successes have transcended as well their own hopes, as their opposers fears. In England there is not one malignant garrison untaken, and in Wales but two or three rocky places hold out for the King, and these too so inconsiderable, that they more advantage their enemies forces, by keeping them from idleness, than they are able to prejudice them by their opposition. The Scots being now to quit the kingdom, the parliament had compounded with them for all their arrears, upon whose payment they are to deliver up their garrisons, and retire into their own country . . .

This day with kingly state was buried the great earl of Essex, having 400 officers, not one so low as a captain, the house of peers, the house of commons, the city, and the assembly of divines, for his mourners, and all the other parting compliments of honour, that ever subject could aspire unto. His sickness was an apoplexy, which did not long make him linger; and thus he, that had escaped so many mutinies, at last perished by a mutiny of the humours. But I have usually observed, that in these great funeral solemnities, the pageantry of sorrow has eaten up the reality . . .

The presbyterian government is at last settled (though I scarce think it will prove long lived) after the great opposition of many, and to their no less dislike; though it seemed very high time unto others, that some established and strict discipline should put a restraint upon the spreading impostures of the sectaries, which have made this distracted city their general rendezvous, which entertains at present no less than 200 several opinions in point of religion, some digged out of those graves, where the condemning decrees of primitive councils had long since buried them; others newly fashioned in the forge of their own brains; but the most being new editions of old errors, vented with some honourable title and modern disguisements; so that certainly if the truth be any where to be found, it is here sought so many several ways, that one or other must needs light upon it . . .

The sadness of your condition I very much resent, and would offer you my assistance to sweeten it, if I did not think the proffer superfluous; but truly I believe it would less afflict you, if you were a spectator of our miseries here, where every day presents us with much more unusual dispensations of providence, where I myself have been fain to borrow money of servants, to lend it to men of above £10,000 a year . . .

And now it is high time I should give you some account both of myself and of my condition; which truly hath been chequered with a great deal of variety of fortune, and a great many vicissitudes of plenty and

want, danger and safety, sickness and health, trouble and ease; wherein
I were guilty of an ingratitude great as the favour I have received, if
I did not acknowledge a great deal of mercy in God's dispensation towards me; which truly hath been so kind, as oftentimes to work my
good out of those things I most feared the consequences of, and changed
those very dangers, which are the object of my apprehension, into the
motives of my joy. I was once a prisoner here upon some groundless
suspicions, but quickly got off with advantage. The roguery of Tom.
Murray gave me a great deal of trouble to discover and prevent; but I
thence reaped the benefit of making further discoveries into œconomical
knowledge, than ever otherwise I should have done . . .

I have been forced to observe a very great caution, and exact evenness
in my carriage, since I saw you last, it being absolutely necessary for
the preservation of a person, whom the unfortunate situation of his fortune made obnoxious to the injuries of both parties, and the protection
of neither. Besides I have been forced to live at a very high rate, (considering the inconsiderableness of my income) and, to furnish out these
expences, part with a good share of my land, partly to live here like a
gentleman, and partly to perform all that I thought expedient in order
to my Irish estates, out of which I never yet received the worth of a
farthing . . .

As for my studies, I have had the opportunity to prosecute them but
by fits and snatches, as my leisure and my occasions would give me
leave. Divers little essays, both in verse and prose, I have taken the
pains to scribble upon several subjects; some of the least bad of which
I shall venture to send you over, as soon as my next vacation spares
me time to lick them into some less imperfect shape . . .

The other humane studies I apply myself to, are natural philosophy,
the mechanics, and husbandry, according to the principles of our new
philosophical college, that values no knowledge, but as it hath a tendency to use. And therefore I shall make it one of my suits to you, that
you would take the pains to enquire a little more thoroughly into the
ways of husbandry, etc. practised in your parts; and when you intend
for England, to bring along with you what good receipts or choice books
of any of these subjects you can procure; which will make you extremely welcome to our *Invisible College,* which I had now designed
to give you a description of, but a gentleman, whom I have been forced
to keep talk with all the while I was writing this, together with the
fear of having too much already trespassed upon your patience, call upon
me to end your trouble and this letter together.[7]

The second letter was written to Francis Tallents from London
on 20 February 1646/7, and it is important because he discusses so

frankly his distaste of sectarian religion, and so delightedly of his intercourse with the group of scientists of London which he fondly nicknamed the Invisible College.

Sir,

I should venture to apologize for my silence, if I thought it not less guilty than meritorious; since to reprieve you from the importunity of my letter, I have hitherto denied myself that happiness, that your civility makes me confident I might have enjoyed by the receiving of yours. I have been every day these two months upon visiting my own ruined cottage in the country; but it is such a labyrinth this London, that all my diligence could never yet find the way out on't, and hath but just now put me in a probability of leaving it within these two or three days. The best on't is, that the corner-stones of the *Invisible,* or (as they term themselves) the *Philosophical College,* do now and then honour me with their company, which makes me as sorry for those pressing occasions that urge my departure, as I am at other times angry with that solicitous idleness that I am necessitated to during my stay; men of so capacious and searching spirits, that school-philosophy is but the lowest region of their knowledge; and yet, though ambitious to lead the way to any generous design, of so humble and teachable a genius, as they disdain not to be directed to the meanest, so he can but plead reason for his opinion; persons that endeavour to put narrow-mindedness out of countenance, by the practice of so extensive a charity, that it reaches unto every thing called man, and nothing less than an universal good-will can content it. And indeed they are so apprehensive of the want of good employment, that they take the whole body of mankind for their care.

But lest my seeming hyperbolical expressions should more prejudice my reputation than it is able any ways to advantage theirs, and I be thought a liar for telling so much truth, I will conclude their praises with the recital of their chiefest fault, which is very incident to almost all good things; and that is, that there is not enough of them.

For news, I believe you do not ignore, what a stream of success the parliament, since I had the honour to see you, has had. I will only now take the freedom to tell you, that I am greatly afraid, most men flatter themselves in their prognostications of peace, which are calculated rather to the meridian of their desires, than to that of their reason. And though I must confess, the traveller seems to be very near the inn, yet I know not why the horse may not stumble at the threshold; for I am somewhat unapt to persuade myself, that the judgement will cease, while the cause continues; but am rather very ready to apprehend, that while adversity makes some obstinate, and others wanton, though the war perhaps may die, the judgement will be kept alive. The pulpits were never more adorned with excellent divines, than they now are here, but with so unsuitable a success in many of the people, that I can sometimes think it no breach of charity to believe, that the small-pox has stricken inward, and many of them have but banished their vices from the body into the heart. For my part, the excellency of the ministry, since waited on by such an improficiency, increases my presaging fears of the approaching misery of the people; for I shall easily be drawn to suspect that horse to be very sick, that thrives not in so plentiful a pasture. And truly, methinks, it is but a very sad symptom, when the physic augments the disease. For matter of sects, it seems, that most of those at Amsterdam have been returned us over by bill of exchange, which our English searchers have been so industrious to improve, that there are few days pass here, that may not justly be accused of the brewing or broaching of some new opinion. Nay, some are so studiously changeling in that particular, they esteem an opinion as a diurnal, after a day or two scarce worth the keeping. If any man have lost his religion, let him repair to London, and I'll warrant him, he shall find it: I had almost said too, and if any man has a religion, let him but come hither now, and he shall go near to lose it. Pray God, it fare not with religion amongst those novelties, as it does sometimes with a great commander, when he is taken prisoner by a company of common soldiers, who every one tugging to have him for himself, at last pull him to pieces, and so each gets a limb, but none enjoys him whole. For my part, I shall always pray to God to give us the *unity of the spirit in the bond of peace,* and desire you to believe, that, amongst all the apostasies of the time, I shall be the least capable of being seduced by that that may oppose my being and continuing so,

Your most affectionate friend and faithful servant,
Robert Boyle.[8]

There is little to relate of Boyle's external life, for the years at Stalbridge passed slowly, and almost without event. He spent much time in the management of his estate and took great pride in keeping it in excellent condition: his pride in his management was increased because he regarded himself as only a life tenant, if he should have no children, to hold it in trust for his brother, Francis, to whom it reverted.

He kept up some social intercourse with his neighbours, but he complained to his sister that they wasted his time, and that he found their local gossip a great bore. For exercise and amusement, he returned to his former habit of taking long walks and rides, during which he let his imagination run unchecked; or he observed the

little homely incidents met on the way. And when he returned
from these excursions, he cultivated the habit of writing them down
in the form of short essays, and amused himself by attaching to
each an appropriate moral tag.

Boyle's life during these long and lonely ten years was chiefly
spent at his writing desk and with his books. With his almost fatal
facility for writing, he composed, besides the rural essays just mentioned, a rapid succession of essays on religious subjects, a novel, and
a mass of poems and casual pieces. Of what he read we have no
record, but it must have covered a very wide range of subjects. One
book we do know he read, and read persistently, even when illness,
travel, or trouble with his eyesight prevented all other reading—the
Bible.

Boyle's greatest pleasure and relief from loneliness were derived
from his frequent visits to London where, as he wrote to Tallents,
'the corner stones of the *Invisible* or . . . the *Philosophical College,*
do now and then honour me with their company.' This group of
scientists, to whom Boyle had been introduced by his sister and
whose kind reception of him he so modestly mentions, immediately
recognized his ability and encouraged him to cultivate the new
experimental philosophy. Hitherto, he had been romantic and wayward in purpose, in spite of the fact that he claimed he had lost
his taste for verbal studies and had turned to more sober and practical branches of knowledge. He believed that his first awaking to
the fascination of scientific work came from his introduction to
mathematics. This study, he said, fascinated him with its exact
logic, and gave him such a distaste for mere words that he became
a master of it. However, this belief is not borne out by any other
evidence. On the contrary, when he later became intimate with
mathematicians he himself admitted he was so deficient he could
not use mathematical analysis in his work; and he certainly never
lost his taste for words, if we can judge from the prolixity of his
writings; and his romanticism persisted throughout his life.

The origin of this Philosophical College and the persons who established it are known from a passage in the *Autobiography* of Dr.
John Wallis: *

* John Wallis, a distinguished and versatile mathematician who led to the discovery of
the Calculus, was also a theologian. He was a strong Parliamentarian, a secretary of the
Westminster Assembly of Divines, and used his extraordinary gift of deciphering codes for
translating intercepted letters and papers of the Royalists. He was educated at Emmanuel
College, Cambridge, was one of the founders of the Royal Society, and was later Savilian
Professor of Geometry in Oxford.

About the year 1645, while I lived in London, (at a time, when, by our civil wars, academical studies were much interrupted in both our Universities) beside the conversation of divers eminent divines, as to matters theological, I had the opportunity of being acquainted with divers worthy persons, inquisitive into natural philosophy, and other parts of human learning and particularly of what hath been called the New Philosophy, or Experimental Philosophy. We did by agreements, divers of us, meet weekly in London on a certain day, to treat and discourse of such affairs; of which number were Dr. John Wilkins (afterward Bishop of Chester), Dr. Jonathan Goddard, Dr. George Ent, Dr. Glisson, Dr. Merret (Drs. of Physic), Mr. Samuel Foster, then Professor of Astronomy at Gresham College, Mr. Theodore Hank [or Haak] a German of the Palatinate, and then resident in London, who, I think, gave the first occasion, and first suggested those meetings, and many others.

These meetings we held sometimes at Dr. Goddard's lodgings in Wood Street (or some convenient place near), on occasion of his keeping an operator in his house for grinding glasses for telescopes and microscopes; sometimes at a convenient place in Cheapside [the Bull-Head Tavern], and sometimes at Gresham College, or some place near adjoining.[9]

Amongst these 'many others' was Samuel Hartlib, who, Evelyn tells us, was a refugee from Lithuania. He soon became an enthusiastic supporter of the new Utopias for improving education and society which were born from the dissatisfaction of the times. He was also interested in improving agriculture, and was a voluminous correspondent—a sort of animated news letter. One of Boyle's intimate friends, he would send him full accounts of the news of London during his absences. From these, we learn that Boyle studied Oughtred's *Clavis Mathematica;* * that he had opinions on the Copernican theory; that he knew Mersenne's works intimately; and that he was deeply influenced by Gassendi's revival of the atomic theory.

Undoubtedly, the London scientists had a decisive influence on Boyle's choice of science as his life work, but we do not know why or when he chose chemistry. Some have suggested that his interest was first aroused by Claudius (or Clod), the son-in-law of Hartlib, and his name, connected with enquiries about chemistry, occurs frequently in their correspondence. Evelyn said of Claudius, 'he

* A very important mathematical textbook used later by Newton. Oughtred was educated at Eton and Cambridge. He was probably the most popular teacher of mathematics of his day.

was a profess'd adeptus, who by the same *methodus mendichandi* and pretence of extraordinary arcana, insinuated himself into acquaintance of his father-in-law'; he was undoubtedly a clever charlatan. Evelyn supposed Boyle was indebted to the virtuosi at Oxford, but this opinion is obviously erroneous, since a chemical laboratory was set up and experiments were made at Stalbridge years before he went to Oxford. It seems certain that the first impetus to his life work was given by that little group in London whom he so affectionately called the Invisible College. He had evidently made up his mind to study chemistry even before he went to Stalbridge, for on 6 March 1646/7, he wrote a humorous account to Lady Ranelagh of his difficulties and of the disastrous conclusion to his soaring hopes to be an Invisible Baconian:

That great earthen furnace whose conveying hither has taken up so much of my care, and concerning which I made bold very lately to trouble you, since I last did so, has been brought to my hands crumbled into as many pieces, as we into sects; and all the fine experiments, and castles in the air, I had built upon its safe arrival, have felt the fate of their foundation. Well, I see I am not designed to the finding out the philosopher's stone, I have been so unlucky in my first attempts in chemistry. My limbecks, recipients, and other glasses have escaped indeed the misfortune of their incendiary, but are now, through the miscarriage of that grand implement of Vulcan, as useless to me, as good parts to salvation without the fire of zeal. Seriously, Madam, after all the pains I have taken, and the precautions I have used, to prevent this furnace the disaster of its predecessors, to have it transported a thousand miles by land, that I may after all this receive it broken, is a defeat, that nothing could recompense, but that rare lesson it teaches me, how brittle that happiness is, that we build upon earth.[10]

There is some mystery about the location of the 'thousand miles by land' over which the unlucky Vulcan had been dragged; even allowing for exaggeration, it must have been bought on the Continent, perhaps when he first visited Marcombes.

His love for chemistry and his desire to use science as a witness of God's plan of the universe grew to be a passion, as is evident from a letter to the same sister, written from Stalbridge on 31 August 1649. The depth of his feelings was intensified by a recent and severe attack of fever and by the news of the death of a near relative:

I will not now presume to entertain you with those moral speculations, with which my chemical practices have entertained me; but if this last sickness had not diverted me, I had before this presented you with a discourse (which my vanity made me hope would not have displeased you) of the theological use of natural philosophy, endeavouring to make the contemplation of the creatures contributory to the instruction of the prince, and to the glory of the author of them. But my blood has so thickened my ink, that I cannot yet make it run; and my thoughts of improving the creatures have been very much displaced by those of leaving them. Nor has my disease been more guilty of my oblivion, than my employment since it has begun to release me: for Vulcan has so transported and bewitched me, that as the delights I taste in it make me fancy my laboratory a kind of Elysium, so as if the threshold of it possessed the qualities the poets ascribed to that Lethe, their fictions made men taste of before their entrance into those seats of bliss, I there forget my standish and my books, and almost all things, but the unchangeable resolution I have made, of continuing till death, Sister, your R. B.[11]

These passions can be regarded as the cornerstones of his character while he was an amateur in science, and later in life when he was regarded as the foremost scientist of his age.

Boyle, as shown by his letters to Hartlib, had a childlike admiration for Claudius, regarding him as an adept in the *arcana majora* and constantly enquiring on what important work he was engaged. In 1652, Boyle was compelled to go to Ireland to attend to his estates, and spent two unhappy years there longing to get back to his beloved laboratory. He wrote in melancholy letters to Claudius that his one desire was to finish his business and leave the unlucky country forever, so he might again sit at the feet of his master. He contrasted the condition of the two: Claudius enjoying the communion of intellectual companions, while he, unhappy man, lives 'here in a barbarous country, where chemical spirits are so misunderstood, and chemical instruments so unprocurable, that it is hard to have any hermetic thoughts in it, and impossible to bring them to experiment.'

Although Boyle's biographers give the impression that he was a proficient and recognized chemist, it is doubtful if he was more, at this time, than the amateur repeating elementary operations. He had had no previous teaching or discipline in the subject, and was not in touch with the alchemists of the day; nor could he have had an adequate laboratory and experience in the use of apparatus. It

was not until he had been some time in Oxford that his apprenticeship was finished.

However much time and energy Boyle may have expended on
science, his principal and, one might say, almost his exclusive interest was the study of theology and the daily practice of the Christian
life. While we lack knowledge of his opinions on most subjects during these years at Stalbridge, we have very full knowledge of his
studies in theology, of his distaste for the excesses of sectarianism
of the time, and of what he thought to be necessary for a life of
Christian piety. How despondently he felt concerning the fate of
Christianity, whose existence was being shipwrecked by the evil
practices of civil strife and of clashing doctrines, has been seen in
his letters to Marcombes and to Francis Tallents, previously
quoted.[12]

But perhaps the most bitter of Boyle's invectives against sectarian
dissension was expressed in May 1647, in a letter to John Dury,
himself well known by his futile efforts to reconcile the Lutherans
and the Calvinists:

It has been long, as well my wonder, as my grief, to see such comparatively petty differences in judgement make such wide breaches and vast
divisions in affection. It is strange, that men should rather be quarrelling
for a few trifling opinions, wherein they dissent, than to embrace one
another for those many fundamental truths, wherein they agree. For my
own part, in some two or three and forty months, that I spent in the
very town of Geneva, as I never found that people discontented with
their own church-government (the gallingness of whose yoke is the
great scare-crow that frights us here) so could I never observe in it any
such transcendent excellency, as could oblige me either to bolt heaven
against; or open Newgate for all those, that believe they may be saved
under another. Wherefore I must confess, it would be extremely my
satisfaction, if I could see, by God's blessing, your pious endeavours of
twisting our froward parties into a moderate and satisfactory reconcile-
ment, as successful, as I am confident they will be prudent and unwear-
ied. As for our upstart sectaries (mushrooms of the last night's spring-
ing up) the worst part of them, if not exasperated by, instead of lighting
them into the right way with the candle, flinging the candlestick at their
heads, like Jonah's gourd, smitten at the root with the worm of their
irrationality, will be as sudden in their decay, as they were hasty in their
growth; and indeed perhaps the safest way to destroy them is rather
to let them die, than attempt to kill them.[13]

As a result of his theological studies, he wrote a surprisingly critical essay on the purpose and authority of the Scriptures, in which he boldly comments on errors of fact and on inconsistencies of details, and yet defends the harmony of their message as a whole. Although the essay was undertaken to satisfy himself and to benefit his family and friends, it was afterwards published in 1661, under the title: *Some Considerations Touching the Style of the Scriptures.*[14]

The essay was written at the earnest request of Lord Broghill, who had been impressed by a letter from Robert, in which he had justified the time and labour he had spent in learning Greek and Hebrew.

Though I think [says he] the authors of our last translation [of the Bible] have made it much more correct than our former was, and preferable to most I have met with in other languages; and have therefore been sincerely and industriously instrumental to the British churches' edification, according to their light; yet that it were very possible, as well as to be wished, that an English translation, yet in many places more correct, might be framed, will scarce seem improbable to an intelligent person, that duly considers, how much the knowledge of tongues, and (what would be highly useful, not to say necessary, in such a work) of Jewish and other Eastern learning, is, since our last version was made, increased and refined, and consequently, how many texts by that greater light, that now shines among critics and antiquaries, may be rendered more fully, or more warily, or more clearly, or more coherently to the context, or more congruously to the analogy of faith, or that of reason . . .

To which purpose I remember, that that excellent Christian scholar and divine Dr. Usher archbishop and primate of Armagh (whose encouragements I gratefully acknowledge to have much engaged me to the study of the holy tongues) talking to me one day in his study of his intended edition of the Septuagint, earnestly implored of him by the transmarine critics, observed to me, not without some just wonder, that for divers ages the church (as to the greater part of it) and even the Apostles, and even those that most flourished in piety, scarce used any other scripture than the Septuagint's translation, which is one of the faultiest versions of the Bible, and wants not gross mistakes . . . Methinks those, that learn other languages, should not grudge those that God hath honoured with speaking to us, and employed to bless us with that heavenly doctrine, that comes from him, and leads to him. When I have come into the Jewish schools, and seen those children that were never bred up for more than tradesmen, bred up to speak (what hath been peculiarly called) God's tongue, as soon as their mother's, I have blushed to think, how many gown-men, that boast themselves to be the true Israelites, are perfect strangers to the language of Canaan; which I would learn, were it but to be able to pay God the respect usual from civil inferiors to princes, with whom they are wont to converse in their own languages. For my part, I . . . that have a memory so unhappy and so unfit to [supply] my intellectual deficiencies, and the rest of my disabilities, that it often strongly tempts me to give over my studies, and abandon an employment, wherein my slow acquists are (by the treacherousness of my memory) so easily lost . . . But in spite of the greatness of these indispositions to the study of tongues, my veneration for the scripture made one of the greatest despisers of verbal learning leave Aristotle and Paracelsus to turn grammarian, and where he could not have the help of any living teacher, engaged him to learn as much Greek and Hebrew, as sufficed to read the old and new testament, merely that he may do so in the Hebrew and Greek, and thereby free himself from the necessity of relying on a translation. And after I had almost learned by rote an Hebrew grammar, to improve myself in scripture-criticisms, in the Jewish way of reading the oracles committed to them, I, not overcheaply, purchased divers private conferences with one of their skilfullest doctors (as St. Hierom had those nocturnal meetings, which so much helped to make him the solidest expositor of all the fathers, with Barraban . . . the Jew) I received of him few lessons, that cost me not twenty miles riding, at a time, when I was in physic, and my health very unsettled. A Chaldee grammar I likewise took the pains of learning, to be able to understand that part of Daniel, and those few other portions of scripture, that were written in that tongue; and I have added a Syriac grammar purely to be able one day to read the divine discourses of our Saviour in his own language: in which I can truly profess, with the famous publisher of the Syriac testament, Guido Fabricius (in his dedication of that book, and his version of it, to the then French King) that I had no instructor to teach me so much as to know the letters . . .

For my part, that reflect often on David's generosity, who would not offer as a sacrifice to the Lord his God that which cost him nothing, I esteem no labour lavished, that illustrates or endears to me that divine book; my addictedness to which I gratulate to myself, as thinking it no treacherous sign, that God loves a man, that he inclines his heart to love the scriptures, where the truths are so precious and important, that the purchase must at least deserve the price. And I confess myself to be none of those lazy persons, that seem to expect to obtain from God the knowledge of the wonders of his book upon as easy terms as Adam did a wife, by sleeping profoundly, and having her presented to him at his awaking. [R. B.]¹⁵

Boyle, during his retirement at Stalbridge, was a prolific writer on religious themes—too prolific for his reputation as a stylist. Besides the *Ethics,* the *Occasional Reflections,* and the *Style of the Scriptures* already mentioned, he wrote two long and loosely constructed tracts, *A Free Discourse against Swearing* and *On Seraphic Love,* and a novel entitled the *Martyrdom of Theodora and Didymus.*

We may be sure that Boyle's family and friends often urged him to marry; and we may be equally sure that he—rich, high-born, of an exemplary character, and admittedly attractive to women because of his wit and courtesy—remained a bachelor from choice and not from necessity. His father had lived to see all his other children married, but had come to fear that this odd son would escape his plans; he had set his heart on a brilliant marriage for his Robyn with the Lady Ann Howard, the very young daughter of Lord Edward Howard of Escrick. On 11 September 1640, Cork noted in his diary that he and his son Dungarvan 'rode to Hatfield to take leave of the Earl of Salisbury. I gave to my Robyn's young mistress a small gold ring with a diamond.'

Even in his will the old patriarch did not relinquish his hope for this alliance; in the very midst of a seemingly endless catalogue of bequests to Robert, he suddenly interrupts with the following memorandum:

I do give grant legate and bequeath to Mrs. Ann Howard Daughter of ye Lord Edward Howard my Silver Cistern weighing 680 ounces, my Silver Kettle or Pot weighing 162 ounces, my Silver Ladle weighing 27 ounces, whereon my Coat of Arms is engraven, with three pieces of Plate I bought of Sir Thomas Jermyn the Younger Knight, and paid him for them £274. 18s. 6d. besides what I paid for Engraving my Arms, if the said Mrs. Ann Howard shall be married to my said Son Robert. But in case she shall not be married unto and become ye wife of my said Son, Then I give the said three pieces of Plate to my said Son Robert if he live and attain unto ye age of twenty one years, Otherwise I give and bequeath them to my Son Dungarvan's eldest Son Charles Boyle.¹⁶

What a man! No detail of his property could be neglected; no purpose ever abandoned. Perhaps the two children met in London while Francis Boyle was being married; if so, they had parted and

had forgotten each other, as Robert went abroad for years, and Ann
Howard married her cousin.

Robert Boyle had seen his brothers and sisters contracted in marriage while they were still children, submissively accepting their
father's choice; he must also have observed the unfortunate results
of several of these bargains for wealth and station. He seems to
have regarded marriage in a different and more serious light, and
to have felt that it imposed embarrassing obligations unless it was
entered into because of an overpowering passion. When he was
twenty years of age, he wrote to a friend, whom he addresses as
'Dear Count,' rather priggishly rebuking him for loose flirtations
and giving his own idea of matrimony: 'I should tell you, that
marriage is not a bare present, but a legal exchange of hearts; and
the same contract, that gives you the right to another's, ties you to
look upon your own as another's goods, and too surely made over,
to remain any longer in your gift.'[17]

Usually, when he was urged to forsake his bachelorhood, he
evaded committing himself by a gentle irony and by his own imperviousness to Cupid's darts. For instance, he once wrote to Lady
Barrymore, his niece, to deny a rumour of his marriage:

You have carried away too many of the perfections of your sex, to leave
enough in this country for the reducing so stubborn a heart as mine,
whose conquest were a task of so much difficulty, and is so little worth
it, that the latter property is always likely to deter any, that hath beauty
and merit enough to overcome the former. But though this untamed
heart be thus insensible to the thing itself called love, it is yet very accessible to things very near of kin to that passion.[18]

There is, however, some evidence that Boyle did not escape heartfree. At least his sister, Lady Ranelagh, once consoled him for a
lost love: 'You are now very near the hour, wherein your mistress
is, by giving herself to another, to set you at liberty from all the
appearances you have put on of being a lover; which though they
cost you some pains and use of art, were easier, because they were
but appearances.'[19] Sisters, however, are sometimes deceived in regard to the seriousness of such attacks. But the most specific evidence that he once courted a lady and was unsuccessful rests on a
statement by his intimate friend, John Evelyn, who mentioned in a
letter to William Wotton, amongst other facts about Boyle, 'That
he courted a beautiful and ingenious daughter of Cary, Earl of

Monmouth; to which is owing the birth of his *Seraphic Love*.' [20] And this rumour is supposed to explain an otherwise mysterious item in his will:

I give and bequeath unto my dear sister, the Lady Katherine, Viscountess Ranelagh, a small ring, usually worn by me on my left hand, having in it two small diamonds, with an emerald in the middle; which ring being held by me, ever since my youth, in great esteem, and worn for many years for a particular reason, not unknown to my said sister, the Lady Ranelagh, I do earnestly beseech her, my said sister, to wear it in remembrance of a brother, that truly honoured, and most dearly loved her. [21]

Attention has been called to Boyle's almost morbid recollection of his childish accidents and ailments; there is little doubt that he was timid about his health and shrank from pain, or that he coddled himself till he was something of a valetudinarian. His letters are full of enquiries about drugs and diseases, and he strove to improve medicine since he believed the physician more to be feared than the disease. God knows the purgings, vomitings, drenchings, blisterings, noxious and filthy druggings, and blood-lettings were enough to make a sensitive person blench with apprehension at the visit of the physician. In spite of the enthusiastic reports by Marcombes of his vermilion cheeks, his breadth of body, and his growing to be an eel, Boyle was delicate from birth.

In addition to recurrent colds, fevers, indigestion, and other minor afflictions, Boyle's eyesight began to trouble him. Such ills were too common to be a matter of note but, at the age of twenty, he was found to be afflicted with stone in the kidney, and he was faced with a future of incurable suffering. In a letter to his friend, Samuel Hartlib, whose wife was a sufferer from the same cause, he wrote of his predicament:

For your bedfellow's receipt for the stone (which certainly wants a parallel, if it be not more easy than effectual) I beseech you to return her (together with the present of my humble service) most humble thanks, which I mean very shortly, God willing, to pay you in an epistle I have drawn up to persuade men to communicate all those successful receipts, that relate either to the preservation or recovery of our health; to which (if you will pardon me a clinch) I shall add, as to the disease last named (so cruel in its tortures, and so fatal in its catastrophe) that they must have their hearts more hard than a very stone, that can refuse a sanative remedy for the stone. As for me, during my confinement to this melancholy solitude, I often divert myself at leisure moments in trying such experiments, as the unfurnishedness of the place, and the present distractedness of my mind, will permit me; which when once my vacant intervals of time will give me leave to blot paper with, and make some short discourses and reflections upon, you may (with all the services you shall be pleased to command their author) confidently expect.[22]

Thomas Birch, in his *Life of Boyle,* gives the following account of Boyle's appearance and health at about this time, which was gathered from his friends:

He was tall of stature, but slender, and his countenance pale and emaciated. His constitution was so tender and delicate, that he had divers sorts of cloaks to put on when he went abroad, according to the temperature of the air; and in this he governed himself by his thermometer. He escaped indeed the smallpox during his life; but for almost forty years he laboured under such a feebleness of body, and such lowness of strength and spirits, that it was astonishing, how he could read, meditate, try experiments, and write as he did. He had likewise a weakness in his eyes, which made him very tender of them, and extremely apprehensive of such distempers as might affect them. He imagined also, that if sickness should confine him to his bed, it might raise the pains of the stone to a degree, which might be above his strength to support; so that he feared lest his last minutes should prove too hard for him. This was the ground of all the caution and apprehension, which he was observed to live in. But as to life itself, he had that just indifference to it, which became so true a Christian . . . The simplicity of his diet was in all appearance that which preserved him so long beyond all men's expectation. This he practised so strictly, that in the course of above thirty years he neither eat nor drank to gratify the varieties of appetite, but merely to support nature.[23]

Boyle lived in constant fear of being drawn into the Civil War. The treatment of his father by Wentworth and Charles I had left him with little affection for the Royal cause; yet he had as little sympathy with the revolutionary ideas of the Parliamentarians. He hated bitterly the religious strife which distracted true piety with its quarrels over creeds and ceremonies; for him, Christian religion was the practice of holy living, and he found in the Anglican Church what fully satisfied him. His experiences in Ireland and Italy had given him a detestation of Roman Catholicism; but he was equally irritated by the wild extravagances of sectarianism which threatened anarchy in both state and church. Though he meddled with politics and religious controversy as little as possible, he was deeply concerned with the miseries which civil war had produced in the country, and the unhappy issue of the strife, whichever side won.

Since Boyle was convinced that the Parliamentary forces were certain to be successful, and since his family, with the exception of Lady Ranelagh and the Warwicks, was Royalist, he saw clearly that his presumed wealth, high social position, and connexion with the peerage would then be an embarrassment rather than an advantage; and it behooved him, like Agag, to walk delicately. But he need not to have worried. We have seen how the influence of Lady Ranelagh secured to him his estates and gave to him a passport. Since then, his brothers had been actively engaged in repelling the Irish rebellion, and had by their ability and bravery prevented Munster from being completely desolated: Lord Broghill, in fact, was for a time in sole command of the army in Ireland. However bitterly the Royalists and Parliamentarians might contend against each other, they were united against the Irish, and neither side could afford to disturb the Boyles while they were doing such service in Ireland.

When the news of the King's execution reached Ireland, horror for the deed united both parties against its perpetrators. Lord Broghill engaged himself in a plot to raise troops on the Continent and to smuggle the young Charles II into Ireland with the hope the country would rise in his cause. To disguise his purpose, he pretended he was about to go to Spa, in Belgium, for relief from an attack of the gout to which he was subject. While stopping on the way at Lady Ranelagh's, he was imperatively summoned into the presence of Cromwell in St. James's Garden. Cromwell, attended by a group of his officers, informed him that his correspondence with Charles was known and is reported to have said: 'The dilemma is short, if you go with me in this expedition to reduce the Irish rebels, you may live, otherwise you certainly die.'[24] Faced with such an alternative, Broghill gave his allegiance to Cromwell with the stipulation that he should be employed only in Ireland. After serving brilliantly in that campaign, he became one of Cromwell's most trusted counsellors and friends, and during the Commonwealth the Boyle interests were safe.

In 1652, it was expedient for Robert Boyle to make a prolonged stay in Ireland in order to attend to his estates, which were now secured but had not paid him any income. He found life there entirely unsuited to his taste, and wrote mournful letters to his friends expressing his boredom and his longing to get away from such a barbarous country. He did however find a new friend, who taught him anatomy and to dissect. In a letter to Dr. Claudius, he describes his pleasure in this new work:

That I may not live wholly useless, or altogether a stranger in the study of nature, since I want glasses and furnaces to make a chemical analysis of inanimate bodies, I am exercising myself in making anatomical dissections of living animals: wherein (being assisted by your father-in-law's [Hartlib's] ingenious friend, Dr. Petty, our general's physician) I have satisfied myself of the circulation of the blood, and the (freshly discovered and hardly discoverable) *receptaculum chyli,* made by the confluence of the *venae lacteae;* and have seen (especially in the dissections of fishes) more of the variety and contrivances of nature, and the majesty and wisdom of her author, than all the books I ever read in my life could give me convincing notions of. Designing, whilst I am kept prisoner in Ireland, to prosecute that study, as I have opportunity; if there be anything relating to it, wherein my knives may give you any satisfaction, I shall be very proud to employ them to so elevated an end.[25]

Dr. Petty, who taught anatomy to Boyle, was an extraordinary and versatile man. After an adventurous boyhood in France, where he learned several languages and mathematics and studied anatomy with Hobbes, he returned to England, entered Brasenose College, and then successively taught music at Gresham College and anatomy at Oxford. He gave up his professorship of anatomy to be physician to the army in Ireland and was remarkably successful also in managing its commissary. In much the same manner as the Earl of Cork, he acquired a huge estate of 50,000 acres in County Kerry and developed its mines, timber, and other resources into a great fortune. Returning to London, he became a leading physician and a founder of the Royal Society. In spite of his support of Cromwell, he enjoyed high favour with Charles II, who knighted him. He was John Aubrey's 'singular friend,' and from him comes the story that Petty amused the King by preaching mock sermons in which he drolly imitated in succession the manner of a Presbyterian, an Independent, a Capuchin Friar, and a Jesuit.

Dr. Petty not only taught Boyle anatomy but also became a great friend and an admirer of his genius. In 1653, the doctor wrote a long letter of advice to the young man, which is a skilful diagnosis.[26] He first tells Boyle that some of his friends are worried about him and then he amusingly enumerates three diseases to be cured.

The first disease is that Boyle reads too much.

I tell you that although you read twelve hours *per diem,* or more, that you shall really profit by no more of what you read, than by what you remember; nor by what you remember, but by so much as you understand and digest; nor by that, but by so much as is new to you, and pertinently set down. But in twelve hours, how little (according to those rules) can you, who know so much already, advantage yourself by this laborious way? . . . On the other side, what a stock of experience have you already in most things! What a faculty have you, of making every thing you see an argument of some useful conclusion or other! How much are you practised in the method of clear and scientifical reasoning! How well do you understand the true use and signification of words, whereby to register and compute your own conceptions! . . .

The next disease you labour under is your apprehension of many diseases, and a continual fear, that you are always inclining or falling into one or other. Here I might tell you, the vanity of life; or, that to fear any evil long, is more intolerable than the evil itself, *etc.* But I had rather put you in mind, that this distemper is incident to all that begin the study of diseases . . .

The last indictment that I bring against you, is practising upon yourself with medicaments not sufficiently tried by those that administer or advise them. It is true, that there is a conceit current in the world, that a medicament may be physic and physician both, and may cure diseases *a quacunque causâ.* But, for my part, I find the best medicament to be but a tool or instrument . . .

Boyle may have regarded his enforced stay in Ireland as a wearisome and barren waste of time; but it was, on the whole, a fortunate episode in his life. During these two fateful years, the Irish rebellion had been crushed, Scotland subjugated, and the Civil War ended by the victory of Worcester which sent Charles II into exile. Since Cromwell returned to Elizabeth's policy of apportioning forfeited Irish lands to English colonists, the estates of the Boyles were secured to them. Robert thus became, for a bachelor, a very rich man; Hooke, who saw his rent roll, told Aubrey that his income was £3,000 a year. Such a fortune relieved him from future financial worry and enabled him to devote his life to science and to exercise his notable generosity.

There is little doubt also that Boyle, while he was in Ireland, was influenced by Dr. Petty to forsake his romantic dilettanteism and to become a professed chemist. Having come to that decision, he saw that Stalbridge was not a suitable place for him. What he needed was contact with scholars who would exchange ideas and stimulate him to work. For such companionship there were but two places from which to choose, London or Oxford.

V

OXFORD AND THE NEW PHILOSOPHY
1654-1660

IT is probable that Boyle, having made up his mind to remove from Stalbridge, inclined first to London, where he could enjoy the companionship of the Invisible College and also live with his sister, Lady Ranelagh. In 1653, he made a hurried trip to London; but, to his dismay, he found the city even more turbulent and distracted than formerly when he had declared it to be distasteful. What was still more discouraging, the weekly discussion meetings of the College had been abandoned. A number of the members had migrated to Oxford; some had left town to accept political positions, and others of the Royalist Party were living in retirement.

While in London, Boyle met Dr. John Wilkins, the recently appointed Warden of Wadham College, who urged him to choose Oxford. There a warm welcome would be given to him by a number of the members of the Invisible College now attached to the University, who, under Dr. Wilkins's leadership, had begun weekly meetings to discuss the new experimental philosophy; also, lodgings would be assigned to him in Wadham. Evidently this offer was the deciding factor in favour of Oxford, for as soon as Dr. Wilkins returned, Boyle received the following official invitation:

Wadham College, Sept. 6, 1653.

Honoured Sir,

You have so well acted the part, which belongs to me, of returning acknowledgements for the favours received at London, that I am as much ashamed, as unable to imitate you. But I have known, Sir, that you are a great master of civilities as well as learning, and therefore shall in all things most willingly submit. I had thought you had gone out of town shortly after the time I waited upon you, which was the reason I did not attempt to trouble you with a visit.

This bearer is the young man, whom I recommended to you. I am apt to believe, that upon trial you will approve of him. But if it should happen

otherwise, it is my desire he may be returned, it being not my aim so much to prefer him, as to serve you, which your own eminent worth will always oblige me unto with my utmost zeal and fidelity. If it be not, Sir, prejudicial to your other affairs, I should exceedingly rejoice in your being stayed in England this winter, and the advantage of your conversation [society] at Oxford, where you will be a means to quicken and direct us in our enquiries. And though a person so well accomplished as yourself, cannot expect to learn anything amongst pedants, yet you will here meet with divers persons, who will truly love and honour you. And it is the more generous kind of felicity to teach and do good, than to learn and receive it. If I knew with what art to heighten those inclinations, which you intimate of coming to Oxford, into full resolutions, I would improve my utmost skill to that purpose; and shall be most ready to provide the best accommodations for you, that this place will afford. I am,
Sir,

your true honourer, and
most faithful servant
Jo. Wilkins *

Before returning to Ireland, in the autumn of 1653, to see to the affairs of his estates, Boyle made a hurried visit to Stalbridge. Since he had determined to forsake his manor, there was much to be done before entrusting it to the care of an agent. In the first place, he made arrangements to maintain the estate in prime condition in order that his brother Francis, on whom it was entailed, should find it to his satisfaction. Alas, poor Francis derived but little benefit from his brother's affectionate forethought. Most of his life was passed in Ireland, practically deserted by his wife, 'black Betty,' who much preferred the dissipations of the Court as a mad companion to her notorious brother, Tom Killigrew, and as a mistress of Charles II, to whom she bore a daughter.

Also, there were legal complications, which arose from Boyle's misunderstanding of the provisions of the entail. To explain these difficulties and the reason for his sudden return to Ireland, he wrote just before sailing the following letter to Mr. John Mallet, the son of his father's friend, Sir Thomas Mallet:

Sir,
If the suddenness of that unwelcome necessity, which hurried me from Stalbridge, would have allowed me so much as two days stay in those

---

* *Works,* Vol. VI, p. 633. The young man recommended to Boyle was probably a young scholar to be an assistant; and possibly it was Robert Hooke, who was such an invaluable aid to Boyle. The credit of recommending him is generally given to Dr. Thomas Willis.

parts, I should not be now reduced to make you an apology for my leaving Stalbridge, before I kissed your hands at Poynington. And though the urgency of my occasions allowed me but one day to pack up bag and baggage, and settle my affairs there, I should have spent part of that day in paying you the duty, and giving myself the satisfaction of a visit, if the greatest obstacle my haste put to my desires had not been the tiredness of my horses by my preceding journies. The apprehension of losing my passage, unless my arrival here prevented the feared change of the wind, posted me so abruptly hither, that it allowed me to comply neither with my civility, nor with my inclinations, the latter of which are never more gratified than in your charming conversation, which the wind's crossness since my arrival here makes me very much regret I did not venture to give myself the happiness of. The sad condition of Ireland making me somewhat irresolute of my going thither this winter, I do not wholly deny myself the pleasing thoughts of being happy in your company at Poynington. But in case a fair wind blow away those thoughts, I must implore, in the want of your immediate conversation, that which is practised by letters, as the next contentment to the former by nearliest approaching it. In the necessity of repairing into Ireland to settle my affairs there, now things seem tending to a settlement in that unhappy country, I shall leave behind me at Stalbridge the bearer, Roger Ball, and with him a lease of that manor for some yet unexpired years; in which lease you were pleased to allow me to have your name put in as a trustee for me. The reason of my mentioning this to you is, that by the mistaking confidence of honest old Mr. Mawdesley, then steward of my courts at Stalbridge, I made several grants there, as presuming I had power to do so; which, upon more knowledge of the law, and a more heedful perusal of my own more than ordinarily strict entail, I found, though hardly overthrowable in equity, yet to be questionable in strictness of law. My just tenderness in cases of this nature made me extremely troubled, that my ignorance had made me do what knowingly nothing should; and therefore by Sir Thomas Mallet's excellent advice, finding a lease of Stalbridge for about thirty years unexpired to remain in the hands of an old servant of my father's, I made it one of my motives to go into Ireland, and one of my concerningest businesses there, to get this lease assigned over in trust to yourself and Roger Ball, with whom I have left order, that in case God should call me to himself before my return to Stalbridge, he shall beg you to join with him in making every tenant, whose grant is questionable, a lease of as many years, as your authority extends to grant, that so these poor men, in case their titles (contrary to my expectation and to probability) should be overthrown as to their first grants, may have a good title to all the unexpired years of your lease; and that number, according to common estimation, will be as advantageous, if not better, than their first grants. I find, Sir, no small trouble in the necessity of giving you this great one; but I am confident you are such a friend to justice, that you will pardon a fault that proceeds only from some tenderness of that virtue in a servant of yours, who very well knowing gratitude to be a virtue as well as justice, if not part of it, is not made more desirous by the laws of the former virtue to secure his tenants, than the duties of the latter will make him of the opportunity of expressing and evincing, how highly he is Mr. Mallet's

affectionate, faithful, and obliged
humble servant
Robert Boyle.[1]

Bristol, Sept. 23, 1653.

In the meantime, Boyle passed the winter impatiently in Ireland and it was not till midsummer of 1654 that, his business ended and relieved of worry, he went to reside at Oxford. He had decided to take lodgings in a private house, rather than to accept the invitation of Dr. Wilkins to live in a college, because of his health and of greater convenience for his experimental work. With this purpose in mind, he had, before leaving England, made a trip to Oxford and engaged rooms from a Mr. Crosse, an apothecary, whose house was in the High Street adjoining University College. It stood on the site now occupied by the Shelley Memorial.*

His sister Katherine, with true feminine doubt that a bachelor was capable of attending properly to his health and comfort, went to Oxford to inspect her brother's selection, and wrote to him a letter of approval and suggestions how he should arrange his rooms in order to solve the problem, peculiarly perplexing to the English mind, of reconciling warmth with fresh air free from draughts.

October 12, [1653.]

My Brother,
It has pleased God to bring us safe to Oxford, and I am lodged at Mr. Crosse's, with design to be able to give you from experience an account which is the warmest room; and indeed I am satisfied with neither of them as to that point, because the doors are placed so just by the chimnies, that if you have the benefit of the fire, you must venture having the inconvenience of the wind, which yet may be helped in either by a

---

* Dr. Fulton, in the Preface to his *Bibliography* of Boyle, erroneously places the lodging of Boyle in the Tavern of the Three Tuns. This tavern was next to Crosse's house; there is some evidence that he established a chemical laboratory in it in which he employed several assistants.

folding screen; and then I think that which looks into the garden will be the more comfortable, though he have near hanged and intends to matt that you lay in before. You are here much desired, and I could wish you here as soon as you can: for I think you would have both more liberty and more conversation, than where you are; and both these will be necessary, both to your health and your usefulness; and as I am sure I have abundantly shared in the latter from you, so I must profess to be very heartily concerned for the former, and must beg that you would be so too, and let me see you are, by your care for its preservation, which are the terms upon which, for aught I see, you must have that blessing; and I am sure you ought not to grudge yourself your cares, since by affording them there you bestow them too upon your friends, and upon me, I am sure, in the most obliging way, who will not give any of that number, that pretend to that relation to you, the precedency in point of the affection belonging to it, though I must many in point of the other qualifications. And alas! how evident is it, that we had need of better things than the best enjoyments of creatures to make us happy; when even friendship itself brings its sensible afflictions as well as refreshments with it? The late experience I have had of this in our parting, will not, I hope, be without instruction to me, as I am sure it has not been without great evidence of the much obligation that lies upon me in point of gratitude, as well as of inclination, to be

Yours affectionately and constantly,
K. R.[2]

Boyle, when he arrived in Oxford to make it his home, found the University scarcely less changed than the nation since the comfortable and easy time when his brother Dungarvan had been an irresponsible gentleman-commoner at Christ Church. The University had steadfastly adhered to the troubled cause of the Stuarts and of the Anglican Church; but, if we can trust contemporary account, it had sunk to a low level of lethargy in both scholarship and morals. When Bishop Laud became Chancellor of his Alma Mater in 1630, he wisely saw what a powerful aid in combatting the spread of Calvinism it would be to entrench his policy of Thorough in the University and to bind it closely to the new church establishment. He at once stiffened the industry and conduct of its fellows and undergraduates; he also undertook to revise and to reform the statutes, which had hardly been changed since the reign of Elizabeth. It is said that the principal work of preparation and the final draught of this three years' undertaking were done by Brian Twyne, Fellow of Corpus, who claimed he 'departed no further from the

ancient statutes than necessary or the genius of the age required.'
When Laud fell from power in 1641, he also resigned the chancellorship; but not before he had left a deep and on the whole good
effect on the university, in spite of a too strict and sometimes gall-
ing supervision of its members.

The following year, Charles I removed the Court from London
to Oxford; and, during the four years he made that city the headquarters for the government and his army, the University, so far as
its academic life and activities were concerned, was practically abandoned. The King and his household occupied Christ Church, and
the Queen, near-by Merton College; while courtiers and army officers dispossessed most of the occupants of the other colleges. The
town and colleges were fortified; trenches were dug in all directions; and the formerly quiet streets were alive with foot-soldiers
and with the troopers of Prince Rupert going to and coming from
frequent forays. Citizens and gown-men were drafted to work on
the trenches; many of the dons and most of the more impressionable undergraduates enlisted for active service. In the constant excitement, studies altogether stopped and student enrollment fell
almost completely, either because of the dangers of travelling, so
vividly described by Boyle on his first journey to Stalbridge, or because of sympathy with the parliamentary cause. The colleges freely,
or from pressure, impoverished themselves by great gifts, or by
loans, never repaid, of money from their chests, and they donated
their precious plate and ceremonial vessels to be melted and coined
in the mint which the King immediately established.*

A bitter day of reckoning came when, on 27 April 1646, Charles,
his army hopelessly defeated, escaped out of Oxford in the disguise
of a servant; and his departure was followed two months later by
the triumphant entrance of the commonwealth forces under the
noble-minded General Fairfax. He dealt wisely and leniently with
his Alma Mater, discouraging vandalism and fostering the return
to normal academic life. Students increased in number, but of a different class—sons of the lesser squires, of the better farmers, and of
merchants, favourable to the now dominant party.

Parliament, clearly foreseeing the importance of inculcating its

* One thing only he was refused. On 30 December 1645, the King sent for a book to be
borrowed from the Bodleian. The librarian apologetically refused, since Bodley's statutes
explicitly and peremptorily forbade any books to be taken out; the King, who, half the
nation believed, considered himself above laws, gave way.

principles in the universities, which had been uncompromisingly royalist and Anglican, first sent down six Presbyterian divines to prepare the way for the new order, so far as preaching could prevail. On 1 May 1647, an Ordinance for the Visitation and Purge of the University was passed; twenty-four Visitors were ordered to enquire into all offences and disorders, and especially to ascertain what members of the University had failed to take the Oath of the Covenant and the Negative Oath not to help the King; had opposed the Parliamentary ordinances; or had fought against the Parliamentary forces. Then followed a period of confusion; many refused to answer questions and were dismissed, many conformed, and some of these kept their offices. As a result of this Visitation and Purge, practically all the Heads of the Colleges and perhaps four hundred members of the Oxford foundations were dismissed. Presbyterians and Calvinists were installed in their places, arousing especial bitterness by the importation of so many from Cambridge, among whom were the already distinguished mathematicians, John Wallis and Seth Ward.

The former indulgent and often loose customs and morals were replaced by rigorous rules; the Book of Common Prayer and the surplice were abolished with the altar and organ playing. Anthony à Wood, who watched the times with cynical aloofness, tells us: 'Presbyterian preachers tried to hold their disciples together by such praying and preaching as to make the prelatical forms ridiculous.' All this doubt and change reduced the enrollment from both parties, for 'some kept their children away for fear of orthodox principles—some keep them at home; others, abroad who return as factious, atheistic, or papistic.' He complained that there were too frequent praying and preaching; but he admitted there were excellent disputations and much zealous coursing, or debates and examinations. Many became morbidly troubled in conscience, and some hanged themselves.

The more fanatic Independents, bitterly discontented with any compromise, became outspoken in their determination to root out and destroy both universities, as obstinate hotbeds of aristocracy and prelacy. Fortunately they failed, for Cromwell, then at the height of his power, accepted the chancellorship of Oxford in 1651. Under his wise and relatively moderate governance, industry and scholarship revived, finances improved, and enrollment increased till Oxford became the centre for the cultivation of the new knowledge and philosophy, far outstripping London and Cambridge, and drawing to it the abler and more ambitious men from both.

It was an extraordinary group of men which, under the leadership of Wilkins, made Oxford famous during the later years of the Commonwealth.[3] Individually remarkable as they may have been, their greater influence resulted from the unanimity of thought and purpose which made them apostles of a new creed. They were passionate believers in the new inductive philosophy of Bacon, by which observation and reason were the divinely ordered keys to absolute truth. The movement begun by them, and culminating in the leadership of Boyle and Newton, led to the founding of the Royal Society and made England the acknowledged leader for a century in the substitution of the mechanistic philosophy for mediaeval scholasticism. Not only has this philosophy guided the physical sciences ever since, but it has also been the model for the later developed biologic and social sciences. Nor would it be difficult to show that Deism, its religious child, is the direct ancestor of our modern humanitarianism.

Dr. John Wilkins, the acknowledged leader of the band of scientists in Oxford and a founder of the Royal Society, was born in the year 1614, and was educated at Magdalen Hall, as the college was then called: at the time of the Visitation and Purge of the University by Parliament he was, because of both his eminent ability and his strong Presbyterianism, appointed Warden of Wadham College. He soon, by his tolerance, his scholarship, and his efficient management, made his college the centre of the new Baconian learning. There he gathered about him a group of young men who met weekly in his lodgings to discuss their new ideas. Of an eager and vivid temperament, he was equally interested in sober and in visionary questions. Although he was in the forefront of the experimentalists of the day, he was also a dabbler in perpetual motion machines, and speculated on the habitableness of the moon and how to get there. In 1656, he got a dispensation to marry Cromwell's sister, which apparently was contrary to the statutes of the College; and two years later he was transferred to Cambridge as Master of Trinity College. While there he revived learning and was honoured and respected by all; however, at the Restoration, his intimacy with Cromwell caused his expulsion. But like most reasonable men, weary of the faction, strife, and intolerance of the past two decades, he later turned Cavalier and became personally popular with Charles II. He was successively Dean of Ripon, Dean of Exeter, and finally Bishop of Chester.

It is no slight tribute to the character and ability of Dr. Wilkins that Anthony à Wood, caustic critic as he was of all his contemporaries and especially so of religious trimmers, should have honoured him thus in his *Athenae Oxonienses:* [4]

. . . This Dr. Wilkins was a person endowed with rare gifts, he was a noted theologist and preacher, a curious critic in several matters, an excellent mathematician and experimentist, and one as well seen in mechanisms and new philosophy (of which he was a great promoter) as any of his time. He also highly advanced the study and perfecting of astronomy, both at Oxford whilst he was Warden of Wadham college, and at London whilst he was of the Royal Society; and I cannot say to the contrary that there was any thing deficient in him but a constant mind and settled principles. Dr. Gilbert Burnet tells us that this Doctor Wilkins (who was for a comprehension and a limited indulgence for dissenters in religion) 'was a man of as great a mind, as true a judgement, as eminent virtues, and of as good a soul as any he ever knew.' And one or more of the Royal Society, say that 'all that knew Bishop Wilkins must needs acknowledge him for his universal insight into all parts of learning, solid judgement, rare prudence and dexterity in the management of worldly affairs and transactions, universal charity, ingenuity, temper and moderation of spirit, to have left behind him but few equals.' Sir Peter Pett in his epistle to the reader before Dr. Barlow's *Genuine Remains,* saith thus of Bishop Wilkins. 'He was an ornament both of that university and the English nation, and one who adorned the gospel itself by his great intellectual endowments.'

Of the group of chemists and physicians, Dr. Thomas Willis was probably the most prominent and influential. He was educated at Christ Church and practised medicine in Oxford with great success. Although there are no notable discoveries attributed to him, he was learned in both anatomy and chemistry, and was reputed to have a deep insight in natural and experimental philosophy. In his house, Beam Hall in Merton Street, he equipped a laboratory and employed as his assistant Robert Hooke, then a student at Christ Church, whom he is generally supposed to have recommended to Boyle. In 1660, he became Sedleian Professor of Natural Philosophy; this position, he held for five years; after which he migrated to London. He was one of the first Fellows of the Royal Society and was regarded as one of the leading physicians of his time. In character, Willis was noted for his piety, charity, and amiability; and, unlike many of his colleagues, he never swerved from his allegiance to the Episcopal Church and the Royalist party. He served in the Royalist army while it remained in Oxford; and he continued to hold Anglican services in his house, probably with the connivance of his political opponents, with whom he maintained friendly relations—in all respects, a sincere and upright man.

Richard Lower was another member of the group. Like Willis, he was educated at Christ Church, and the two men remained intimate associates and friends all their lives. He assisted his older friend in medical practice in Oxford and went with him to London in 1665. Anthony à Wood held him in great esteem and recorded that he helped or rather instructed Willis in anatomy. Lower's chief fame rests on being credited with having performed first the experiment of the transfusion of blood. However, Aubrey claimed that he and Francis Potter, a life-long friend and notable 'for his delicate inventive wit,' had ten years earlier transfused the blood of a hen. Oddly enough, Potter got the idea while reading Ovid's tale of Jason and Medea. Transfusion became one of the important enquiries of the Royal Society; many operations were tried on men and animals, and great hopes were entertained that the introduction of new blood would alter character and cure disease. After Willis's death, Lower was probably the most noted physician in London; but, towards the end of his life, he lost much of his practice because of his politics. He was so strong a Whig that James II complained, 'he did him more harm than a troop of horse.'

A third influential chemist was Ralph Bathurst, also an intimate friend of Willis. He was a Fellow of Trinity and educated for the Church; Wood tells us that he was Chaplain to the Bishop of Oxford, but, finding he had little hope of preferment, he turned to medicine. At the Purge, he submitted to the Presbyterians and kept his fellowship; at the Restoration, he again shifted his faith and, in 1664, he was elected President of Trinity and proved to be 'a good governor but of a poor spirit.' Bathurst was a friend and admirer of Wood and, with Wallis, gave him access to the archives, thus starting him on his antiquarian researches; but his patronage did not prevent Wood from accusing him of wenching and bribery. In 1670, Bathurst left Oxford for London, and, returning to the Church, was appointed Chaplain to the King and Dean of Wells.

Jonathan Goddard completed the quartette of chemists who gave distinction to Oxford. He was a member of the Party of Independents and served as Cromwell's personal physician, accompanying him on his campaigns in Ireland and Scotland. In recognition of his services, Cromwell appointed him Warden of Merton, as Charles I had previously appointed William Harvey. His intimacy with Cromwell was too close to be forgiven and, in 1660, he was ejected. A few years later he moved to London, where he held the important position of Professor of Medicine at Gresham College until his death by apoplexy in February 1674/5, while riding in his coach. He lived in the college and equipped at his own expense an admirable chemical laboratory. Goddard was familiarly known as the drudge of the Royal Society; he seems to have been given the task of solving chemical problems when others failed. He was known to rely on a few simple remedies to cure many diseases, and 'Goddard's Drops' was a famous panacea.

While Boyle profited greatly from contact with these physicians and chemists, it is safe to say that next to Wilkins and Wallis, Seth Ward and Christopher Wren were the conspicuous leaders of the New Science.

Seth Ward, a precocious mathematician when a boy, was a student and then a Fellow of Sidney College, Cambridge. When the Civil War broke out, he, the servitor, disciple, and devoted friend of its Master, Dr. Samuel Ward, voted a college loan to the King. When Cromwell established himself at Cambridge and imprisoned Dr. Ward in St. John's College, his young friend voluntarily accompanied him and helped to relieve his tedium until he died in 1643.

Seth Ward was formally evicted from Sidney in 1644. After several years occupied in various ways, he migrated to Oxford, 'for the sake of Wilkins'; there he entered himself as a gentleman commoner of Wadham and shared with Wren the Tower Chamber. For some years, these three brilliant men made Wadham the centre of learning in the University, and Oxford the centre of the New Science. In 1648, at the Visitation by Parliament, he was appointed Savilian Professor of Astronomy. The Fellows of Jesus College elected him to be their President but the choice was quashed by the Visitors. He was appointed President of Trinity in 1659 but was ejected from the University—this time by the Royalists. Pleading before Charles II his early imprisonment for the royal cause, Ward was taken into favour and successively appointed Dean, and then Bishop, of Exeter, and finally Bishop of Salisbury.

Ward was undoubtedly ambitious, and his first experience, resulting from constancy to his principles, made him resolve for the rest of his life to be more pliant. His impulsive and domineering nature tended to make steadfast friends and strong enemies, who have left to us divergent opinions of his character. Aubrey, his friend, summed him up as a prudent, learned, and good man, of a magnificent and munificent mind; athletic, handsome, and a benefactor of the Royal Society. But Anthony à Wood, who disliked all trimmers and, especially, the Cambridge men imported by Oxford, tells us he was expelled from Cambridge for good cause, and that he obtained his many preferments by cringing to the party in power. But he grudgingly admits that Ward was a real scholar and liberal with money, even though he was smooth and suave.

So much has been written about Sir Christopher Wren and the monuments to his genius are so abundant that there is little need to sketch his career here. It is, however, often forgotten that he was only thirty-four years old when, as a result of the Great Fire, his energies were absorbed as architect and public surveyor; and that even before then, he and Boyle were regarded as the wonders of the age. Their conspicuous abilities were so tempered by modesty and amiability that neither jealousy nor malice was directed against them. To his contemporaries, Wren was 'that astonishing young scholar to whom no form of knowledge came amiss—as a boy, a prodigy; as a man, a miracle; already recognized as a scientific genius.' Nor was there any doubt that his accomplishment as a mathematician, astronomer, and anatomist would have been equally great. Even as it was, no one was more influential in promoting the interests of the Royal Society and of the New Science.

Of the leading members of the group there remains only Robert Hooke.[5] Perhaps no other man of science has been the subject of such divergent criticism. There is, however, since the publication of his *Diary*,[6] no longer any reason for such misunderstanding. It is evident that he was cursed with a jealous and irascible temper; his chronicle of headaches and nausea, and his mistaken regime of emetics and purgatives, must excite sympathy and mitigate criticism.

On the other hand, the accepted opinion of Hooke as a lonely recluse, without friends, feared and hated because of his caustic tongue, is entirely wrong. He was an intimate friend of Boyle,

Wren, and the other distinguished scientists of his day; he was a daily frequenter of the taverns and coffee houses; * and he was an active participant in the life and affairs of the city. It is no exaggeration to say that he, more than anyone else, bore the burden of the difficulties besetting the Royal Society, and contributed to its success. As an architect and as a planner to rebuild London, he was second only to Wren.

Such was Oxford when Boyle arrived to pass fourteen of the happiest and most fruitful years of his life. He at once entered prominently into the best life of the University and formed intimate friendships with its leading scholars. He established laboratories, hired many assistants, spent much money, and entertained so lavishly that he maintained a second establishment at Stanton St. John's, four miles out of town, where he could retire when he desired rest and quiet from visitors. His routine of life was interrupted only by short but frequent visits to friends, to his family, and to London.

Boyle's biographers and critics have given us the impression that he at once took the position of an acknowledged master of the sciences with which his name and fame are connected. But even a cursory consideration of his character and previous education, as given by himself and by his contemporaries, should prevent that error and should, on the contrary, prove that he spent somewhat short of six years as an apprentice to the foremost scholars of the day. This erroneous opinion must have been derived from complimentary letters to him, from his sudden fame in 1660, and from casual statements in his autobiographic sketch; but one should not neglect to weigh the customary flattery of letters of the period, especially when addressed to one of high social rank, or to discount the memory of early achievements which were merely indicative of future accomplishment.

There is no better way to understand Boyle's character and his preparation for his life work than to contrast them with Newton's. Newton, from a humble birth and fortune, rose to eminence by sheer ability and used his scientific reputation to secure wealth and high social position. As a youth of twenty-three years, his genius unrecognized and unknown, he retired to Woolsthorpe from Cambridge because of the plague, and there in solitude, in a year and

* The astonishing number of 154 of these resorts is mentioned in his *Diary* as being occasionally, or frequently, visited by him.

a half, discovered the laws of the nature of light, of calculus, and of universal gravitation. Without divulging his astounding discoveries or seeking advice from anyone, he meditated on these subjects for many years; when, at long last, he reluctantly published his results, they were final, complete, and unassailable. He was the exaggerated type of the solitary worker, making it almost impossible to discover the influence of others on his genius.

Boyle, on the other hand, born to wealth and high social rank, sought no further advance in either, and used them to aid his scientific aims. Friendly and modest, he made a host of friends, eagerly learned from them, invited criticism, and gathered data and ideas from all the world. In return he excited wonder and admiration because he, a gentleman, engaged in scientific work; his companionship was sought and his accomplishments were exaggerated because he could foster scientific undertakings and dignify their importance.

Boyle's reputation does not rest on great inventions, such as Newton's does, but on his ability to popularize empiric science and to supersede the scholastic and mediaeval philosophy by the Baconian and corpuscular philosophy. His influence on thought was profound, and although he was the founder of modern chemistry, he made no epoch-making discoveries. He himself was the first to acknowledge this. He says repeatedly that he was a historian of science, accumulating a mass of experimental data of all sorts in order that others might later build on it a sound knowledge and philosophy.

That Boyle had much to learn when he went to Oxford is evident from Anthony à Wood, who recorded in his Diary that Boyle brought to Oxford a certain Peter Sthael,* a noted chemist and Rosicrucian of Strasbourg, who taught him geometry, the Cartesian philosophy, and chemistry. Sthael lived for a year or two with Boyle at Mr. Crosse's in the High Street. Besides his duties as private tutor, he was permitted to give lessons to three other pupils. Then he moved to a house next door but one, a tavern kept by Arthur Tillyard. Finally in 1663, when his work became established and his classes increased, he went to an ancient hall, 'a back-side house to

---

* *Works,* Vol. VI, p. 122. Hartlib wrote, 1659, to Boyle that he had been suffering grievously from stone, but he had acquired an 'excellent spirit of salt' which he uses daily and which works mightily upon stone: 'I had a letter from him, who made it, I mean Mr. Stahl, expressing a resolution to come over shortly into England.'

the Ram Inn in All Saints Parish'; there, he established his laboratory and his classes. Wood himself was a member of them, and he mentions amongst others John Wallis, Christopher Wren, Dr. Ralph Bathurst, and Dr. Richard Lower. He also noted that John Locke * was of the number, and caustically added: 'He was a turbulent spirit, clamorous, and never contented; while others listened and took notes, he would not—he would be prating and troublesome.' Sthael afterwards became an operator of the Royal Society. He died in London, about 1675, and was buried in St. Clement Danes.

The conviction that Boyle was still in the status of the apprentice is strengthened by the fact that he did not publish any work until he had lived in Oxford six years. While the date of publication is no clue to the time when any of Newton's work was done, it is for Boyle's, unless he specifically mentions that publication had been delayed. He ordinarily published hurriedly and voluminously, and was the despair of his proof readers and printers, who complained that his manuscripts were muddled, corrected, and added to during the printing. There is, I think, no work of his which does not allude, in the preface, to this habit of carelessness and hurry. The apology made to the reader and prefixed to his first book, in 1660, is typical and proves that he issued it as soon as he had material:

They [the experiments] are not still set down so much as in the order wherein they were made; but most commonly in that casual one, wherein my occasions induced me to dispatch them to the press. And, which is worse, I did usually send quite away the former experiments, before the latter were written, or perhaps so much as made: whereby I lost the advantage of correcting and supplying the imperfections of what I had formerly written, by the light of my subsequent trials and discoveries.

Besides all this, the distemper in my eyes forbidding me not only to write myself so much as one experiment, but even to read over myself what I had dictated to others; I cannot but fear, that besides the author's mistakes, this edition may be blemished by many, that may be properly imputed to a very unskilful writer (whom I was oftentimes by haste reduced, against my custom to employ) and may have escaped the diligence of that learned friend, that doth me the favour to oversee the press; especially there being the distance of two days journey betwixt it and me.[7]

* Locke was then a Student of Christ Church and was ignominiously dismissed by the order of Cromwell for his fractious refusal to obey. Lord King, in his *Life of Locke,* severely criticized Dean Fell for servilely and treacherously carrying out this order, but others exonerated Fell from blame. Wood, *Life and Times,* Vol. 1, p. 472.

Even stronger evidence of Boyle's apprenticeship can be drawn from the character of his earliest publication, *On the Spring and Weight of the Air,* than from its date. The entire credit for this work, which immediately established his reputation as the foremost scientist of his day, has always been ascribed to him; but a critical study of the subject and its treatment should transfer an equal, if not a major, share to his assistant, Robert Hooke.

In the preface, which is in the form of a letter to his nephew, Lord Dungarvan, Boyle explained how his attention was drawn to the problem, and the difficulty of securing an efficient air-pump, without which the work was impossible:

You may be pleased to remember, that a while before our separation in England, I told you of a book, that I had heard of, but not perused, published by the industrious Jesuit Schottus; * wherein, it was said, he related how that ingenious gentleman, Otto Guericke, consul of Magdeburg, had lately practised in Germany a way of emptying glass vessels, by sucking out the air at the mouth of the vessel, plunged under water [1650-54]. And you may also perhaps remember, that I expressed myself much delighted with this experiment . . . Wherefore to remedy these inconveniences, I put both Mr. G. and R. Hooke (who hath also the honour to be known to your Lordship, and was with me when I had these things under consideration) to contrive some air-pump, that might not, like the other, need to be kept under water (which on divers occasions is convenient) and might be more easily managed; and after an unsuccessful trial or two of ways proposed by others, the last-named person fitted me with a pump.[8]

Because of Boyle's known probity, we should unreservedly accept his claim to the idea of investigating the properties of the air; and we know that the idea did not occur to him before 1657, at least three years after he had established himself at Oxford. Now, the elusive properties of the atmosphere and of gases in general, which had put them in a mysterious class by themselves and had given rise to Aristotle's much abused doctrine of nature's *horror vacui,* rested entirely on the mechanical difficulty of manipulating them. Just so soon as an efficient gas-pump and accessory apparatus were available, the weight and elasticity of the air and its effects on life and combustion were as readily discoverable as were the new marvels of astronomy when the telescope was invented.

* *Mechanica Hydraulico-pneumatica,* 1657. It is thus certain Boyle had had no idea of undertaking this work until he had been at least three years resident in Oxford.

It is a significant fact that there was no mention in the first edition of Hooke as the creator of the air-pump. This is no reflection on Boyle's character, since Hooke had been engaged at first as a mechanic, for which art he had remarkable skill; and it was not customary to mention specifically laboratory assistants.* When, probably to the surprise of the author, the tract made a dazzling success and the air-pump was regarded as an eminent invention comparable to that of the telescope, Boyle generously gave full credit in the second edition to Hooke. But the scientific and the social world had already hailed Boyle as its inventor. The original apparatus presented to the Royal Society is exhibited in the Library as Boyle's Pump. Evelyn's *Diary* and other contemporary writers refer to the frequent and exciting demonstrations of Boyle's Engine; and that opinion still persists.

The fact that the success of all these experiments depended on the pump was acknowledged by Boyle in 1669, when the second and improved apparatus was designed:

After I had presented the great Engine I formerly made use of to the Royal Society, partly the difficulty of procuring such another of that size and make, and partly the desire of making some improvements invited me to make some alterations in the structure; some suggested by others, (especially by the ingenious Mr. Hooke,) and some of them that I added myself, as finding that *without them I could not do my work.*†

Lastly, if we consider the plan and conduct of this work, they are exceptional for Boyle, who was a chemist interested in the composition of bodies; and customary for Hooke, whose taste and genius directed him to mechanical and mathematical problems. The specific experiments point to Boyle, but the method of attack, which involved the physical and mechanical properties of the air, shows the influence of Hooke. The final and convincing proof that air, like other bodies, had a definite weight was first given in the second edition, to answer the objections of Linus, by a crude determination of Boyle's law—that the pressure of a gas is directly proportional to its density. That same year, 1662, Hooke moved to London, as Curator of the Royal Society. Boyle, although he afterwards frequently discussed the properties of the air, abandoned any further work of a quantitative and mathematical nature; while

* This is the opinion also of Dr. Fulton. *Bibliography*, p. 21.
† Fulton, *Bibliography*, p. 21. Italics mine.

Hooke devoted his time to that type of work, and in fact included Boyle's law in his general formula for elasticity: *ut tensio, sic vis.*

The time when Boyle reached his full power is important; if this extended argument be sound, he was *in statu pupillari,* or at least greatly assisted by others and especially by Sthael and Hooke, for his first six years at Oxford. We may even assume that the success of his discovery of the spring and weight of the air convinced him that his ability did not lie in the field of physics, which requires delicate apparatus and involves quantitative and mathematical experimentation. Otherwise, it is difficult to explain another statement in the preface to that work:

Ever since I discerned the usefulness of speculative geometry to natural philosophy, the unhappy distempers of my eyes have so far kept me from being much conversant in it, that I fear I shall need the pardon of my mathematical readers for some passages, which, if I had been deeply skilled in geometry, I should have treated more accurately. And indeed, having, for reasons elsewhere deduced, purposely kept myself a stranger to most of the new hypotheses in philosophy, I am sensible enough, that the engine [Hooke's pump] I treat of hath prevailed with me to write of some subjects, which are sufficiently remote from those I have been most conversant in.[9]

Amidst the chorus of praise, there were only two hostile voices; Boyle was attacked by Franciscus Linus,[10] an English Jesuit and Professor of Physics in the University of Liége, and by Thomas Hobbes,[11] then at the height of his fame as a materialistic philosopher. It is both interesting and instructive to compare the reactions of Boyle and Newton to criticisms of their maiden efforts. It will be remembered that Newton's great monograph on the nature and composition of white light was severely objected to by several scientists who could not endure to have their darling speculations destroyed and who would not accept the clear evidence of facts. Newton, it also will be remembered, was induced by Oldenburg, the Secretary of the Royal Society, to answer his critics led by this self-same Linus, who, as a Jesuit, was dogmatically committed to scholastic Aristotelianism. The controversy dragged on till Newton, weary and disgusted, threatened to renounce science as a master more litigious than the law.

Boyle, on the other hand, courteously answered his opponents and then dismissed the subject from his unruffled mind. He opened his defence by summarizing Linus's absurd Funicular Hypothesis thus:

The hypothesis that the examiner would, as a better, substitute in the place of ours, is, if I mistake it not, briefly this; that the things we ascribe to the weight or spring of the air are really performed by neither, but by a certain Funiculus, or extremely thin substance, provided in such cases by nature, *ne detur vacuum,* which being exceedingly rarefied by a forcible distension, does perpetually and strongly endeavour to contract itself into dimensions more agreeable to the nature of the distended body; and consequently does violently attract all the bodies whereunto it is contiguous, if they be not too heavy to be removed by it.[12]

Then he added a large number of new and convincing experiments, among which he measured roughly the variation of the pressure of the air with its density and announced what is now the familiar Boyle's law.

As for Hobbes, he had sneered at Boyle for submitting to the immense waste of time and effort in experimentation when any ingenious mind could arrive at true conclusions about natural phenomena by cogitation. He contemptuously exposed his cogitations in a farrago of nonsense. Boyle, with great restraint,[13] answered him, and contented himself with this stinging rebuke:

If Mr. Hobbes thinks fit to say anything to the following discourse, it will not be amiss, that his reply be as inoffensive as I have endeavoured to make my examen. For having dispatched as much as I think requisite to say of this controversy myself, and having other (and I hope better) employments for my leisure hours, if I can get any; I must leave the further disputes, if any shall arise, to be managed by others, who, if Mr. Hobbes refuse to imitate my way of writing, will possibly make no scruple to imitate his, and put him in mind of that law of Vespasian, upon which himself would be thought to ground that heap of strange titles he bestows upon the two learned Savilian Professors, *That it is unlawful to give ill language first, but civil and lawful to return it.*[14]

Boyle's reference to 'the two learned Savilian Professors' is to a controversy which had recently amused and excited the scholarly world. Hobbes, who was a self-taught mathematician, immensely proud of his accomplishment and equally contemptuous of academic discipline, ventured to write a book on geometry. It was not at all a bad book so long as he confined himself to ordinary problems, but he rashly included solutions for squaring the circle and others of the demonstrated insolubles. Wallis and Ward, the Savilian Professors, gleefully took up the challenge and overwhelmed the author with stinging sarcasm and wit, in which Wallis was a master. The paper fight waxed hot and furious; as a sample of the amenities of their words, Hobbes's characterization of his opponents may be cited: 'So go your ways you uncivil ecclesiastics, inhuman divines, dedoctors of morality, unasinous colleagues, egregious pair of Issachars, most wretched Vindices and Indices Academiarum; and remember Vespasian's Law.'

Boyle's interests, as always, were not confined to science. His eyesight was still strong enough to permit him to continue his studies in the oriental languages, and in the Bible. He eagerly sought and made friendships with a group of humanists.

Among these friends was Edward Pococke, of whom Wood remarks that he became honoured and famous for his oriental knowledge and publications; a modest, candid man, and an ornament to Oxford. He travelled for several years in the Orient and collected an oriental library for the University. Chancellor Laud appointed him first Reader in Arabic, and he was later Professor of Hebrew and Canon of Christ Church. He it was who did most of the translation of the New Testament into Malayan, and from his letters to Boyle we learn that he was constantly aided financially by the latter in the publication of his books.

There was also the famous oriental scholar, Samuel Clarke of Merton College, who had the imposing title of First Architypographus of the University. When Boyle went to Oxford, Clarke was in London correcting the manuscript and publishing the Polyglot Bible, but he returned to Oxford in 1658, and they became lifelong friends.

Of this group of humanists, Thomas Barlow was probably the most eminent and the closest to Boyle. He was a Fellow, and later Provost, of Queen's College. On the strength of his strong Calvinism and tolerance even towards the Anabaptists and Independents, he retained his fellowship at the Purge and was in 1652 appointed Head Keeper of the Bodleian. Into this work he threw himself heart and soul, and under his direction the Library grew with leaps and bounds. Considered by his contemporaries to be the most learned man of his day in theology and Christian history, and with an encyclopaedic memory, he also had the talent for entertaining visitors to the Library, and he rarely permitted them to escape without enriching the collection. In spite of his former Calvinism, he was able by skilful trimming not only to escape dismissal at the Restoration, but even to be appointed a Royal Visitor to purge the University of Calvinism, and later to be made Margaret Professor and Bishop of Lincoln by Court influence, in spite of the protests of Archbishop Sheldon. Barlow was of great assistance to Anthony à Wood in his antiquarian researches, giving him many privileges in examining manuscripts; and, in return, Wood assisted in arranging the great Seldenian gift of 8,000 volumes. However, Wood's anger was aroused by a few restrictions imposed on his use of manuscripts, and one suspects that the antiquary was not innocent of occasionally purloining a choice specimen. But his chief grievance arose when Barlow permitted Wallis to see Wood's manuscript copy of the *Athenae Oxonienses* and to delete certain offensive passages about him. In his sketch of Wallis, he had mentioned the mathematician's skill in deciphering intercepted letters and documents of the Royalists. Wallis was very proud of this accomplishment before the Restoration and just as reluctant to have it mentioned afterwards; hence his anxiety to remove the passages in the manuscript, and hence the author's ire. In revenge, Wood dubbed him 'false, insincere, and not the scholar he was supposed to be'; but Boyle's and Evelyn's long and intimate friendship is a safer estimate of Barlow's character. Barlow, as Bishop of Lincoln, was a bitter opponent of James II and of the Pope, whom he always referred to as 'the old gentleman at Rome.' In his few letters to Boyle which we have, he mentioned many portents of punishment for the sins of England; and he confidently predicted that the abdication of James was prophetic of the downfall of the papacy, sure to occur in the year following.

Thomas Hyde, the last of this group of humanists, was a younger man than the others. From his very early years he showed his inclination to oriental languages, which he studied with his father. He first went to King's College, Cambridge, but after a year he was called to London to assist Dr. Clarke as a corrector of the Polyglot Bible; that finished, he entered Queen's College, Oxford; and already an acknowledged authority in Persian, Arabic, Syriac, and Samaritan, he was appointed reader, or professor, in Hebrew. He later succeeded Barlow as librarian of the Bodleian, and Pococke as professor of Arabic.

When we recall Boyle's interest in oriental languages and his ardent support of the translation and spread of the Gospels in the Orient, in Ireland, in America, we readily appreciate what such friends meant to him and what he meant to them.

In addition to those who may be termed professional companions, Boyle made many personal friends. Two sons of his oldest brother, the Earl of Cork, were students at Oxford, and Boyle began his practice of trying (vainly) to turn such youths to a studious life by dedicating his *Spring of the Air* to the young Lord Dungarvan. Dick Jones, the son of his sister, Lady Ranelagh, also came up to Oxford with his tutor, Henry Oldenburg, for a year before leaving on a continental tour. To this wayward and fascinating boy, under the pseudonym of Pyrophilus, his uncle dedicated his *Physiological Essays*. Apparently, Jones was a more promising neophyte. His life was a curious blend of dissipation and studiousness. Under the one influence, he became a boon companion of deGrammont and the Court rakes; and under the other, an intelligent Fellow of the Royal Society. In the end, he figured as an important man, fat and witty, and as a result, advanced his family to the earldom of Ranelagh. He it was who built the great estate, Ranelagh House in Chelsea, which was afterwards sold and turned into the Gardens where the gallants of the next two centuries congregated and flirted.

In 1656, Evelyn mentions in his *Diary* that Boyle and Dr. Wilkins dined with him at Saye's Court. This was the beginning of a friendship which grew ever stronger and more tender with the years. There are many references to Boyle in the *Diary;* and at Boyle's death, Evelyn was made a trustee to administer the Boyle Lecture Fund.

In 1657, Oldenburg left Oxford with young Jones for their tour of the Continent, and from his letters we have some interesting news of Boyle. In one letter, he sends a recipe for invisible writing in order that they may express themselves freely; in another, he sends some 'grains of bama muscata' which, when properly prepared, he hoped would be useful in curing Boyle's gravel in the kidney; also the recipe of an oil, valuable in curing 'megrims, palsies, lamenesses, crookednesses, and all ricketing diseases,' and adds that it 'answereth your *Ens Veneris.*' Another letter tells of a fixed salt drawn from a potter's earth at Arcueil, 'which salt being for some time exposed to the sunbeams, became salt-petre, then vitriol, then lead, tin, copper, silver, and, at the end of fourteen mouths, gold.' He has some doubt about this most protean salt, but the author of the fable was a 'very authentic gentleman' who had observed the auto-transmutation. From these letters also we learn that Boyle had already begun his inveterate habit of devising remedies and of collecting recipes from all sources for curing all manner of diseases; especially for those real or imagined ones which afflicted him. Also, we learn that he was an alchemist and had begun his search for the philosopher's stone, making transmutations of all sorts one of the axioms of his philosophy.

After his return from the tour on the Continent, Oldenburg, on Boyle's recommendation, became Secretary of the Royal Society, and as a voluminous correspondent did much to promote its interests. He kept Boyle constantly informed on what was new and interesting in the scientific world as, later, he also served Newton. He acted as Boyle's agent in London and saw his works through the press, a complicated task; when he died impoverished, his patron generously supported his family.

It will be recalled that Cromwell had returned to the policy of granting Irish estates to English landlords and colonists and that, through the influence of Lord Broghill, much property had been assigned to the Boyles. These grants included some, at least, of the church property of the Earl of Cork which the Earl of Strafford and Charles I had compelled him to restore to the parishes. What to do with this portion of his enlarged estate seems to have troubled the conscience of Robert Boyle; he finally decided to accept the church property, but to devote it to the advancement of the New Science. There is reason to believe he had in mind to endow an institution such as afterwards became the Royal Society.

We learn of Boyle's purpose from a letter of Oldenburg's to him, in which he says:

I am hugely pleased, that the council hath granted your desires for the promotion of knowledge; which I suppose to be those that were couched in a certain petition you were pleased to impart to me at Oxford; wherein, if I remember well, a matter of twelve thousand pounds sterling was offered to purchase confiscated lands and houses with in Ireland, and to commit the profit thereof into the hands of certain trustees, for to employ it in the entertainment of an agent, secretary, translators, for keeping intelligence, distributing rewards, *etc.* in order to the end aforesaid.[15]

In order to assist Boyle in perfecting the details for this proposed
foundation of learning, John Evelyn wrote to him a long letter,
dated from Saye's Court, 3 September 1659.[16] In this letter, he out-
lines a scheme for a fantastic mathematical college where a few
choice spirits could, under a sort of monastic regime, retire from the
horrid disturbance of the age to 'resign themselves to live profitably
and sweetly together,' and, like a little army under the command of
the spirit of Bacon, march forward in the conquest of the New
Philosophy. He desired to devote his own small fortune to the
project, were he not an 'aggregate person,' and so obliged, as well
by his nature as by the laws of decency and by their merits, to provide for his family and dependents. And then note the position
Boyle had already attained as a patron of learning:

I propose, that if any one worthy person, and *quis meliore luto,* so
qualified as Mr. Boyle, will join in the design (for not with every one,
rich and learned; there are very few disposed, and it is the greatest
difficulty to find the man) we would not doubt, in a short time (by
God's assistance) to be possessed of the most blessed life that virtuous
persons could wish or aspire to in this miserable and uncertain pilgrim-
age, whether considered as to the present revolutions, or what may happen for the future in all human probability.

Evelyn proposed for his monastic college the purchase of thirty
or forty acres of land some twenty-five miles from London, on
which to erect various buildings at a cost of not more than £1,600.
He and his wife would live there as abbot and matron. Some of the
orders for the fellows were to be: prayers at six in the morning and
study till half past eleven; dinner at one, prayers again at seven, and
to bed at nine; all play and amusement interdicted; and every one
to cultivate his garden and to work in the laboratories. A few
strangers might be entertained, and reports of the results of studies
should be made weekly.

Under more favourable circumstances, Boyle might have been
persuaded to foster Evelyn's visionary scheme; but it was proposed
at a time of the deepest perplexity and despair: Cromwell was dead,
and under the nerveless guidance of Richard, no one knew whether
anarchy or the restoration of the monarchy would result. In either
case, new rebellions in Ireland were a certainty and his newly acquired estates would yield no income for years, even if they should
not be altogether lost.

The winter of 1657/8 was, according to Evelyn, the severest ever known by any living man, and it lasted well into June. Such weather, in those days, was certain to be accompanied by widespread illness; it was so in this case and, in May, a public fast was ordered 'to avert an epidemical sickness, very mortal this spring.' This was the beginning of the epidemics which annually increased and swept over England till they culminated in the terrible plagues of a few years later. Cromwell, exhausted by the great burdens of his life and even more by anxiety over his daughter's illness, was known, on 21 August, to be ill of an ague; and, on Sunday the 29th, public prayers were said for his recovery. On the next day occurred the most terrible storm on record in England. The superstitious regarded it as a portent; his followers, as a divine warning of retribution; his enemies said the devil was riding in the whirlwind to claim the soul of the great traitor. Isaac Newton, when an old man, still remembered that he, then a lad of sixteen at Woolsthorpe in Lincolnshire, had tried to estimate the force of the wind by measuring how much farther he could jump with it than against it. Boyle and his friends at Oxford were filled with anxiety, which increased with the news of the Great Protector's death on 3 September.

Every member of the Oxford group owed the security of his position to Cromwell's protection; they had, at the Purge, received or maintained their positions either because they were Parliamentarians or because they had abjured the Royalist cause. And now during this year, and the dismal one following, all knew that Richard Cromwell was incapable of governing the country. If the fanatics won, then they could expect the destruction of the University; if the Royalists restored the monarchy, there was sure to be a new purge, and it would be difficult to succeed twice as a trimmer.

Even before the death of Cromwell, the magic circle had been broken, for Wren had gone to London as professor of astronomy in Gresham College, and Cromwell had sent its dominant spirit, Dr. Wilkins, to Cambridge as Master of Trinity College. The meetings were transferred to Boyle's rooms, but much of their charm and vigour was lost. During the two years preceding the Restoration, the meetings were discontinued and Boyle left Oxford; just when, we do not know, but for a considerable while he was a guest of his friend, the poet Waller, at Beaconsfield. While there, he prepared his *Seraphic Love* and his *Spring of the Air* for publication.

While Boyle was quietly waiting at Beaconsfield the outcome of the strife of party, his brother, Lord Broghill, went again to Ireland and remained loyal to Richard Cromwell till he was convinced of the hopelessness of that government; then he dispatched a letter by his brother Francis to Charles, begging him to come to Ireland and, with his help, restore the monarchy. Although this letter was, perhaps, received by Charles before General Monk had declared for the Restoration, the scheme was unnecessary; but the intention of the author was remembered by Charles II when he distributed favours to those who promoted his return from exile.

VI

LAST YEARS AT OXFORD

1660-1668

WHATEVER fears the Boyle family may have had regarding its fate at the Restoration were allayed by the astute policy of Lord Broghill, and all its members were received in high favour by Charles II. Even Robert Boyle left his retreat at Beaconsfield and took his part in the national welcome; he may have been amongst those who made the crossing to escort Charles from The Hague. At least Pepys records in his *Diary*, 11 April 1660: 'A gentleman came from my Lord of Manchester for a pass for Mr. Boyle, which was made him'; and on 20 April: 'This evening came Mr. Boyle on board, for whom I writ an order for a ship to transport him to Flushing. He supped with my Lord, my Lord using him as a person of honour.'

Boyle's oldest brother, the Earl of Cork, who had quietly remained a Royalist, was now given an English peerage and took the title of Earl of Burlington and Cork. Like his father, he loved ostentatious display, and he built Burlington House, one of the first great mansions in Piccadilly, adjoining Clarendon House—the former is now the home of the Royal Society, the latter did not outlast the fortunes of the Lord Chancellor. Here Cork entertained lavishly, and we have the amusing anecdote that Pepys, dining there, was so excited by the honour that he set his wig on fire when nervously bending his head too close to the candles.

In the autumn of 1660, Broghill was created Earl of Orrery, his services to Cromwell forgiven, and Francis was made Viscount Shannon. Robert Boyle took part in the festivities of the investiture and also enjoyed a milder triumph. He stayed with his sister, Lady Ranelagh, in Chelsea, and there Evelyn dined with him and after dinner saw 'divers experiments' performed with the new and marvellous pneumatic pump. He found favour with the new King, who was an amateur of chemistry and astronomy, with the Lord Chancellor Clarendon, and with the Earl of Southampton, Lord High Treasurer. He, too, was offered a peerage, but declined it on the ground that, as he was, he enjoyed all the privileges of wealth and rank; whereas if he became the head of a great family, he would be burdened by the cares and distractions of managing its affairs. Clarendon even advised him to enter into holy orders and promised him the highest preferment in the Church. This temptation, also, he put aside, again with the excuse that he had no interest in religion except to save his own soul, and he believed he could accomplish that better if he had no share in the patrimony of the Church and could pursue his philosophical studies in such a manner as to support religion. As a scientist, his new air-pump and experiments on the spring of the air, fresh from the press, had at once given him fame, and he was constantly sought to demonstrate the wonders occurring in a vacuum, even by Royal command showing them to the King.

When Boyle returned to Oxford after the festivities for the return of the King, he found the University and city recovering from a delirious celebration. On 8 May, Richard Cromwell had resigned as Chancellor, and, on the fateful 29th, the loyalists lost all restraint, and the wild jollity lasted until the next morning. Anthony à Wood wrote: 'The world of England was perfectly mad.' Wood's picture of the moral laxity at Oxford during the reign of Charles is not without justification. But with the appointment of the Earl of Clarendon as Chancellor, a period of high Court favour began for the loyal university.

When Clarendon returned as Chancellor, 'mistrustful and censorious, to the beautiful city which he knew so well, he marvelled to find it, in spite of malice and rebellion, yielding an extraordinary harvest of sound knowledge. Even students, wickedly introduced, had applied themselves to the practice of virtue. Even Puritan scholars had learned to appreciate the meaning of duty and obedience, qualities which it could hardly be expected that any rebel should be taught.'[1] The purge which followed was relatively mild; some few of the obstinate Calvinists were dismissed, but most were so weary of strife that they conformed to the new order, and Oxford quickly reverted to *ante bellum* customs, to Anglicanism and the Royalist Party.

But Boyle found his circle of scientists not only depleted but broken up, and the home of the new science was transferred to

London. Wilkins, who had gone to Cambridge, had been dismissed, and Seth Ward lost his professorship at Oxford; although both returned to favour, they forsook science and became prominent bishops. Wallis stayed on at Oxford and, although Wren returned as Ward's successor, he was mostly occupied in London. Of the physicians and chemists, all except Bathurst soon left to practise in London. Even more serious to Boyle's work, Hooke and Sthael left to accept positions in the new Royal Society. On the other hand, most of his humanist friends and associates remained in the University and his interest in their work increased steadily.

Boyle returned to Oxford a famous man; the popularity of his early works was extraordinary both in England and abroad, even reaching to the American colonies. One great cause of this popularity was their ease and simplicity of style. Pepys, who can be taken as typical of the age, always mentions the purchase of Boyle's books as they came off the press, and reading them, often as he rode in a wherry on the Thames; even when he confesses that the subject is too chemical for him to understand much, 'yet enough to see he is a most excellent man.' From 1660 to 1666, Boyle published ten large books while at Oxford, and twenty papers in the *Transactions of the Royal Society;* then followed a period of silence for five years, except for six papers in the *Transactions.*

It is somewhat of a mystery how Boyle could achieve such a great quantity of work. The best explanation seems to be that he was rather a director of a laboratory than an individual experimentalist. As such, he employed numerous assistants and mechanics, who made the observations and did the detailed work on the problems he set them. And he must have had a staff of secretaries, who managed his great correspondence, collected the mass of data and recipes he published, read to him, and wrote to his dictation. There are a number of circumstances that support this opinion. After the Restoration he was frequently absent from Oxford, in London and visiting friends and relatives; he was often incapacitated by illness, once for a period of almost two years; and, although he refused many offices and appointments, he accepted some which required time and attention.

Industry and perseverance might have conquered other distractions, but the persistent and increasing weakness of his eyes made it almost impossible for him to read, to write, or to observe consecutively for long periods; in his correspondence and publications there are frequent references to this unsurmountable handicap to his personal work, and apologies for errors because of his inability to give personal supervision. As was to be expected, since his interest in medicine was especially keen when the subject touched his own real or imagined troubles, he studied the structure and function of the eye, and gathered recipes of cures from all sources, learned or ignorant. If he actually tried them, the wonder is that his eye-sight did not altogether fail; one, which he mentions as having aided him, was dried and powdered dung blown into the eyes.

The weakness of Boyle's eye-sight became acute in the autumn of 1664. While on a trip to the western counties, he consulted his friend, Dr. Turberville, a skilful oculist of Salisbury, who watched and attended to his eye-sight the rest of his life; when Pepys suffered from the same affliction, he was induced by Boyle to seek the same aid. A pathetic letter to Dr. Turberville written only three months before Boyle's death is typical of his interest in the subject:

London, Oct. 8, 1691.

Worthy Doctor,
If you knew how very ill my sister and I have been, since you left this place, you would not wonder, that you have not had from me an enquiry, how you bore your journey to Salisbury . . . Your constant kindness to me, and the benefits I have received from your skill and experience in your profession, urge me to acquaint you with the distemper in my eyes, that did much surprise me, and does still much afflict me, having continued with me for about a month. The case in short is this; in the day time, I see, thanks be to God, as I use to do, and so till five o'clock in the afternoon; but then, as soon as candles are brought in, I find a very sensible decay in my sight; so that, though I can see all the same gross objects as I did before, and could, if I durst, read printed books, as I have often tried, yet the reflection from those objects is not vivid, as it was wont to be; and if I look upon somewhat distant objects, methinks I see them through a thin mist, or a little smoke; but when the candles are newly snuffed, and so the light increased, I see far better, for a little while, till it begin to have more snuff: this distemper continues, as long as I make use of candlelight, but the next morning, by God's goodness, I find myself as before, only now and then there seems to fall slowly down, sometimes in one eye, and sometimes in another, a faintly shining vapour, which immediately disappears. I have such apparitions of late, for these two or three years, without any bad consequence. What this distemper may proceed from, I know not, though I remember I have heard you more than once take notice of the

narrowness of my pupil. Sight is a thing so dear to all men, and especially to studious persons, that I earnestly beg, you would be pleased to consider my case deliberately, and acquaint me with your thoughts of the cause; and more particularly, to send prescriptions of the receipts you would have me employ, and your directions what else you would have me do towards the cure of it. I have had too much trial of your friendship, to doubt, that, upon so important an occasion, you will refuse me the effects of it, which will exceedingly add to your former favours, and oblige me to study the ways of shewing myself,

Sir,

your most affectionate
and most humble servant.

[R. B.]

P. S. I have, of yours, the water for clearing the sight, which I much esteem, and have more than once used; but I sometimes use, upon your authority, a little honey diluted with succory; but I much want the constant eye-water, to be used every night, or oftener, especially if it may be fitted for the present state of my eyes; and therefore beg, that you would be pleased to prescribe me one, that I may make here. I forgot to tell you, that, for some months last past, I have been much troubled with what they call vapours, of fumes of the spleen, and with some scorbutic disaffections. [R. B.] [2]

One of the first and important interests in Boyle's life, on his return to Oxford in 1660, was the founding of the Royal Society. When London had returned to its former orderly life after the reign of terror and the excitement on the return of Charles II, the lectures and meetings of the philosophers at Gresham College were resumed. To promote science, a more formal organization was considered advisable, and on 28 November 1660 a memorandum was drawn up as follows:

These persons following, according to the usual custom of most of them, met together at Gresham College to hear Mr. Wren's lecture, viz. The Lord Brouncker, Mr. Boyle, Mr. Bruce, Sir Robert Moray, Sir Paul Neile, Dr. Wilkins, Dr. Goddard, Dr. Petty, Mr. Ball, Mr. Rooke, Mr. Wren, Mr. Hill. And after the lecture was ended, they did, according to the usual manner, withdraw for mutual converse . . . And because they had these frequent occasions of meeting with one another, it was proposed that some course might be thought of, to improve this meeting to a more regular way of debating things, and according to the manner in other countries, where there were voluntary associations of men in academies, for the advancement of various parts of learning, so they might do something answerable here for the promoting of experimental philosophy.[3]

The original members of the Royal Society were those then present, and forty-one other names were proposed and accepted. Sir Robert Moray, who had joined Charles II in his exile and was now in great favour at Court, was elected temporary president and was commissioned to secure the interest of the King. In this he was entirely successful, and the charter, 15 July 1662, of the Royal Society (the name seems first to have been used by Evelyn) was passed under the Great Seal. The King declared himself as Founder and Patron, and presented the society with a silver mace, a harbinger of future benefits not fulfilled. Since the first charter did not give the Fellows all the privileges they desired, a second charter was granted in 1663; and a third, which contains only some minor changes, passed the Great Seal in 1669. Boyle was one of the Founders and a member of the first Council.

The motto *Nullius in Verba* * was chosen to epitomize the intention of the Society to be free from the dogmatic authority of all philosophic schools, and had, of course, particular reference to Aristotelian scholasticism. The motto is commonly translated by men of science as 'Nothing in Words.' While such a rendering plays fast and loose with the Latin language, it does express vaguely the purpose of the Society as announced from its beginning: that the Fellows aimed to seek the truth by experimental demonstration, and to give no credence to hearsay or to authoritative dicta. In this purpose, they were following the dictum of Galileo, a century earlier, that knowledge of the phenomena and laws of nature cannot be investigated by texts and bare authority, since they concern a sensible world and not one of paper.†

The desire to reform the pursuit of knowledge was extended to simplification of the English language. How seriously the Society considered this aspect of its work is forcibly expressed by Bishop Sprat, whose *History of the Royal Society* was regarded as the official declaration of its principles and the defence of its practices:

* The motto is taken from a line of Horace, Epistles I, I. 14. *Nullius addictus jurare in verba magistri;* or, I am not bound over to swear as any master dictates. Horace is speaking of his not being pledged to accept the formula of any school of philosophy.

† Venite non con testi e nude autorità, perche i discorsi hanno a essere intorno al mondo sensibile, e non sopra un mondo di carta.

I daresay, that of all the studies of men, nothing may be sooner obtained, than this vicious abundance of phrase, this trick of metaphors, this volubility of tongue, which makes so great a noise in the world. But I spend words in vain; for the evil is now so inveterate, that it is hard to know whom to blame, or where to begin to reform . . . They [the Fellows of the Society] have therefore been more rigorous in putting in execution the only remedy, that can be found for this extravagance . . . They have exacted from all their members a close, naked, natural way of speaking; positive expressions, clear senses; a native easiness; bringing all things as near the mathematical plainness as they can; and preferring the language of artisans, countrymen, and merchants, before that of wits, or scholars.[4]

It is by no means certain that Bishop Sprat spent his words in vain, and it would be interesting to trace the influence of the Royal Society as one of the chief causes for the change from the florid and involved diction of the Elizabethan and Stuart writers to the direct and nervous style of Addison, Steele, Swift, and the other writers of the age of Queen Anne.

Lord Brouncker was elected first president; and the first anniversary of the Society was celebrated on 30 November 1663: 'It being St. Andrew's Day, who was our patron,' Evelyn records in his *Diary,* 'each fellow wore a St. Andrew's Cross of ribbon on the crown of his hat. After the election we dined together, His Majesty sending us venison.' *

From its beginning, the Royal Society did not restrict its membership to professional scientists but included influential peers, bishops, literary men, statesmen, and others who expressed curiosity in the new philosophy. In spite of such powerful support, the Society travelled no easy road. It was embarrassingly poor, and its early records are full of pitiful pleas for the Fellows to pay their small dues, and of stringent rules to compel them to settle their arrears. Its solemn proceedings were lampooned by the wits; and the Fellows trembled under the sarcasm of Butler, knowing that the fickle King carried a copy of *Hudibras* in his pocket. The Universities turned against it bitterly as a new rival, threatening to grant academic degrees and to replace their conservative curriculum with its new-fangled ideas.

* The witty Dr. Petty grumbled: 'I had rather have had it been St. Thomas's Day, for he would not believe till he had seen and put his finger into the holes, according to the motto, *Nullius in Verba.'* Such then was the confidence in observation as the key to absolute truth, and the popular interpretation of the motto had an early beginning.

Nor did the young Royal Society escape other criticism. Although several of the most important bishops and physicians were included in its membership, the Church and the medical profession as a whole were outspoken against it—the one saying that the new philosophy encouraged free thinking and atheism; the other, that such rash ideas of disease and cure were unorthodox and a menace to health and life.

These criticisms, which were widespread enough to endanger the life of the Society, were the cause of Bishop Sprat's *History of the Royal Society,* published in 1667. It was so excellent a discussion of the aims and work of the Society that it did much to allay suspicion, and it is said, no one could be induced to continue the history lest his reputation should suffer by contrast. Joseph Glanvill, Rector at Bath, also became its champion with his *Plus Ultra: or, the Progress and Advancement of Knowledge since the Days of Aristotle.*

Glanvill's tribute to Boyle shows the reputation he had obtained, and the influence he had in the Society:

[Mr. Boyle] alone had even then done enough to oblige all mankind, and to erect an eternal monument to his memory; so that had this great person lived in those days, when men godded their benefactors, he could not have missed one of the first places among their deified mortals . . . In his writings are to be found the greatest strength and the genteelest smoothness, the most generous knowledge and the sweetest modesty, the noblest discoveries and the sincerest relations, the greatest self-denial and the greatest love of men, the profoundest insight into philosophy and nature, the most devout, affectionate sense of God and religion.[5]

To turn to the other side of the picture, the bitterest and most voluble opponent of the Royal Society was a certain Dr. Henry Stubbe,* a physician of some repute, located first at Stratford-on-Avon and later at Bath. Beginning in 1670 with two tracts; one entitled *Legends no histories,* against Bishop Sprat, and the other *The Plus Ultra reduced to a Non Plus,* against Glanvill; these were followed by others, and by a correspondence with Boyle. In spite of the virulence of his attacks, Stubbe and Boyle remained friends because Boyle believed him to be sincere and thought his criticisms useful.

A final quotation from this war of words, a letter of Stubbe,

* Dr. Stubbe probably became a friend and admirer of Boyle while he was 'second library-keeper of the Bodleian Library under Dr. Thos. Barlow' during the years 1656-59.

shows, in contrast to Glanvill, that Boyle's reputation may have suffered:

Do you not hear, how much the serious and sober men do blame you? You are much a stranger to the discourse and sentiments of men, if you know not, that your name is frequently questioned, and that the integrity of Mr. Boyle is disputed . . . I tender you this testimony of my sincere respects, that I am thus free with you; and whilst others flatter you, there is an old servant of yours informs you of the truth.[6]

Boyle's relations with the Royal Society were influential and cordial during his life. He was one of the original members and served on the Council. The presidency was urged upon him several times, and he was actually elected to that office in 1680, but he declined to serve and, in a letter to Hooke, requested the Society to choose some one else, as he had a singular hesitation about subscribing to an oath of office. But, even if his 'great (and perhaps peculiar) tenderness in point of oaths' had not influenced him, his health was by then far too delicate to permit the regular attendance and duties of the office. Evelyn sadly comments on the election: 'that excellent person and great philosopher Robert Boyle, who indeed ought to have been the very first; but neither his infirmities nor his modesty could now any longer excuse him.'[7]

Until the fame of Newton eclipsed his, Boyle was the chief glory of the Society. He published some thirty-five papers in the early numbers of its *Transactions*,[8] and its *Record Books* are full of references to his experimental work and to problems proposed by him for discussion and investigation. In the Library of the Society, his original air-pump holds an honoured place with Newton's telescope and a few other cherished relics.

Mention has previously been made of Cromwell's grants of land to Boyle, which included expropriated church property;[9] of Boyle's scruples over its use, and of his inclination to divert it to the founding of an institution for advancing the new science. This plan was abandoned when, after the death of Cromwell, all his Irish property was jeopardized by renewed revolt. Although Charles II confirmed, by a new grant, this church property without Boyle's solicitation or even his knowledge, new perplexities arose regarding its use.

When his kinsman, Michael Boyle, Bishop of Cork, learned of this grant, he hurried to Oxford and exposed the destitution of the Irish parishes and their ministers, thus deprived of the income from their expropriated estates; and he begged that they should not suffer by any plan, however worthy its purpose might be.

It is fortunate that Boyle's answer to the Bishop of Cork has been preserved for us, for it gives a noble picture of his character, and of his care to investigate claims on his justice and generosity:

May 27, 1662.

My Lord,

You will not, I presume, think my silence strange, when I shall have acquainted your lordship, that the reasons of it have been partly, that I was informed, that the parliament of Ireland had adjourned itself for a long time, and partly because an honest gentleman of public employments, and very well versed in the affairs of that country, did some days after your lordship's departure hence, undertake to procure me, with all convenient speed, an account, how those impropriations, which are within the grant made me by his Majesty are, or are like to be, provided of ministers and maintenance . . . I would not have what I intend to do reflect upon those persons of honour, that (though unknown to me) made use of my name to obtain the grant from the king, since in such disputable cases, persons, that act very differently from one another, may yet all satisfy their own judgements and consciences in their proceedings. But in regard my intention in general was to apply an addition of revenue, if my friends procured any for me, to good uses, though, I confess, I designed it rather for the advancement of real learning, than to any other purpose; yet since it so falls out, that unknown to me it is cast upon impropriations, it is very likely, that by the account I expect of the state of them, I may see cause to make the more immediate service of religion, (by relieving the poor in those places, and contributing, if need be, towards the maintenance of ministers there, or elsewhere, or promoting other good works, as from time to time occasion may require) the principal of these good uses, to which I have thoughts to apply about two thirds of what will, *de claro,* come to me out of my share of this grant . . . And I should possibly employ the other third part also the same way, but that his majesty has been pleased, without my seeking, (or so much as knowledge) to appoint me governor to a corporation for the propagating of the gospel among the heathen natives in New England, and the other parts of America . . . I think, after having advised with the Bishop of Lincoln in the case, that it becomes me, on such a juncture of circumstances, to apply the other third part, or thereabouts, of what the king's grant will yield me for six or seven years at least, to the carrying on of so unquestionably good a work . . . And by this, I hope, your lordship will be confirmed in the belief of what I formerly assured you of, namely, that had I known, that any thing was asked for me, whose grant would have been prejudicial or unwelcome to the church, I should not have consented to have my name made use of for a much greater matter, than the proviso is like to yield me . . .

> My lord,
> your lordship's most humble,
> and most affectionate servant.[10]
>
> [R. B.]

Bishop Boyle, in his answer to this explanation, expressed his approval of Boyle's intentions, but he added:

I must humbly take leave to acknowledge myself unsatisfied, why that additional revenue, which his Majesty designed and promised for the better support of the clergy here, that they may with greater comfort attend the cures of their several churches, should be diverted to any other use, though in itself it be generous and handsome . . . For although at present your piety provides all that possibly you may, to prevent these sad consequences; yet you know not how they shall be minded, who succeed you; nor are you certain, that those other persons (whoever they may be) that have obtained this grant under your patronage, will be as inclinable upon that account as you are.[11]

So far as we know, Boyle held to his decision of using two thirds of his grant for the benefit of the Irish, and the other third to promote Christianity amongst the American Indians, a work very dear to him the rest of his life. In his letter to Bishop Boyle, he mentions that he had just been appointed by the King to be governor of the Corporation for propagating the Gospel in New England and the parts adjacent in America, and that its revenue had been diverted from its use.

The case, as told by Birch, was as follows:

In July 1649, there was an ordinance passed in the Parliament, for the promoting and propagating of the Gospel of Jesus Christ in New England, by the erecting a corporation in perpetual succession, to be called by the name of the president and society for the propagation of the Gospel in New England and to receive and dispose of monies in such a manner, as shall best and principally conduce to the preaching and propagating the Gospel amongst the natives, and for the maintenance of schools and nurseries of learning for the education of the children of the natives; for which purpose a general collection was appointed to be made in and through all the counties, cities, towns, and parishes of England and Wales, for a charitable contribution, to be as the foundation of so pious and great an undertaking. With the monies thus collected, lands were purchased to the value of between five or six hundred pounds a year, and settled in a corporation of citizens of London in trust, Henry Ashurst, Esq., being their treasurer. Upon the restoration of King Charles II, the corporation being dead in law, Colonel Bedingfield, a Papist, who had sold an estate of £322 *per ann.,* which had been settled for the use of it, repossessed himself of it, and at the same time refused to pay back the money which he had received for it. Mr. Boyle therefore used his interest with the Lord Chancellor Clarendon, to prevent that act of injustice; and the corporation being revived in 1661, by an express charter, he was made governor of it, and the estate, which had been detained by Bedingfield, was restored by the Chancellor's decree.[12]

Boyle must have been an ideal governor of the corporation. His scrupulous honesty and his shrewd business ability made it certain that funds would be safely kept and wisely distributed. He achieved a great reputation and influence amongst the American Colonists and, in return, they kept him informed of their affairs and sent to him news of scientific wonders and strange events.

For example, Governor Winthrop of Connecticut wrote to him of the capture of Manhattan from the Dutch, and of a mysterious slaughter of fish in a pond which the Indians attributed to its having been struck by lightning. William Penn described the character of the Indians and his dealings with them in his Quaker Colony. Others asked for information about alchemy and the alkahest of Paracelsus and of Van Helmont, commonly supposed to be more potent in transmutations than the philosopher's stone. But the most satisfactory relationship was that which flourished between him and John Eliot, the devoted and extraordinary missionary to the Indians. Boyle was his main support in his efforts to Christianize them, to transliterate their dialects, and to make the New Testament accessible to them. He wrote many letters to Boyle, describing his work and his heart-breaking difficulties, addressing him as 'Right honourable, right charitable, and indefatigable, nursing father.'[13]

Lest these Irish estates should be diverted to other uses by his heirs, Boyle made a careful disposal of them in his will.[14] His unentailed estates in Ireland and his personal effects not specially mentioned, he left to three Trustees to be sold; £500 was to be given to the poor of the parish of Stalbridge and to the Irish where his land lay, and, by a codicil, £200 to poor preachers, their wives, and children. By another codicil, he directed his Trustees to use one fourth the tithes and revenue of the impropriated church property, granted to him by Charles II for thirty-one years, for good and pious purposes.

Although Boyle refused various honours and appointments, he was unable or unwilling to avoid all such obligations. In 1664, he accepted membership in the Company of Royal Mines and passed the winter in London. This position involved work after his own heart; he made many inspection trips, exploring the minerals and soils of the country, and their possible uses for both industrial and medicinal purposes. He also gradually made a rich collection of ores and minerals, which, in his will, he left to the Royal Society.

In 1665, he was appointed Provost of Eton by the King, but declined, for one reason because it would require him to enter into holy orders.[15] In the same year, he was created doctor of physic by Oxford.[16] He was also for many years a Director of the East India Company, and did not resign that office till he was too feeble to attend the meetings.

The evidence goes to show that Boyle, in all his official work, was an upright and zealous officer; running through all of it was a passionate desire to educate and Christianize the native population of Ireland, America, and the Orient. This ambition was fixed in his earliest years in Oxford and persisted unabated to the end of his life. Thus:

He gave a noble reward to Dr. Edward Pococke, who translated Grotius's incomparable treatise on *The Truth of the Christian Religion* into Arabic, and was the charge of a whole impression, which was finished at Oxford in 1660, in quarto, and which he took care to order to have dispersed in all the countries, where that language is understood. He was resolved to have carried on the impression of the New Testament in the Turkish language; but the [East India] Company thought, that it became them to perform that work, and so suffered him only to give a large share towards it.[17]

He also employed in this work a Mr. Will Seaman, who was highly recommended by Oldenburg. But, his chief adviser and co-adjutor in translations into the Turkish, Arabic, and especially of a Malayan text of the Four Gospels and the Acts, was Thomas Hyde, many of whose letters are extant and show the warm friendship between the two men.[18] The knowledge of so munificent a patron as Boyle must have subjected him to many requests for aid from impecunious scholars. A typical case is the following letter, amusing and also instructive regarding the attitude of a client towards a great patron.

London, Bell-Savage-yard, on Ludgate-hill, May 15, 1683.

Sir,

To your honour's hands, as the great patron of languages and arts, this impolite grammatical tract of the Malayan dialect presumeth to make its submissive addresses, and to stand the fate of your judicious and impartial censure; who have judgement enough to correct any faults, and goodness enough to pardon all; nor dares this pigmy, without such assurance, attempt a public exposal in this critical, humourous, and fanciful age. The success of this previous manual will much contribute to the animation or abortion of my impregnate intentions for a Malayan dictionary, and the translation of the sacred Evangely, *etc.* into those Oriental idioms. But since it is your honour's countenance and favour only, that can give life and being to this, or them, I humbly submit it to seek its happy or unhappy fortune from your doom, as deeming my ambition gratified, if I may attain a gracious admittance into the catalogue as,

Sir, your honour's most humbly devoted
and faithful servant,
Wm. Mainston.[19]

Boyle's influence as a director of the East India Company seems to have been successful in raising its standard from a mere mercantile venture to exploit the resources of India, to one which would have also an interest in improving the social and religious state of the natives. In 1677, as he was then too feeble to attend its meetings, he sent a letter of resignation, reviewing his services and urging the directors to continue to foster this work:

The continuance of my distemper not permitting me to wait on you, as I gladly would, in London, you will, I doubt not, give me leave to present you in this paper some of the things, that I would more fully have acquainted you with by word of mouth. You may remember, that when my health, and the kindness of the East India Company, allowed me to sit in your committee, I ventured to make a motion, that some course might be thought on of doing some considerable thing for the propagation of the Gospel among the natives, in whose countries we have flourishing factories. And it seemed to me very fit, that we, whose endeavours God had of late so signally prospered, should pay him some little acknowledgement of his many blessings, and that remembering ourselves to be Christians, as well as merchants, we should attempt to bring those countries some spiritual good things, whence we so frequently brought back temporal ones. And I was somewhat the more concerned to succeed in the motion I made, because I wished the company were enough to desire, that they in particular should have the honour to silence the reproaches of those who I wish had less pretence to upbraid the Protestants, and among them the English, with the neglect to making proselytes to the Christian religion; to the advancement of which I endeavoured to excite you by what hath been done by the Dutch Company in Batavia . . .[20]

Although Boyle was sympathetic to every appeal by a worthy cause, he was primarily interested in aiding the Irish. Their condition was, indeed, desperate. No one knows how much he gave to relieve their distress, but it amounted to a great sum. He was also eager to improve education and to increase Protestantism, which was made difficult by the fact that few could read English and there was no Gaelic translation of the Bible. He first secured the service of a young Irish scholar, Dr. Andrew Sall, for whom he obtained, in 1678, a post in Christ Church, Oxford, and commissioned him to translate the New Testament into Irish. When that work was published in 1681, the more difficult task of rendering the Old Testament was begun; at the premature death of Sall, this was completed by Narcissus Marsh, Provost of Trinity College, Dublin, and afterwards Archbishop of Armagh. Hundreds of these Bibles, for which Boyle had undertaken the entire cost, were distributed in the parishes throughout Ireland and Wales, and also in the Scottish Highlands. The difficulties encountered in this work are evident from the letters of Sall and Marsh.[21] There not only were the troubles inseparable from the translation and publishing of such an arduous work, but there was also serious opposition from the clergy and people. Thus Sall complains:

The best and greatest men of this kingdom do highly commend your pious zeal appearing in this work, and do approve of our endeavours to procure the spiritual welfare of this miserably deluded people. But beside the private opposition of the Romish clergy, who would have themselves to be the only teachers, we have a more public and bolder opposition by some of our own apparent but very false brethren, who are not ashamed to profess a dislike of our endeavours to convert the natives of this country, upon maxims like those of the American planters, in hindering the conversion of their slaves to the Christian religion. One of them had the gallantry to tell me in my face, and at my own table, that while I went

about to gain the Irish (to God I mean) I should lose the English. Our
good archbishop has continued battles with them upon this subject.

For several years, beginning in 1662, all England and Ireland
were excited by the marvellous cures wrought by Valentine Greatraks, the Irish Stroker. The fact that he accomplished many cures,
exaggerated as they undoubtedly were, is too well attested to be ignored. There seems to have been no suspicion of imposture; and of
the reliable witnesses, some ascribed them to miracles and others to
natural causes. Boyle was one of the witnesses, and his approval was
very valuable. Flamsteed, the Astronomer Royal, in his youth was
sent to Ireland by his father to be stroked in the hope of curing him
of his persistent ill-health. He 'went down to the Assuane, and was
by him the third time touched; but not finding any amends, I determined to depart.' [22] But he was convinced of the Stroker's gift:
'Some seem to asperse him each way, for my part I think his gift
was of God; and for the course of his cures, I dare fully acquiesce
with what Dr. Stubbe hath written of him. For though I am an
eye-witness of several of his cures, yet am not able to remember or
fitted to write them out as I saw them.' The most reliable evidence
was probably that of Lord Conway, who brought the Stroker from
Ireland to try his skill on his wife, who suffered excruciating headaches.* While no relief was afforded her, Lord Conway reported
many successful cures in Worcestershire.

Greatraks—his name is spelled in a dozen ways—was the son of
William Greatraks of Assuane by a daughter of Sir Edward Harris,
a Justice of the King's Bench in Ireland. He was well educated in
England in the humanities and divinity. On his return to Ireland,
he 'almost died from depression of spirits' because of the miserable
condition of its people. He became a friend to Lord Broghill and
served in the army under his command; it was Broghill, then Lord
Orrery, in fact, who recommended him to Lord Conway.

About 1662, Greatraks became obsessed with the persuasion that
he was gifted with a power to cure scrofula, the 'king's evil.' This
vision he concealed for a time, but finally confessed it to his wife,
who discouraged him. However, an opportunity of trying his gift on
a boy, who suffered from an advanced case of the disease, presented
itself; and, to his astonishment, the boy was entirely cured within

* Lady Conway, the friend of Henry More and the Cambridge Platonists, was one of the
most attractive figures of the period. Cf. the *Conway Letters*.

a month. For three years, he limited himself to laying on his hands, or to stroking, for that disease; then, during an epidemic of ague, he succeeded with that, and afterwards with other ills.

Boyle was brought into the controversy over Greatraks by Dr. Henry Stubbe, who, on the invitation of Lord Conway, had been a witness to the cures in Worcestershire, and then published a pamphlet in the form of a letter addressed to the Hon. Robert Boyle. In the letter he enthusiastically exclaimed that, 'in fine, without any prejudice to this age be it said, he seemed to me, by his faith and by his charitableness, to include in his soul some grains of the golden age, and to be a relic of those times, when piety and miracles were sincere.' As to the cause of this gift, he falls in with the prevalent belief in effluvia, as we, today, rely on electricity, and adds: 'God had bestowed upon Mr. Greatraks a peculiar temperament, or composed his body of some particular ferments, the effluvia whereof being introduced sometimes by a light, sometimes by a violent friction, should restore the temperament of the debilitated parts, reinvigorate the blood, and dissipate all the heterogeneous ferments out of the bodies of the diseased, by the eyes, nose, mouth, hands, and feet.'[23]

This letter Stubbe published before Boyle had seen it or had given his permission. He had forgiven the irascible doctor's attacks on the Royal Society, but he could not stomach this liberty with his name nor the comparison of the miracles of Greatraks with those of Christ and the Apostles. In a long answer he severely rebuked the author, and followed it with an explanation of his own views. It is unfortunate that his answer is too long to quote in full, since such a spontaneous expression may give a juster knowledge of his character and ideas than do his formal works. But the following excerpts may suffice:

March 9, 1665-6.

Sir,

It was so late yesternight before I received your account of Mr. Greatrak's stupendous performances, that I had much ado to run it over before I went to bed; and this morning being to take care of some little affairs in order to a remove, that I am to make in the afternoon for some days, I am obliged to answer your letter in as much haste as you tell me you writ it in . . .

To begin with, I must confess to you, that I was somewhat surprised to find this epistle of yours brought me from the press, before I had seen it any other way; and it is no small trouble to me, both upon your score and my own, that I did not see the manuscript before it came abroad. For if I had seasonably seen what you wrote about miracles, I should freely have dissuaded you from publicly addressing to me, what I cannot but much dissent from; and perhaps I should have been able to prevail with you to omit all that part of your epistle . . . But by what hitherto appears to me of Mr. Greatraks's cures, I must take leave to think, that either they are not real miracles; or, if they have any thing in them of a supernatural gift, it is so far short of the gifts of our Saviour Christ and his apostles, that I presume your friends will think, that if it were not the effect of your haste, it was rather to shew your wit than declare your opinion, that you seem to make a parity between them. And for my part I should in that case, reflecting upon the passage you cite, that *there are differences of administrations, but the same Lord,* think it more fit to look upon this gift of Mr. Greatraks, as a distinct and inferior kind, than degrade the unquestionable miraculous gifts of the apostles, to depress them to the same level with his . . .

Perhaps I should not believe those that I find recorded in the scripture itself, if the relations of them were not recommended by such concurrent characters of credibility, as would make my rejecting them an obstinacy, and as are of another guess weight than those that countenance those relations whereto I do not give credit. And I little doubt, but if the pretended miracles of Pyrrhus and Vespasian had been watched and considered by Mr. Stubbe as narrowly as those of Mr. Greatraks's had been, you would have found at least as much reason to ascribe their cures, as his, to physical causes, if not to some mistake, collusion, or flattery, which the persons on whom those wonders are fathered, render the more suspicious . . .

As to what seems your main hypothesis, that Mr. Greatraks performs his cures by the strengthening and reinvigorating of nature, which being relieved and fortified by the sanative effluvia that pass from his body into the body of the patient, doth afterwards vanquish the disease herself, I doubt not, that you will have many of your readers of that opinion with you; and particularly those Helmontians and other chemists, that hope or plead for universal medicines, operating by way of restoratives, will be glad to find you to countenance their tenet. For my part, unless I could send you what I once drew up by way of disquisition about the received notion of nature (wherein perhaps I do not acquiesce) I cannot think it proper to mention to you my particular thoughts of the power of strengthened nature. But some scrupulous person will not only deny, that nature alone, though fortified with any thing, that is but a cordial, can cure all diseases (as for instance, the stone in the bladder, or kidneys, when it is confirmed and grown too big to be voided by the urinary passages) but will perhaps enquire, whether it does appear that Mr. Greatraks's touch is positively a cordial, and not barely or chiefly so, as it relieves nature by freeing her from some distempers that oppressed her, as when burned feathers remove the faintings of hysterical women . . .

What you say of the subtlety of the effluvia, and of the great efficacy they are capable of, will not be much struck at by a Corpuscularian. And if I could think it proper here to add some of the instances of that kind, which I have lying by me in my notes about Occult Qualities, (as they are commonly called) perhaps they would afford no despicable confirmation both to what you here say, and to what I have elsewhere written about the power of invisible corpuscles. And I am the more persuaded to think great matters performable by them, both by some odd observations, that I have since met with of the efficacy of the even solid parts of dead animals, and particularly of a sea-horse tooth outwardly applied to the body, and by considering, that a sanative temperament may reasonably be supposed capable of diffusing its virtue by contacts more plentifully and more powerfully in a living body of a sanguine complexion, where the natural heat of the blood and spirits, being vegete and active, incessantly emit so great a plenty of insinuating steams, as living bodies, that transpire freely, appear to do by the notable observations of Sanctorius's ingenious *Medicina Statica* (not to mention my own trials to the same purpose) . . .

Sir, your very humble servant,

[R. B.] [24]

Boyle passed the early part of the summer of 1665 in London, as we learn from a letter of Oldenburg's, but he returned to Oxford early in July, probably because of the Plague. Beginning with the rigorous winter of 1657, contemporary chronicles give a dismally increasing record of illness, usually in the form of agues and periodic fevers. During the summer of 1665, these culminated in the Great Plague. Oldenburg pluckily stayed at his post as Secretary of the Royal Society. Writing to Boyle in July, he expressed the hope that the news of his intention to leave Oxford was not because the infection had attacked that place; as for himself, he was perplexed what to do with the books and papers of the Royal Society. For fear that he would fall ill and they be lost, the best he could think to do was to 'make a list of them all, and put them up by themselves in a box, and seal them together with a superscription; that so, in case the Lord should visit me, as soon as I find myself not well, it may be ready to be immediately sent away out of mine to a sound house, *et sic deinceps.*' [25] And later he wrote that he had taken the same precautions with Boyle's books, papers, and his Latin translations of them, which were in his possession. When the Plague reached alarming proportions, the Court moved first to Salisbury and then to Oxford; the meetings of the Royal Society were adjourned, and most of its members left town. Hooke, with Dr. Wilkins and Sir William Petty, intended to retreat to Non[e]such, but finally betook themselves, and their scientific apparatus, to Durdans, the seat of Lord Berkeley, near Epsom; there they engaged in philosophic talk and experimenting till it was safe to return to town.

Boyle stayed in Oxford through September; then, having declined an invitation of Lady Ranelagh to come to Leeze, where she and her daughters were staying with her sister Mary, Lady Warwick, he simply vanished. Apparently, he was driven to take that step, less from fear of the Plague than from the annoyance of excessive visitors and the distractions of the Court. So strictly did he conceal his whereabouts that even his sister, worried by lack of news of him, wrote to him by way of London, hoping the letter might be forwarded to wherever he might be. By the following February, he had recovered from an attack of illness, and we learn from Oldenburg that he had about decided to quit Oxford and to live with his sister in London.

Boyle had definitely decided to move to London, now that the Plague had subsided, but seems to have been hesitant about the city itself, and had taken temporary lodging at Newington, a suburb on the Surrey side. Oldenburg, solicitous as usual about the comfort of his invalid friend, wrote to him on 17 March 1665/6:

I doubt not but you have received a full account of the lodging-place designed for you at Newington. Mr. Coxe, soliciting me to give him a visit there, I walked thither on Thursday last; and though I was not within the house that is to be taken up for you, yet I looked upon the places about it, and must needs say it seems to me very convenient for you; there being a large orchard, a walk for solitary meditation, a dry ground round about, and, in all appearance, a good air; all which Mr. Coxe affirms to be accompanied with a civil landlord and fair landlady.

At our meeting on Wednesday last at Gresham, the president took some account what several of the members then present had been employed in, during the late sad and long recess. Some related what had been done by them in the matter of chariots and watches; others, what in masonry, and the extraction of lead out of the ore; others, what in the nature of salts; others, what in the perfecting of the experiments touching the injection of veins, and particularly about the transfusing of blood out of one animal into another; concerning the last whereof Dr. Clark affirmed, that he had tried that experiment two years ago, but found it so difficult that he gave it over: whereupon Sir R. Moray mentioned, that Mr. Boyle had hopes of mastering the difficulties that are met with in that experiment. Dr. Wallis being present, and desired to acquaint the company what had been chiefly done at the meeting in Oxford last summer, related some of the musical experiments that had been made; and being solicited to give them in writing, he made answer, that Mr. Boyle had recorded them, whereupon the secretary was ordered to take notice of it in writing, that Mr. Boyle be desired to impart the said experiments, with all their circumstances.[26]

According to Oldenburg's letters, Boyle was probably at Newington during April and May; then he made a short visit somewhere, and on his return went to lodgings in Chelsea, which he seems to have maintained permanently. He stayed during the summer and perhaps was there during the Great Fire of 2-5 September; if so, he immediately retired again to Oxford. We may infer that he was present and then left town, because both his sister and Oldenburg in letters addressed to him at Oxford mention the after-effects of the catastrophe, but they give no details as they would if he had not witnessed it.

Lady Ranelagh wrote on 12 September to enquire if he had got to Oxford in good health, and added, 'I dispensed your charity amongst some poor families and persons, that I found yet in the fields unhoused.' And Oldenburg wrote two days earlier that he would have waited on him at Chelsea if he had known the least word of his retiring to Oxford. Alas for the books and manuscripts of the Royal Society he had so sedulously guarded during the Plague! 'I doubt I shall find it very difficult to continue the printing of the *Transactions,* Martin and Allestry being undone with the rest of the stationers at Paul's church-yard, and all their books burnt they had carried for safety into St. Faith's church, as they call it; besides that, the city lying desolate now, it will be very hard to vend them.'[27]

Early in 1666, Boyle published his important treatise on the *Origin of Forms and Qualities,* in which he appeared as a thorough-going corpuscularian, and in which he explained the qualities of bodies by purely mechanical causes. The book made a great sensation and was widely quoted, especially by Locke, Newton, and other physicists. On the other hand, it aroused opposition amongst the religious who saw in it a likeness to the atheistic and mechanical philosophy of Descartes. Such an effect would be shocking to Boyle, and he was particularly chagrined to have it expressed by the pious Platonist, Henry More, in his bitter attack on Cartesianism published later in the same year. That Boyle was deeply offended by being classed with Descartes is apparent from the following letter from More:

Christ Church College, December 4, [1667].

Honoured Sir,

Mr. Foxcroft being at my chambers yesterday, and acquainting me so explicitly how you have taken offence at what concerns you in my *Enchiridion Metaphysicum,* it has quickened me to do that, which I was sometimes thinking to do, since I saw you last. For I had some such inklings before now. But when I was with you, you seemed not to be concerned for yourself, but for Descartes. I shall now briefly answer as touching both. And truly, whatever I have written in that book, touching Descartes, I confess, I have not the least dislike of it, it being so exceedingly requisite for me to do as I did. I have, from my very first letters to Descartes, till this last book of mine, always expressed my opinion, that this mechanical way would not hold in all phaenomena, as I always verily thought . . . Wherefore what could I have done less, than declare my sense of the Cartesian philosophy, and vindicate myself from the imputation of so fond a blindness, as not to be aware of the danger of that philosophy, if it be credited; and, which is best of all, to put it quite out of credit, in that sense I oppose it, by demonstrating the great weakness thereof, in its pretences of solving, though but the easiest and simplest phaenomena, merely mechanically? which, I think, I have done irrefutably, nay, I am unspeakably confident of it: and have therewithal ever and anon plainly demonstrated the necessity of incorporeal beings; which is a design, than which nothing can be more seasonable in this age; wherein the notion of a spirit is so hooted at by so many for nonsense . . . But come it in what circumstances it will, Sir, I will assure, it came from one, that does very highly honour you and love you, and whatever displeasure you may conceive against him, is resolved, whether you will or no, to love you and honour you, and wish you all good possible, and, in this sense and resolution, does heartily subscribe himself,

Honoured and dear Sir,

Your most humble, and

most affectionate servant,

Hen. More *

---

* *Works,* Vol. vi, p. 513. Boyle takes occasion many times in his various religious works to express his conviction that Descartes was not an atheist, and that his philosophic system is based on the existence of God.

These two men were of too noble and pious a character not to respect each other, or to allow a difference of opinion to mar their mutual regard and friendship.

By November 1667, Boyle's arrangements for moving to London had so far progressed that his sister could write: 'I have ordered Thomas to look out for charcoal, and should gladly receive your order to put my back-house in posture to be employed by you, against your coming, that you might lose no time after.'[28] But again there was a long period of an unaccountable hesitation and delay; and it was not till more than a year and a half later, in the summer of 1668, that Boyle finally went to live with Lady Ranelagh in her house in Pall Mall. But, once established, he remained there during the rest of his life.

VII

LIFE IN LONDON

1668-1691

PALL MALL, although it had changed greatly since the time when Boyle, a lad unknown and almost penniless, on his return from the Continent had found a welcome refuge with his sister, was still rural and suburban. Lady Ranelagh's house on the south side is no longer standing, but the ornate façade of Nell Gwyn's house, given to her by Charles II, still is to be seen only two doors away. Another neighbour was Isaac Barrow, who deserted mathematics for divinity and had been Newton's predecessor as Lucasian Professor at Cambridge. But of all his neighbours, Boyle would find Dr. Thomas Sydenham the most congenial. He was then a fashionable and rather eccentric London physician; it was only after his death that his originality was recognized and he was given the title of the father of English medicine. Boyle and he had long been correspondents, exchanging recipes and ideas. Both of them were warm advocates of simplicity in drugs, and many of the stories told of the physician illustrate this innovation. Thus, he once startled the profession by the caustic remark: 'There are cases where I have consulted my patient's safety and my own reputation most effectually by doing nothing at all.'

For almost a quarter of a century, Boyle's house was a focus for the best society of London. It must have been a charming place to visit with such a host and hostess, who were themselves bound together by a peculiarly tender affection. Boyle, at the height of his reputation, was sought after by all distinguished foreigners visiting England; of his sister, who was in 1669 set free from the bondage of her brute of a husband by his unlamented death, it was said at her death: 'She had lived the longest on the most public scene, and made the greatest figure in all the revolutions of these kingdoms for above fifty years, of any woman of that age.'[1]

In spite of Boyle's long evasion of matrimony and his present

comfortable provision for the future, some of his friends evidently
still were seeking a wife for him. He had hardly settled down in
his new home before Wallis proposed a fantastic alliance. After describing with disgust the boisterous and rather disgraceful Encaenia
when the Sheldonian Theatre was dedicated, he wrote that Sir James
Langham, his wife, and other persons of quality had dined with
him. Sir James had extolled his sister-in-law, the Lady Mary Hast-
ings, as so excellent that he would marry her himself, except for
the slight impediment that he was married and she was his wife's
sister. They all agreed that she was particularly suited to be the wife
for Esquire Boyle, and he closed the letter with the wish: 'If I might
be the happy instrument in making two so excellent persons happy
in each other, as he persuades me I might, if you think fit, I do not
know, in what else I could more approve myself.' [2] We are ignorant
how Boyle escaped from this paragon of all the virtues and her
dowry of six thousand pounds.

At the time Wallis was attempting to dispose of Boyle's fate, his
family was deeply worried about a different prospect for Lord Orrery. Shortly before, the Earl of Clarendon had fallen from power,
had resigned the Great Seal, and had been driven into exile; Lord
Orrery, according to Dr. Morrice, his chaplain, had foreseen Clarendon's fall and had warned him in vain to abate his imperious attitude. Orrery, who had been living in great splendour at Charleville
as President of Munster since the Restoration, was now back in
England because, as Morrice notes, his credit at Court also had declined, and he was advised to be on the spot. He was more pliable
than the haughty Lord Chancellor and, as usual, his urbanity and
diplomacy stood him in such good stead that he not only regained
favour with the King but was even offered the vacant Chancellorship. The Boyle family had had too frequent examples of the fickle-
ness of the Stuarts to be tempted; and the wily politician, with expressions of gratitude for the honour, declined on the plea that he
was a decrepit man and afflicted with the gout.

Lord Orrery again had shown his wisdom in avoiding conspicuous place, for only a few months later he was impeached in the
House of Commons. At the time, he was suffering from a severe
attack of the gout and could scarcely mount the steps from Westminster Hall to the Court of Request. A friend, remarking that he
walked with difficulty and pain, was answered: 'Yes, sir, my feet are
weak; but if my heels will serve to carry me up, I promise you my

head shall bring me safe down again.' Orrery made an able defence, and the foolish impeachment, as Dr. Stubbe called it, was dismissed. For this time, at least, the King remembered the long services of the Boyle family and ended the case by proroguing both Houses of Parliament.[3]

In spite of his fragile health, his poor eye-sight, his many attacks of fever, colds, and kidney stones, Robert Boyle seems to have escaped the virulent diseases so prevalent at the time; but he was now attacked by a disorder so grave that to most men it would have meant the end of active life. In June 1670, he was afflicted with his first paralytic stroke.[4] With the same indomitable fortitude which enabled his father to conquer the same calamity and to repair its ravages when his enemies thought they had wounded him to death, so now his son gathered his forces and continued his work. His paralysis was certainly not caused by passion against his enemies, as was his father's, but it may have been induced by anxiety for his brother, on trial for his life. Evelyn, who met Boyle intimately and often, in a letter to Wotton,[5] imputed his 'frequent attacks of palsies' to constant attendance on chemical operations. And he continued: 'It has plainly astonished me to have seen him so often recover, when he has not been able to move, or bring his hand to his mouth.'

If one examines the publications of Boyle, he will be amazed to find that some of his most important work appeared during the five years following his paralysis. Unable to read or to operate, he must have dictated in laborious speech to amanuenses, and have directed the experimental work of several assistants. Eleven months after the attack he was still prostrated; his grim determination to restore his nerves and his muscles, his patience and his serenity, will be sympathetically appreciated from the following letter, written to John Mallet, his friend and companion during the years at Stalbridge:

London, May 23, 1671.

Sir,

I am much obliged to you for the favour of hastening to me such welcome news, as that of my brother Orrery's being already put to sea with so fair a wind, as promised he would get quickly to the other side of it. Since Monday, when I received the favour of your letter, there came to my hands a desire from him relating to your kinsman, Mr. Pitt, which was very needless; the relation, that gentleman has to you, and the concern you express for him, being more than sufficient to make me forward to do him all the service I am able. But this, I fear, will not be very much; for though, through the goodness of God, my paralytical distemper is much lessened, yet I am far from being fully cured of it; and during the space of an eleven months past since it first invaded me, I have taken so many medicines, and found the relief they afforded me so very slow, that it is not easy for me to tell you what I found most good by. The things, which to me seem the fittest to be mentioned on this occasion, are, that cordial medicines, especially such as peculiarly befriend the *genus nervosum,* were very frequently and not unusefully administered. That I used during this sickness less purging physic, and that gentle, than in many years before; and found cause to think such evacuations very weakening, and, when they are not very necessary, dangerous. That the dried flesh of vipers seemed to be one of the usefullest cordials I took; but then I persevered in taking it daily for a great while. That I seldom missed a day without taking the air, at least once, and that even when I was at the weakest, and was fain to be carried in men's arms from my chair into the coach. That the best thing I found to strengthen my feet and legs, and which I still use, was sack turned to a brine with sea-salt, and well rubbed upon the parts every morning and night with a warm hand. That for my hands I use several things, and particularly palm oil, which comes from Guinea, and a liquor somewhat like the *spiritus lavendulae compos.* of the dispensatory, and also fomentations with cephalic flowers and herbs, one or other of which I yet daily continue. But yet I found nothing so available as frequent exercise of my hands and feet, in which I continued as far as my strength would possibly allow me, getting sometimes others to bend the joints of my arms and hands for me. And though this course makes me every day sore and weary, yet I continue to undergo it, because I think I find more benefit by it alone, than by all the outward applications of physicians and chirurgeons. These, Sir, are in brief the chief things that I have observed about my own distemper; but how far they will be applicable to that of your friend, I do not know half so well, as that in case he use them, they will prove very effectual, if any thing can be added to their virtue by the good wishes of,

Sir,

Your most humble and affectionate servant,

R. B.[6]

There is not much more to narrate of Boyle's life. He and his sister continued to live a quiet life in the house at Pall Mall. They had suffered deeply from the deaths of Mary, Countess of Warwick, so vivacious and stubborn in her girlhood and so broken by sorrows in her later life, and of Lord Orrery; but their mutual love comforted them. He, in spite of increasing infirmities, continued to publish steadily on all manner of subjects, and carried on a correspondence with the noted men in foreign countries; and their house was a rendezvous for the best society England had to offer. In fact, the constant stream of visitors and guests finally so fatigued him, and so interfered with his work, that he published a notice stating that he would not be at home to visitors on Tuesday and Friday forenoons, and on Wednesday and Saturday afternoons. And, in addition, he hung a board on his door, stating when he did and when he did not receive visits.

In 1691, both Boyle and his sister were very ill, so ill, that on 18 July, he drew up his will,[7] in which with scrupulous care he disposed of his property which had not been entailed by his father. Besides many gifts to relatives, friends, and dependents, he provided for the continuance of his various charities; and, in addition, he devised property with an income of £50 a year to establish an annual salary for a learned divine, or preaching minister of London, to deliver eight sermons in a parish church of the city 'for proving the Christian religion against notorious Infidels, viz. Atheists, Theists, Pagans, Jews, and Mahometans, not descending lower to any controversies, that are among Christians themselves.' As executors of this trust, he named Sir John Rotheram, Sir Henry Ashurst, Thomas Tenison, D.D., and John Evelyn, Esq.

These celebrated Boyle Lectures have, by an additional gift from Archbishop Tenison, been given annually, with few exceptions, to the present time. Boyle's specific purpose was to counteract the fashionable atheism widely spread through England by the philosophy of Spinoza and Hobbes, and to demonstrate that his own corpuscularian hypothesis was, when rightly understood, a powerful support to the Christian religion. The executors chose for their first preacher, in 1692, Mr. Richard Bentley, then chaplain to Bishop Stillingfleet and later the Master of Trinity College, Cambridge.

Bentley preached his first sermon in St. Martin's, where Boyle had been buried, and the other seven at St. Mary-le-Bow's. His general topic was *A Confutation of Atheism,* and the sermons were said to have surpassed the high expectations of his patrons. Bishop Monk, in his *Life of Bentley,* wrote: 'We are assured that the effect of these discourses was such, that atheism was deserted as untenable ground; or, to use his own expression, the atheists were "silent since that time, and sheltered themselves under deism." ' These sermons are also notable because in the last one his concluding argument was the demonstration of the necessity of a Divine Providence from the constitution of the universe as demonstrated in the *Principia*. Before committing the sermons to the press, Bentley submitted the manuscript to Newton for criticism. The four letters in answer by Newton are well known. For the most part he approved Bentley's views; and he advanced some other arguments in support; some opinions he corrected and modified. It was in regard to these letters that Dr. Johnson made the famous remark, 'how even the mind of Newton gains ground gradually upon darkness.'

Unfortunately, the fond hope of Boyle and Newton, that the mechanistic philosophy, as developed by them, would be a lasting proof of the existence of a Divine Creator, and a strong buttress to the Christian religion, was not realized. As developed by the French Encyclopædists and the mathematical physicists, this philosophy induced an atheism which far exceeded the feared influence of Hobbes. And, in the nineteenth century, when it was expanded to explain the phenomena of life by Spencer, Huxley, and the evolutionists, it at its best superseded spiritual other-worldliness as the goal of life by a benevolent humanitarianism, and at its worst replaced a planning Creator with a vaguely personified Nature.

Lady Ranelagh's illness terminated in her death on 23 December 1691. This unexpected loss was a fatal blow to her brother, and he survived her but a week, dying peacefully, and without the pain he had so dreaded, during the night of Wednesday, 30 December, in the sixty-fifth year of his life. He was buried in the chancel of St. Martin's-in-the-Fields near his sister. His funeral was without pomp, as he had wished it to be, but it was followed with true grief. The sermon preached by Bishop Burnet was eloquent in telling of his excellent life, and as Evelyn noted in his *Diary*: 'truly all this was but his due, without any grain of flattery.'

There is little need to add a critical analysis of Boyle's character. He was blessed with such a simple and transparently clear integrity of mind that his contemporaries, intimate friends and casual acquaintances alike, were singularly unanimous in their estimates of him as a man and scholar; and he himself was so expansive and so self-revealing in his published works and letters that there is little difficulty in knowing the whole man. Evelyn's reminiscences of the habits and traits of his friend for forty years, which he wrote to Dr. Wotton, present a picture that can, I think, be trusted as far as can be anyone's estimate of a friend:

He was the most facetious and agreeable conversation in the world among the ladies, whenever he happened to be so engaged; and yet so very serious, composed, and contemplative at all other times; though far from moroseness, for indeed he was affable and civil rather to excess, yet without formality.

As to his opinion in religious matters and discipline, I could not but discover in him the same free thoughts which he had of philosophy; not in notion only, but strictly as to practice, an excellent Christian; and the great duties of that profession, without noise, dispute, or determining; owning no master but the Divine Author of it; no religion but primitive, no rule but Scripture, no law but right reason. For the rest, always comformable to the present settlement, without any sort of singularity. The mornings, after his private devotions, he usually spent in philosophic studies and in his laboratory, sometimes extending them to night: but he told me he had quite given over reading by candle-light, as injurious to his eyes. This was supplied by his amanuensis, who sometimes read to him, and wrote out such passages as he noted, and that so often in loose papers, packed up without method, as made him sometimes to seek upon occasion, as himself confesses in divers of his works. Glasses, pots, chemical and mathematical instruments, books and bundles of papers, did so fill and crowd his bed-chamber, that there was but just room for a few chairs; so as his whole equipage was very philosophical without formality. There were yet other rooms, and a small library (and so you know had Descartes), as learning more from men, real experiments, and in his laboratory (which was ample and well furnished), than from books.

I have said nothing of his style, which those who are better judges think he was not so happy in, as in his experiments. I do not call it affected, but doubtless not answerable to the rest of his great and shining parts; and yet, to do him right, it was much improved in his *Theodora* and later writings.

In his diet (as in habit) he was extremely temperate and plain; nor could I ever discern in him the least passion, transport, or censoriousness, whatever discourse or the times suggested. All was tranquil, easy, serious, discreet and profitable; so as, besides Mr. Hobbes, whose hand was against everybody and admired nothing but his own, Francis Linus excepted (who yet with much civility wrote against him), I do not remember he had the least antagonist.

In the afternoons he was seldom without company, which was sometimes so incommodious, that he now and then repaired to a private lodging in another quarter of the town, and at other times (as the season invited) diverted himself in the country among his noble relations.

He was rather tall and slender of stature, for most part valetudinary, pale and much emaciated; not unlike his picture in Gresham College; which, with an almost impudent importunity, was, at the request of the Society, hardly extorted, or rather stolen, from this modest gentleman by Sir Edmund King, after he had refused it to his nearest relations.

In his first addresses, being to speak or answer, he did sometimes a little hesitate, rather than stammer, or repeat the same word; imputable to an infirmity, which, since my remembrance, he had exceedingly over-come. This, as it made him somewhat slow and deliberate, so, after the first effort, he proceeded without the least interruption, in his discourse. And I impute this impediment much to the frequent attacks of palsies, contracted, I fear, not a little by his often attendance on chemical opera-tions. It has plainly astonished me to have seen him so often recover, when he has not been able to move, or bring his hand to his mouth: and indeed the contexture of his body, during the best of his health, appeared to me so delicate, that I have frequently compared him to a chrystal, or Venice glass; which, though wrought never so thin and fine, being care-fully set up, would outlast the hardier metals of daily use: and he was withal as clear and candid; not a blemish or spot to tarnish his repu-tation . . .[8]

VIII

EARLY WORKS

THE biographer of Boyle has a peculiarly difficult task in attempting to give a just estimate of his work; if Boyle himself could never quite decide whether he was a theologian or a scientist, so also his biographer must endeavour to maintain a balance between those two fields which now seem so separate that most readers will be interested in only the one or the other.

The problem of criticism is further complicated by the fact that Boyle's contemporaries perceived no such antagonism; the theologians were often scientists, and the scientists were versed in theology. And in both subjects there was the confusion of ideas which must attend an age of transition. But it is just this ebullience of the Renaissance, passionately trying to destroy an earlier civilization and to create a new one—yet like a Janus facing two ways, using and clinging to the past and unwitting of the results to follow from the new ideas—which makes the seventeenth century so fascinating and so profitable a study. And one could hardly find another Englishman so typical of the age as Robert Boyle. As a humanist, he strove to preserve a just balance between worldliness and otherworldliness, and yet he unconsciously fostered the ever-accelerating preponderance of science over religion; he is rightly called the innovator of modern chemistry, and yet he remained an ardent alchemist; he was a convinced mechanistic corpuscularian, and, at the same time, he ascribed mystical powers to nature and believed his life was directed by Divine Providence; in politics, he wavered between allegiance to the absolute authority of the king and the popular rights of the commonwealth; in religion, he rejected both Papacy and Calvinism and found contentment in the *via media* of the Anglican Church with its authority restricted to matters essential to salvation. By his contemporaries, he was affectionately portrayed as 'The Christian Gentleman.'

In agreement with Boyle's declared belief that the true character and genius of a man are best revealed in his youth before he has been subjected to the distractions of maturity, and before the necessity to compromise induces him to assume a character rather than to be himself, a rather extensive review of his early works will be given as a preface to a critical analysis of his mature contributions to religion and science.

During his residence at Stalbridge, from 1644 to 1654, Boyle completed four tracts which have been preserved, and several manuscripts which were destroyed or have disappeared. Though none of them was published till after the Restoration, they were circulated privately and highly approved by their readers, so that he gained a very considerable literary reputation in a limited, but influential, circle. If he had not later attained so eminent a reputation, these early works would probably have been forgotten; they are, however, of value to the student as indicative of his later and mature work. In general, they show clearly that he had, before he was twenty years of age, a distinctive literary style and a fixed purpose in life. He was, first and last, the teacher, the lay preacher, and the propagandist. All his work might be classed as sermons out of the pulpit; whatever he wrote and whatever he did was designed to incline first his friends and then the world to the Christian life. He early adopted Bacon's motto, that science is valuable for its fruits, and extended that doctrine also to religion; while he wrote much philosophy and theology, his emphasis was always on the advantageous uses to which both could be applied. As for his style, although it was careless and wearisomely discursive, and often marked by the *sprezzatura* of the fine gentleman who would conceal his learning with the appearance of ease, yet it was infused with charm and illustrated with a vivid imagination.

Boyle, in his first letter to Lady Ranelagh after arriving at Stalbridge, mentioned that his *'Ethics* go very slowly on,' as if she were well acquainted with the project; and we can be pretty certain that he had begun its composition in Geneva, for he wrote shortly afterwards to Marcombes:

The *Ethics* hath been a study, wherein I have of late been very conversant, and desirous to call them from the brain down into the chest, and from the school to the house, I have endeavoured to make it not only a lanthorn, but a guide, in a just, though a brief treatise, that I am writing of it; having already with much trouble in some sixteen chapters travelled through the most difficult part of it, and that wherein I saw others deficient, I believe I shall leave the rest to be completed by those, who enjoy more leisure.*

Although the manuscript has disappeared, it is probably fortunate that Boyle's executors did not publish the *Ethics,* if we may judge from another juvenile essay, *A Free Discourse against Customary Swearing: And a Dissuasive from Cursing,*† which they found amongst his papers and entrusted to John Williams, Bishop of Chichester, to edit for posthumous publication in 1695.

In the introduction to this essay against swearing, the editor admits that, if the honourable author had composed the tract in his riper years, he would have given his argument, illustrated by his vast store of learning and thought, more forcibly; yet he justifies its publication since 'there is in the management of it such a strain of modesty and of unaffected piety, such an affectionate zeal for the honour of almighty God, and such a passionate concernment for the well-doing and happiness of those of his acquaintance, for whose use this seems more especially designed.'

Boyle's thesis is that unnecessary oaths are flatly forbidden in both the Old and the New Testaments. He therefore examines singly, and in order, the pleas the swearer makes for excusing the habit, 'and tear off those fig-leaves of evasions and excuses, the devil teaches him to sew together, to hide his own deformity from himself.' [1] The first excuse is that, while swearing is a sin, it is a little one. The answer is, omitting the long discussion, that one might as well say pistols are little and not dangerous because there are large cannon. Secondly, some explain that they seldom swear; but who would say of poison they seldom take it? Thus, he proposes thirteen possible reasons the swearer may allege, and each one he combats or turns to ridicule with quotations and illustrations: some clever, and others dull; some apposite, and others inappropriate. The first section ends with the swearer, all his pleas rebutted, forced to admit that, because long custom has so habituated him to his sin and folly, he cannot leave off.

* *Works,* Vol. i, p. xxxiv. Birch notes that the manuscript in his own handwriting was then extant.

† Ibid. Vol. vi, pp. 1-32. Cf. also Fulton's *Bibliography,* p. 125. Dr. Fulton remarks: 'The publisher would have us believe that the second tract of the "Discursive," although mentioning "Our friend, Mr. Boyle" at several places in the text and signed "W.D.," is "but a decent cover for the concealment of himself." The attribution appears to me unconvincing.' Dr. Fulton's opinion seems to me justified, since the style of the 'Dissuasive' differs largely from Boyle's.

Boyle then gives the penitent six directions to forsake the vice. He must seriously acknowledge swearing to be a sin; he must make 'a zealous and incessant solicitation at the throne of grace, for power to subdue this stubborn vice'; and he must forsake the company of professed swearers. Also, he should pay a fine, or inflict a punishment on himself, every time he swears—and be sure the fines go to relieve distressed Christians; he should resolve to renounce the habit at once, and not by degrees; and lastly, he should reflect on the vanity and foolishness of swearing.

The interest in this tract lies in the fact that Boyle was singularly averse to emphasizing his speech with even the mildest expletives; so averse was he that he was observed invariably to make a reverent pause before pronouncing the name of God. Is it not possible that, as a youth, he drew up this protest against oaths to confirm himself against the habit rather than to influence others, and, since it had served its purpose, abstained from publication? If so, he must, at some time, have wavered in his decision, because he added as a postscript:

To prevent all mistakes that may arise from some apprehensions of mine, which (seeming to censure oaths without distinction) may possibly be stretched beyond my meaning, I thought myself obliged to declare, that in no part of this discourse my intention was to justify that plausible error of our modern Anabaptists, that indiscriminately condemn all oaths as absolutely and indispensably prohibited and abolished by the gospel; my design being only to restrain the needless abuse, not interdict the necessary use of swearing.

In addition to Boyle's 'great (and perhaps peculiar) tenderness in point of oaths,' mention has been made of his persistent study of the Bible. It is not surprising that one of his earliest attempts in writing should relate to a subject so dear to his heart. Like all his early work, his essay on *Some Considerations Touching the Style of the Holy Scriptures* * was written for private circulation; it was not published till 1661, some nine or ten years later, and then only

---

* *Works,* Vol. ii, pp. 247-322. Fulton cites four editions of this work in English and three in Latin during the author's lifetime. It was also published twice in the nineteenth century. He regards it as 'a remarkable forerunner of modern higher criticism which began nearly a century later with Astruc (1753). Boyle compares the Gospels in truly scientific fashion, commenting on the incongruities but emphasizing their essential harmony.' In diction he classes it as not 'a readable book, for it represents Boyle in his most discursive style.' Fulton, *Bibliography,* p. 38.

after he had been urged to do so by many friends and specially by
his brother, the Earl of Orrery, to whom it was dedicated. As became his habit, he employs the form of a letter, addressed to a
friend, Theophilus, a person of rare character who, he assures us,
resembled his brother in many particulars. He also apologizes for
its careless style and his presumption in treating such a subject
'when my green youth made me very unripe for a task of that
nature; whose difficulty requires, as well as its worth deserves, that
it should be handled by a person, in whom nature, education, and
time have happily matched a senile maturity of judgement with a
youthful vigour of fancy.'

It is fortunate that Boyle had the habit of inserting unexpected
items about his life and ideas in his dedications and prefaces, since
from them we can add to the meagre details of his life which have
been preserved. Thus, from a statement in this preface we can
date roughly as prior to 1661, the time when he adopted the atomic
theory which had been revived by Gassendi, and discarded the
Aristotelian, or rather the scholastic, philosophy of natural phenomena:

I confess to you also, that since the physiological writings I have been
induced to publish of late,* and the sort of studies, to which (for reasons
to be told you at a fitter opportunity) I seem, at present, to be wholly
addicted to, make many look upon me as a naturalist; and since some
persons, as well philosophers as physicians, have either faultily, or at
least indiscreetly, given many men occasion to think, that those, that
being speculatively studious of nature's mysteries, depart, as I often do,
from the vulgar peripatetic philosophy, and especially if they seem to
favour that, which explicates the phænomena of nature by atoms, are inclined to atheism, or at least to an unconcernedness for any particular
religion: Since, I say, these things are so, I was not unwilling to lay hold
of this opportunity, to give a public testimony, whereby such as do not
know me may be satisfied, (for I presume, all that do know me, are so,)
that, if I be a naturalist, it is possible to be so without being an atheist,
or of kin to it.

Boyle states his purpose in this essay concisely and clearly: an answer to 'divers witty men' who acknowledge the authority of the

* These were *The Spring and Weight of the Air* in 1660; *Certain Physiological Essays* and
The Sceptical Chymist in 1661. The word 'physiological' is used in its original Greek sense
of natural knowledge.

Scriptures, but take exception to their style, and thus deter many others from reading them. He develops his argument in the form of questions and answers, but he is unfortunate in his inability to exercise restraint in adorning its argument with illustration. He sarcastically wonders why anybody is brave enough to read the Bible, so many and so various are the contemptuous criticisms of its style and content. It is declared by the critics to be obscure, incoherent, and contradictory; much of its matter is trivial or impertinent; its style is flat, unadorned, and repetitious. His retort is that these cavillers at the style judge from reading it in a translation and do not realize how much is lost by rendering it into another language, especially when the tongues differ so greatly as do those of the Orient and Occident.

Besides the general difficulties inherent in translations, the Scriptures are particularly unfortunate because their sacred and infallible nature constrained interpreters to render the Hebrew and Greek passages literally into Latin and English word for word, instead of by phrases; thus the style in our versions is neither idiomatic nor elegant.* There is also a peculiar difficulty of the Hebrew tongue which leads to unavoidable obscurities and inaccuracies. This arises from the fact that pure Hebrew has been unhappily lost except for what remains in the Old Testament; and the meaning of many words which seldom occur in it cannot be interpreted because they cannot be compared with examples in other texts.

Again: 'We should carefully distinguish betwixt what the Scripture itself says, and what is only said in the Scripture. For we must not look upon the Bible as an oration of God to men, or as a body of laws; . . . but as a collection of composures of very different sorts, and written at very different times.' If we regard its composite nature, its many authors and periods of time, we should expect the Bible to be a chronicle rather than an example of literature; as for its obscurities, the Old Testament was written primarily for those to whom it was addressed, and it is not surprising that there are many references to the forgotten events of such remote times. Many parts, also, are prophetic of times future to our own and therefore unintelligible to us. Finally:

It was fit, that there should be some obscure passages left in the inspired volume, to keep those from the knowledge of some of those divine

* An unexpected criticism of the diction of the King James Version, if he was referring to it.

mysteries, *that are both delightful and useful, though not absolutely necessary,* who do not think such knowledge worth studying for. It was also fit that there should be some clouded and mysterious texts, to excite and recompense the industry and speculation of elevated wits and religious enquirers.*

Enough attention has been given to this most important of Boyle's early works to make clear his attitude towards the Bible. It is remarkable, not only as an early textual criticism of a book which was regarded as excluded from the field of scepticism; but even more so because Boyle was one of the first to apply the method of verbal scrutiny to the text. The awakening of the scientific spirit during the seventeenth century had excited a firm reliance on observation and reason as the canons of truth, and had led to a timidly critical questioning of the authority of the Bible and a vigorous revolt from the authority of the Church. The English had seen and had suffered from the confusion resulting from the complete loss of authority of the Church and worse from the domination of the Bible imposed by intolerant and fanatic sectaries. Boyle in his early youth by his persistent study of the Bible had convinced himself that no translation could agree literally with the original text, and therefore that the English and Latin versions could not infallibly express the messages of God. But also, in the original texts, he found erroneous statements of natural phenomena and of the history of the ancient peoples; and even more significant to him was the fact that there were obscurities in the presentation of matters of faith which caused unavoidable controversies about God's dealings with men.

The question inevitably had to be answered: if the Bible is not literally infallible, and if the claims of the Roman Church to a living inspiration are not justified, how far can we go in accepting either as a divine or revealed guide? Where must criticism stop and authority be found? As the temper of the age was rationalistic, the movement called Deism developed, the essentials of which were reliance on the individual's responsibility of judgement, and on the authority of some inward and common sentiment of knowledge that guided human society in the path of righteousness. According to Lord Herbert of Cherbury, familiarly called 'the father of Deism,' the principle of certainty is to be found in a 'natural instinct,' or the

* Italics are mine.

'common notions' of mankind: 'Thus universal consent will be the sovereign test of truth, and there is nothing of so great importance as to seek out these common notions, and to put them each in their place as indubitable truths.' * Since the test of truth is that it shall be a 'common notion,' understood and consented to by all people, and since God desired the redemption of everyone, no obscure passage in the Bible can refer to matters *necessary to salvation*. It will be seen at once that Boyle, either independently or by the influence of Lord Herbert, expresses the same idea in the phrase in the passage quoted above which I have italicized.†

Sometime during his years at Stalbridge, Boyle wrote a full-dress romance, *The Martyrdom of Theodora and Didymus*.[2] Like all the work of this period, the manuscript was circulated widely amongst his friends and apparently found great favour; but, for some reason, it was not published till 1687, more than forty years after its composition. Even then, it was subscribed as by a person of honour, and it was not till the second edition was issued in 1703, after his death, that his name appeared on the title page.

Boyle tells in his preface how he 'came to meddle with this subject,' and why, when published, it was so badly maimed:

Having had occasion many years ago to turn over a martyrology, and some other books, that related to the sufferings of the primitive Christians, I chanced to light on those of a virgin, who, though (to my wonder) she was left unnamed by the other writers that mentioned her, seemed plainly to be the same that is by one of them expressly called Theodora. I own, I was not a little affected, at the reading of such moving and uncommon adventures as hers, and finding her story to be related by the author, that named both her and her lover, not only succinctly and imperfectly, but very dully too; I found myself tempted so to enlarge this story, so that it might be contrived into a somewhat voluminous romance . . . This piece, having been perused by those for whose sake I wrote it, was so fortunate, that it having, without my leave, been ventured into several hands, as a book of a nameless and unknown author, it was lucky enough to be, by some indulgent readers, attributed to one, and by some to another, of the two persons, that were at that time counted the best writers of disguised histories.

* Cf. Basil Willey's *Seventeenth Century Background*, London, 1934, pp. 121-32. The excerpt is from his translation of the French version, 3rd ed., 1639. The work *De veritate* was first published in Latin in 1625. He states that it has never been translated into English.
† The influence of Boyle on theology will be treated more fully later when his mature religious works are discussed.

During its travels, the loose sheets of the manuscript were so carelessly or maliciously handled that practically all the first part and much of the second were lost. Boyle was but little disturbed, since he had never intended to make the papers public. When at the earnest solicitations of some eminent persons he did set himself to put them in order, he found the first part was gone beyond repair; yet he was able to restore out of his memory, or otherwise from the recovered sheets, sufficient of the second part to satisfy the importunities of his friends. Thus the romance, as we have it, is but the revised second part of the original as it came from his hands.

This romance deserves attention, if for no other reason than Dr. Johnson's dictum on it: 'The attempt to employ the ornaments of romance in the decoration of religion was, I think, first made by Mr. Boyle's *Martyrdom of Theodora;* but Boyle's philosophical studies did not allow him time for the cultivation of style; and the completion of the great design was reserved for Mrs. Rowe.'[3] If it be true, and one may place great faith in the opinion of Dr. Johnson, that this romance was the predecessor of the long and swelling line of religious novels, then, in spite of its evident faults, this invention of a youth in his early twenties assumes high value.

Boyle tells us that, in the missing first part, he developed the characters of both Theodora and Didymus, and the rise of his love for her. The scene of the story is set in Antioch at a time of a bloody persecution of the early Christians, in which Theodora, a young virgin of the noblest birth and of a dazzling beauty, became involved; when summoned before the 'president' of Antioch, she resolutely confessed her Christianity and resisted both his promises of favour and his menaces of punishment. She was doomed by her judge, either to sacrifice to the Roman gods, or to be prostituted in the public stews. She is led to the infamous place and shut up alone in a room; there 'she employed the little time, that was granted her, to consider, whether she would yet burn incense to the Roman idols, in fervent prayer to the true God, for a rescue of her purity, not her life; in order whereunto, she designed, and hoped, by resistance and contumelies, to provoke her first assailant to become her murderer, rather than her ravisher.'

The second part opens with the chaste Theodora in this deplorable situation. Didymus, learning of her predicament, at once resolves to rescue her by a contrivance to enter her prison, substitute himself in her place, and take upon himself a martyr's death. In this design he addresses himself to his intimate friend, Septimius, who happened to be the officer of her guard:

Generous Septimius, says he, I cannot but look upon it as one of the chief advantages I have obtained by venturing my life in the Roman camps, that I had the happiness to be acquainted with you there, and to be a spectator of your gallantry; which did not only then raise me to a desire of imitating it, but allows me now to own a request to you, that none but a gallant person ought to be entrusted with, or would easily grant. Generous Didymus, replies the Roman, when I accompanied you in following our propitious eagles, I found so great a contentment in your acquaintance, and so strong a spur to glory in your examples, that I looked upon the advantage of having been your fellow soldier, as preferable to the honour of leading the most numerous troops I may at any time command; and shall think all the hazards I then exposed myself to, abundantly rewarded, if any power they have procured me may enable me to do you service . . .

Didymus then proceeded to say: 'If you have ever had the happiness to be acquainted with Theodora, or so much as to have seen her, it would be needless, as well as improper, for me to offer at giving you a character of her, which you must needs think injurious to her: but if you have not, the shortness of the time will only permit me to assure you, that not only she has given me those sentiments of her excellencies, that I never had, nor ever thought myself capable of having, for any of her sex . . . This admirable person, for exercising among other virtues, that of an invincible constancy to her religion, and refusing to sacrifice to Venus, Flora, and some other of those deities, whom her perfections might, though her religion did not, exempt from adoring, is by your savage president condemned to be exposed to the public lust . . . You may easily guess by this, continues he, that my request is like to prove an earnest one; that you would please to treat with some of those soldiers of yours, in whom you think you have the greatest interest, and dispose them to assist me in rescuing Theodora out of so infamous a prison, and accept from me greater recompences for doing a handsome action, than they can expect from the president, for doing a barbarous one.'

Septimius is won by the passionate plea of Didymus. A member of his troop provided a military cloak for a disguise; the desperate lover was passed by the guards as one who, having been scornfully slighted by Theodora, is now desirous of satisfying his lust and his revenge.

When first admitted, Didymus is thought by Theodora to be the first of her ravishers. Then he, without approaching too near, calms her fear by this address: 'Do not, madam, I beseech you, add to your other troubles, the apprehension, that, because I appear in the circumstances of a ravisher, I come to commit a rape.' No; he begs her to disguise herself in his cloak and to go freely out of her shameful prison; while he, Didymus, by remaining in her stead will not only regard such a service as a full recompence of his love but a high obligation of his religion. Then follows a long and touchingly tender dialogue. Theodora will not accept her life, which she values but little, at the sacrifice of another's; if suicide be forbidden so also she would be an accessory to murder if she should owe her freedom to his substituted death. And so they serenely and calmly argue this question on the highest moral grounds.

Didymus claims it was not a sin for him to hazard his life a thousand times as a soldier for mere excitement, or glory, or for the welfare of his country; how much more worthy to take the same risk to save her chastity. Theodora finally is moved by the acknowledged right of a virgin to protect herself by extraordinary means and exclaims:

Since, then, an untainted purity is a jewel, that the possessors are allowed to preserve and defend, even by uncommon ways, if others will not serve, and such as would in other cases be unwarrantable; though I do not, as I lately told you, think it lawful, as many do, to secure virginity by self-murder, yet I cannot disapprove their opinion, that allow a virgin, in case of extremity, to implore that death from another's hand.—Deny me not therefore, concludes Theodora, with tears in her eyes, the last request I shall ever make you; but by sheathing your sword here, (at which words she pointed, with blushes, at her fair and innocent breast) be pleased, by one quick and charitable stroke, to perfect my deliverance, without making me stain it with the blood of my deliverer; free us both from eminent danger, me of being dishonoured, and you of being tormented; and by the same act of friendship secure me the coronet of virginity, and procure me the crown of martyrdom.

Didymus convincingly points out that if he should accede to the desperate proposal of the chaste Theodora it would result in his death also; and thus he finally overcomes her refusal to escape. He divests himself of his military coat. Then follows a scene true to the spirit of the age that a virgin was a delicate creature, all blushes and modesty, however plainly she might use words now avoided in polite conversation:

[She] permitted him (tho' not without strange disorder in her mind and looks) to assist her; for it was absolutely necessary to do it, so he did it with all imaginable care, to distress so nice a modesty as little as was possible; and therefore, as soon as ever he had done that, with all the respect and decency the place and occasion would by any means permit, all that could be done without him, he left her to do herself, withdrawing to a part of the room whence he could not see her: which retreat he was induced to make, not only out of civility and respect, but perchance because [of] the dangers that threaten internal chastity.

These two most delicately proper lovers, propriety having been resumed, then discuss many profound questions at very great length while the lusting soldiers outside grow impatient for their turns. Theodora, now disguised, safely passes her guards and hurries to the house of Irene, her bosom's friend. There, she finds a gathering of Christians, lamenting her fate. Again follow inordinately long discussions, till a friend enters to tell them that Didymus had been discovered and was then being interrogated by the president of Antioch, who not only condemned Didymus to death, but, unmoved by his heroic conduct, vowed that if he could lay hands on Theodora he would not again attempt to 'reclaim her by the fear of infamy but by the terror of death.'

When Theodora learns that martyrdom and not infamy would be her fate, she leaves Irene to join her lover. She expounds her faith to the obdurate president and the joy of martyrdom as a witness to the crucified Christ. We omit the tedious harangues. Didymus is executed in her presence: after a final discourse, 'with a countenance, wherein serenity was mingled with joy,' she too suffers martyrdom. Nothing is said of the soul of Didymus, who would seem to have been the nobler spirit of the two, but of her: 'The glad soul was by the angels, (whom she had aspired to resemble in purity and devotion) carried to that happy place, whose glories are neither to be conceived by those, that have not seen them, nor described by those, that have; such supernatural felicities as much transcending man's ideas and his expressions, as they surpass his merit.'

With all its too obvious faults of false emphasis on the traditional picture of the virgin in distress, of stilted diction and moralizing, and of inordinate length, the story is one of arresting interest. One wonders, if Boyle had pruned his exuberant romanticism with the sobering influence of matured literary practice instead of immersing his thought in natural philosophy, whether it would not have resulted, as Dr. Johnson believed, in his taking a leading and commanding place amongst English men of letters.

Miss Masson, in her *Life of Boyle,* ventured the opinion that the *Martyrdom of Theodora* was inspired by a personal love affair, and that Boyle drew the character of Theodora from life as his ideal of noble womanhood. There seems to be no other warrant for such a surmise, save that the subject is on love, and that it was written at an age when young and romantic youths are apt to be in love; there is, however, stronger evidence that another essay, *Seraphic Love,* written in 1648, was inspired by a personal experience. In this piece the shadowy heroine, Hermione, is portrayed as a beautiful, alluring, and fickle jilt; certainly she and Theodora are diametrically opposite in character, and if they both are drawn from his life, Boyle had two unlucky affairs.

The evidence that Hermione was drawn from life rests directly on a statement of Evelyn in a letter to Dr. William Wotton: 'Though amongst all his experiments he never made that of married life, yet I have been told he courted a beautiful and ingenious daughter of Carew (or Carey), Earl of Monmouth; to which is owing the birth of his *Seraphic Love,* and the first of his productions,' and there is supporting evidence to this gossip. Lady Ranelagh was, at this time, proudly showing to her friends the manuscripts of her young brother and, to advance his interests, gave one to the Countess of Monmouth. This very important personage not only liked the production, but also invited the author to visit her at her celebrated Moore Park; there, the youth made a short visit, read an essay to the Earl and Countess, and must have met their daughters, of whom there were many then unmarried. In August of the same year, he was visiting his sister Mary, the daughter-in-law of the Earl of Warwick, at 'delicious Leeze' in Essex; and there he finished *Seraphic Love* on the sixth of the month.

Seraphic Love,* as it was commonly known, was not published till 1659, when Boyle had been for some five years living at Oxford. The essay appeared at a critical time: 'the dismal year,' as it was

---

* Boyle's *Works,* Vol. 1, pp. 243-93. The full title is: *Some Motives and Incentives To the Love of God. Pathetically discours'd of, in A Letter to a Friend.* By The Hon. R. B. Esq. Fulton, in his *Bibliography,* states that it is now as little known as any of Boyle's works. The book is scarce and only five copies have been traced. By 1708, there had appeared nine English editions; also translations in French and German, and in the collected Latin edition of Geneva. It was republished in Edinburgh in 1825.

labelled by Bishop Sprat in his *History of the Royal Society* to contrast it with the following *annus mirabilis* of the glorious Restoration, had sunk all England into the depths of gloom. So this earnest plea of Boyle, backed by his distinguished and powerful family connexions, to return to the Christian principles of peace and good will of their fathers awoke an enthusiastic response of hope.

This hope for peace, in almost ecstatic terms, was expressed to Boyle in a letter by John Evelyn, which cemented an intimate friendship that was to last more than forty years between these two noble gentlemen.

I was . . . ready to cry out with St. Paul, *cupio dissolvi,* and to be in the embraces of this seraphic love, which you have described to that perfection as if in the company of some celestial harbinger you had taken flight, and been ravished into the third heaven, where you have heard words unutterable, and from whence you bring us such affections and divine inclinations, as are only competent to angels and yourself: for so powerful is your eloquence, so metaphysical your discourse, and sublime your subject . . . Dearest Sir, permit me to tell you, that I extremely loved you before; but my heart is infinitely knit to you now: for what are we not to expect from so timely a consecration of your excellent abilities? [4]

We may smile at Evelyn's extravagant and flowery praise, which reflects the formal fashion of the time; but we would do well to ponder over his underlying conviction that the spiritual values of religious piety and unity are the only safeguards from the tyranny of the dictator or of the mob. And we, with our chill indifference to religion, as they with their hot fanaticism, have also sunk into a 'dismal year' and must learn to realize that our *annus mirabilis* can come only when we shall restore a balance between worldly and otherworldly ideals.

Boyle explains, at length, in a dedicatory preface to his sister Mary, why this private letter on *Seraphic Love* to a friend, written in 1648 at 'delicious Leeze,' was now, eleven years later, given to the public. Addressed to his friend Lindamor, a traveller, a linguist, and a scholar, who had been jilted by Hermione in spite of her apparent encouragement of his passion, the letter was a plea to effect a cure by concentrating his attention on another and nobler kind of love. Even so, he declares, it would never have been published if his sister, in her enthusiasm, had not made several copies and shown them to many friends; as it chanced, a broken sample fell into the hands of a necessitous person who thought to obtain a little money by offering it to a stationer. Fortunately, Boyle was informed of this circumstance in time; since two or three copies were already abroad, and publication by someone was believed to be certain, he was persuaded to undertake it himself.

'My dearest Lindamor, I am very much delighted to learn, both by the voice of fame and the information of much more credible relators, that Hermione's cold usage has cured you of the fever her scorching eyes had given you.' He then proceeds to tell his friend that there is something weak, and even degrading, in allowing such amorous excesses to bind him in chains to any woman; no one should allow his reason and his independence to be overcome by such extravagance of emotion. 'For, wherever a passion has these properties, or any of them, conspicuous in it; it cannot, but by being consecrated to God, avoid being injurious both to him and to itself.' Boyle would not, however, be thought to quarrel with love itself, since to love with moderation the person one would marry is both allowable and expedient.

Then Boyle, who had perhaps seen too much of the bargaining for wives and husbands in his own family, of whom only Mary and himself had rebelled successfully against the Earl's use of his children to extend his power and his estates, gives his opinion of marriage:

Though I am no such an enemy to matrimony, as some (for want of understanding the raillery, I have sometimes used in ordinary discourse) are pleased to think me, and would not refuse you my advice (though I would not so readily give you my example) to turn votary to Hymen; yet I have observed so few happy matches, and so many unfortunate ones; and have so rarely seen men love their wives at the rate they did, whilst they were their mistresses; that I wonder not, that legislators thought it necessary to make marriages indissoluble, to make them lasting.

So, having emphasized the frailties of human or carnal love, Boyle would have his friend turn to the seraphic love of God; not because he had suffered defeat at the hands of Hermione, but because it is the explicit commandment of both the law and the gospel. While excessive passion for a woman is not only blameworthy but even ridiculous, there can be no excess in seraphic love. Love to a creature is something given as a present, but to God it is a tribute;

though we may as prodigals easily squander our substance by gifts to a beloved one, we shall scarcely overpay our debts.

Lindamor loved Hermione because he believed her full of loveliness and excellencies, and that her love for him was great, free, and constant. Yet all these properties eminently exist and illustriously concur in God, alone; 'and his love, I must now Lindamore, (with strong desires of doing it prosperously) attempt to manifest.'

'First then, our highest love is made God's due by the excellency and prerogative of his nature.' It is not necessary to give the many illustrations Boyle produces from the Bible and elsewhere, yet one unusual application from science, as typical of his conflation of science and religion, may be given: 'Methinks, seraphic and our common lovers behold exterior beauties with a difference resembling that, wherewith children and astronomers consider Galileo's optic glasses (with one of which telescopes, that I remember I saw at Florence, he merrily boasted, that he had *trovato la corte a Giove;*) which the one prizes most for what they appear; the other, for what they discover.'

Secondly, as God transcends all else by his own nature, so we can repay only a little part of our debt to him for what he is to us. Boyle's argument is that the supreme gift of love was the sending of his Son for the remission of our sins, and, as he and the Father are one, so God himself participated in the redemption.

So, also, God's love is disinterested, free, and constant. The universe is the Lord's and he has given it to us that we may be partakers of it with him and as witnesses to his glory. Boyle's explanation for the existence of suffering and sickness is the stock excuse that God so hates sin that he mercifully afflicts his children to bring them to repentance.

When Boyle is confronted with the question of predestination, which had torn the Church and had split it into warring sects, he has only this to say:

Concerning the controversies betwixt the Calvinists and the Remonstrants about predestination, and the coherent doctrines, it were improper to give you here my sense. Those, that are truly pious of either party, are perhaps otherwise looked on by God than by any other, as contending, which of God's attributes should be most respected; the one seeming to affirm irrespective decrees, to magnify his goodness; and the other to deny them, but to secure the credit of his justice . . . I think it not amiss to advertise you, that the doctrine of predestination is not necessary to justify the freeness and greatness of God's love.

Such an opinion as this would be a sufficient reason why Boyle postponed the publication of this letter until the zealots for predestination had lost the power to enforce their doctrines with carnal weapons.

As a final and crowning impulse to the cultivation of Seraphic Love, there is the ineffable reward of heaven. In Boyle's opinion it is perfectly proper to guide one's life with the purpose of hoping for such a reward; although

many, not undeservedly, applauded preachers have of late been pleased to teach the people, that to hope for heaven is a mercenary, legal, and therefore unfilial affection. Indeed, to hope for heaven as wages for work performed, or by way of merit, in the proper and strict acception of that term, were a presumption, to which none of the divines, we dissent from, can be too much an enemy, nor perhaps more so than I am . . . But to forego readily all the pleasures of the senses, and undergo cheerfully all the hardships and dangers, that are wont to attend a holy life, is Lindamor, such a kind of mercenariness, as none, but a resigned, noble, and believing soul is likely to be guilty of.

While we are unable, Boyle concludes, to describe the nature of heaven, we can state positively that the baffling question of what may be true happiness will be answered, and 'we shall have clearly expounded to us those riddles of providence, which have, but too often tempted, even good men, to question God's conduct in the government of the world.'

So ends this self-revelation of piety. Evelyn, and probably many others, pointed out that the logic is faulty—that the two sorts of love are not incompatible, and that to expel human passion is not the purpose of seraphic love; indeed Boyle contradicts himself by his portraiture of the love of Theodora and Didymus. We may also find his exposition to be cast in too stereotyped a form; but like Evelyn also we could love him for the character of himself which he unconsciously reveals as a just man without guile.

In addition to the more formal works which Boyle composed during this period of life at Stalbridge, he began the habit—perhaps even before his return to England—of observing incidents during his walks and at other times on which he would meditate to see if he could not draw from them a moral lesson. He found that, to fix these lessons in his mind, they should be written in an easy and familiar style, more to encourage devotion than to satisfy the professional critic. As usually happens, these little pieces accumulated and, having been loaned to his sister Katherine and other friends, some were returned and others travelled into unknown hands. As the sketches met with unexpected favour, his sister persuaded him to make a collection of them and to publish it anonymously, with the title, *Occasional Reflections upon Several Subjects; whereto is premised A Discourse about such kind of Thoughts.*[5]

Boyle was not, of course, the originator of the short essay form; we have only to mention Aesop, Plutarch, Cicero, and Seneca to assure ourselves of its popularity with the classical writers. While this form of prose is difficult to define because of its variety in length, purpose, and style, it is not difficult to recognize; the classic essay had been revived with dazzling success by Montaigne and Bacon, and those authors had been followed by many successors in the seventeenth century.* Yet the *Occasional Reflections* was formerly widely read and is, as will be shown, strikingly original in a number of ways.

Boyle outdoes even himself by prefixing to this work a dedication to his sister, Lady Ranelagh, as Sophronia; a preface to the reader; and a long discourse, in the form of an essay, justifying the habit of meditation, for which he coins the uncouth name, *meletetics.* The dedication to Sophronia is perhaps the best of his many tributes to relatives and friends; it is less overloaded with florid compliment and, in its simplicity, it witnesses a deep love for this sister, an affection stronger probably than for anyone else in the world. She had commanded him to publish; he must obey even though he will not publicly own them, for they are unfinished and unpolished trifles, and likely to interfere with work of the very different and serious nature now expected of him. It should be remembered that Boyle had recently published the first fruits of his scientific work and had become a noted man of science.

In his preface, Boyle apologizes, as was his usual habit, for the carelessness of his writing and the haste of his publishing as if he must, as a great gentleman and dilettante, excuse himself for adopt-

---

* *Seventeenth Century Essays,* Scribners, 1926. Professor Zeitlin lists nineteen important essayists, but oddly enough does not include Boyle in the list nor even mention his name.

ing the unusual rôle of scholar and religious writer. Nevertheless, he warns his readers that if they 'try their skill in making meditations indifferently upon the occurrences that shall happen, and wander no further from the circumstances of their themes, nor lard them any more with sentences and other passages borrowed from the fathers, or the poets, than in most of the following papers I have done; [they] will not find the task so easy.' He claims two novel inventions for his work. He has, he says, ventured for the first time to put some of the essays in the form of dialogues, and he adds that the reader will be less startled by this and other deviations from 'Bishop Hall's * way of writing occasional meditations, when he acknowledges that till of late he had purposely neglected to read that eloquent prelate's devout reflections.'

As another novelty in this form of writing, Boyle claims that sections two and four, 'though by far the longest in the whole book, are entirely taken up; the former by meditations on accidents relating to an ague that once afflicted me; and the latter by those, that occurred to anglers by the river side.'

Boyle's *Occasional Reflections* are preceded by a critique on essay writing, in which he discusses the delight and advantage of meditating, and explains the proper method of cultivating the habit. Meditation, he says, 'conduces to keep the soul from idleness, and employments worse than idleness.' Perhaps, one should not criticize such an essay too seriously, but take it genially as a whimsical display of youthful fancy.

There is no doubt that a Milton meditating persistently on *Paradise Lost* was kept from idleness and was filled with good thoughts; but Boyle's meditations are not of such a type. In his first one, he holds a bit of meat just above the reach of his spaniel; if the dog does not leap up for it, he certainly cannot have it; if he does leap, then Boyle lets it fall half way into his mouth. His moral is that we cannot attain virtue if we do not try, but virtue is so far above us that our own efforts would be vain unless God in his mercy accepts good will for accomplishment. Now, such a meditation as that is in itself commonplace, its moral is trite and needs no meditation to attain. Its excuse is solely in the pleasing picture, pleasingly expressed, of a wistful, panting spaniel and his fondly tantalizing master.

* Joseph Hall, Bishop of Norwich, called the first English satirist, was said by Thomas Fuller to be very good in his *Characters*, better in his *Sermons*, best of all in his *Meditations*.

Yet there is one phase of Boyle's thought in these meditations which is important—the interpretation of piety from natural phenomena, which apparently he introduced into English literature and which has its counterpart two centuries later in the early nature poetry of Wordsworth. An example or two will make this clear: 'He that can (as it were) make the world vocal, by furnishing every creature, and almost every occurrence, with a tongue to entertain him with, and can make the little accidents of his life, and the very flowers of his garden, read him lectures of ethics or divinity . . .' Again: 'It was doubtless a very great pleasure to Aesop, that by his ingenious fictions he could, in a manner, lend reason and speech to lions, foxes, crows, and other animals, to whom nature had denied both; and I know not why it should be less delightful, by occasional reflections, to turn not only birds and beasts, but all kinds of creatures in the world, as well mute and inanimate, as irrational, not only into teachers of ethics, but oftentimes into doctors of divinity.'

There is, however, an essential difference between the philosophy of Aesop and that of Boyle and Wordsworth. To make, on the one hand, the sly habits of the fox teach a moral lesson against slyness in men by giving speech to the fox is an ingenious and striking analogy. But to have 'the very flowers of his garden, read him lectures of ethics or divinity' as did Boyle, or to find 'sermons in running brooks' as did Wordsworth, merely confuses the aesthetic sentiments aroused in us by beautiful objects with moral responsibility.

It would seem that this attempt of Boyle and Wordsworth to derive moral lessons from inanimate objects and plants was induced by a common cause. In the seventeenth century the dazzling achievements of the line of physicists, from Copernicus to Boyle and Newton, in developing a mechanistic philosophy of the universe had made science a popular study and fashionable in general society. Their discoveries of natural law and phenomena had introduced serious problems in religion; for such astonishingly accurate results obtained by the exercise of observation and reason inevitably led to enquiry by the same method into the accuracy of the Scriptures and of the Church. This new self-reliance led, on the one hand, to the rapid spread of the atheistic philosophy of Hobbes and to the belief privately expressed by such a conforming Christian as Newton, that the doctrine of the Trinity is not necessary to salvation because it is humanly unintelligible: and on the other hand when Bentley, in the Boyle lectures, attacked the atheism of Hobbes, he could find no better support for religion than Newton's mechanistic theory of the cosmos. In fact, this whole movement to rationalize religion, which received the name of Deism, may be said to have adopted the motto from Newton, that natural law required a rational Creator who was an excellent geometer.

A similar effect of rationalizing religion and of compelling it to take account of scientific discoveries occurred with the popular interest awakened in the nineteenth century by the Darwinian theory of evolution. Again, as in the former period when science became fashionable, we find, on the one hand, the clergy seeking to buttress a shaken religion by an appeal to observation and reason; and, on the other hand, amongst the 'virtuosi' the diluted substitute for atheism which passes under the name of humanitarianism. In literature, Tennyson replaces the doctrines of free will and grace of the individual with a natural law of evolution, which constrains all society to progress independently of the individual and with the same rigour as the solar system obeys the Newtonian laws. And Wordsworth, like Boyle, made flowers and stones and brooks preach sermons as morally eloquent as were those of the most devout doctors of divinity.

The *Occasional Reflections* of Boyle are so uniform in style, and so naïve in purpose, that the quotation of one from the collection of seventy-five will suffice to acquaint the reader with a book once very popular, but now almost completely forgotten.

REFLECTION III.

Upon his being in great danger wandering, on Mendip hills, among covered lead mines, that he knew not of.

How have I travelled all this while upon the brink of the grave! I thought only to be out of my way, but little dreamed to be so near the end of all my journeys, in that of my life by traversing to and fro amongst those deep and covered pits, upon any one of which if my horse had but chanced to stumble, (and the very mine-men I at length met with, think it a kind of miracle he did not) I had been killed and buried at once, and my fate had been for ever as much concealed from my friends as my body: and all this escape a work so totally of God's goodness, that I did not so much as know my danger till I was past it; so that it seemed sent, but to give me occasion of rejoicing in my deliverance. How vast a debt of gratitude then do I owe to God? and how extremely do I fall short of acquitting myself of it? since, I often fall into dangers that I know not, and of distrusts of God's providence, since I have found it so watchful to deliver me from those that I feared not.[6]

There is no doubt that Boyle's early works, and notably his *Occasional Reflections,* aroused contemporary enthusiasm and placed him amongst the popular writers of the day; his popularity is, perhaps, most clearly shown by the fact that he and the new philosophy of the Royal Society were picked out as targets for the satires of the period. Samuel Butler wrote an *Occasional Reflection on Dr. Charlton's feeling a dog's pulse at Gresham College,* which was published with his posthumous writings; and one of Swift's cleverest parodies, *A Meditation on a Broomstick,* had the same source.

The origin of this parody, as told by Thomas Sheridan in his *Life of Swift,* is too amusing to be omitted. It seems that Lady Berkeley had a great liking for Boyle's *Reflections,* and after her devotions, which were conducted by Swift, who was then her private chaplain, she was accustomed to have him read them aloud to her. It is easily understood that such sentimental writings would bore the impatient doctor; so to put an end to the task he wrote his *Meditation on a Broomstick* and slyly inserted it between the pages of the book. Then the next time he was called upon, he, 'with an inflexible gravity of countenance, proceeded to read the *Meditation,* in the same solemn tone he had used in delivering the former.' Some company coming in, Swift left the room, and Lady Berkeley soon began to praise the heavenly *Meditations* of Mr. Boyle. 'But,' said she, 'the doctor has been just reading one to me, which has surprised me more than all the rest—, I mean that excellent *Meditation on a Broomstick.'* The company, full of wonder, opened the book and found it indeed there, but in Swift's handwriting.[7] The cleverness and biting sarcasm of Swift's parody are illustrated in its beginning and ending sentences:

This single stick, which you now behold ingloriously lying in that neglected corner, I once knew in a flourishing state in a forest: It was full of sap, full of leaves, and full of boughs: But now, in vain does the busy art of man pretend to vie with nature, by tying that wither'd bundle of twigs to its sapless trunk: 'Tis now at best but the reverse of what it was, a tree turned upside down, the branches on the earth, and the root in the air . . . But a broom-stick, perhaps you will say, is an emblem of a tree standing on its head; and pray what is man, but a topsy-turvy crea-

ture . . . His last days are spent in slavery to women, and generally the
least deserving; till worn to the stumps, like his brother bezom, he is
either kick'd out of doors, or made use of to kindle flames, for others to
warm themselves by.

Another of Boyle's *Meditations,* the *Reflection Upon the Eating
of Oysters,* warrants especial mention, as it was rumoured to have
led Swift to the idea of his *Gulliver's Travels.* Two friends, Eu-
genius and Lindamor, with other acquaintances are pleasantly eating oysters. Lindamor falls into a strain of moralizing on the pro-
vincialism of people who ignorantly praise their own customs: 'I
acknowledge it to be one of the chief advantages I account my self
to have obtained by my travels, that as I do not easily admire, so
I am not forward to deride, the practice of any people for being
new, and am not apt to think their customs must be therefore
worse than ours, because they widely differ from them.'
Lindamor then cites examples from our eating and drinking, of
how other people may regard us:

We impute it for a barbarous custom to many nations of the Indians,
that like beasts they eat raw flesh. And pray how much is that worse
than our eating raw fish, as we do in eating these oysters . . . Lastly, as
the highest degree of brutishness, our travellers mention the practice of
the Soldanians, at the Cape of Good Hope, who not only eat raw meat,
but, if they be hungry, eat the guts and all of their cattle, with the dung
in them. I will not answer, that I know several among us, (and perhaps some fair ladies too) that, to prevent the scurvy and the gout, drink
their own or boy's urine . . . But I will rather demand, how much less
we do ourselves, than what we abominate in those savages, when we
devour oysters whole, guts, excrements, and all?
[Eugenius replies:] 'You put me in mind of a fancy of your friend
Mr. Boyle, who was saying, that he had thoughts of making a short romantic story, where the scene should be laid in some island of the southern ocean, governed by some such rational laws and customs, as those of
Utopia, or the *New Atlantis;* and, in this country, he would introduce
an observing native, that, upon his return home from his travels made in
Europe, should give an account of our countries and manners, under
feigned names, and frequently intimate in his relations, (or in his answers to questions that should be made him) the reasons of his wondering to find our customs so extravagant, and differing from those of his
country.'[8]

Although Swift never acknowledged any indebtedness to Boyle for the idea of *Gulliver's Travels,* Boyle's brother, Lord Broghill, lamented: 'To what a height must the spirit of sarcasm arise in an author who could prevail on himself to ridicule so good a man as Mr. Boyle.' It is easy, by looking back, to see that ridicule and the new scientific spirit were changing most of the ideals, including the definition of goodness, of Elizabethan England.

Perhaps too much space has been given to these youthful works of Boyle, now almost completely neglected even by critical scholars; but they are important in revealing the character of Boyle, and they are even more important in showing how Boyle and other thinkers of the day were attempting to use the new science to replace the dogmas of a religion revealed to us by God, by a Deism satisfactory to our perceptions and to our reason.

IX

BOYLE AND ANGLICAN THEOLOGY

A COMPARISON of the Anglican movement of the seventeenth century with the religious beliefs and works of Boyle, will convince the student how thoroughly in sympathy he was with it and how influential he was in steering its course in the *via media* between Romanism and Calvinism.* Fortunately, he revealed himself so clearly and so fully in his writings, in his correspondence, and to his associates, that we can form a just estimate of his ideas and character as a Christian, and of his scholarly equipment as a theologian.

In the first place it should be kept in mind that Robert Boyle was in many traits said to be very like his father, and that the fortunes and prejudices of his family were deeply affected by its Irish environment. While Robert himself was rarely in Ireland and could not speak the native language, both the good and bad fortune of his family were caused by the Irish and must have been constantly discussed. His father was an unquestioning adherent of the Church of England; he despised the native Irish Catholics and he feared the Roman priests, to whose religious influence he attributed the disturbances and rebellions which endangered England and wrecked his ambitions. In spite of continual controversies with the government, in politics he was unwavering in his loyalty to the Crown and to the King, and had the Englishman's rooted fear of the political interference of Rome. These influences were permanently implanted in his son. Also the belief of Lord Cork that he was led by divine guidance in every affair of his life was so impressed on Robert Boyle that he too saw the intervention of God in all the

* By the permission of Mr. Linden H. Morehouse, I am able to include as an Appendix to this work an Essay on *The Spirit of Anglicanism* by my brother, Paul Elmer More. This Essay served as an introduction to *Anglicanism: An Anthology of Religious Literature of the Seventeenth Century,* Compiled and Edited by Paul Elmer More and Frank Leslie Cross: Morehouse-Gorham Co., New York and Milwaukee, 1935. The importance of Boyle in this movement is fully recognized by the Editors.

events of his life, and this belief even affected his scientific work to the extent of stopping him short of determinism.

Boyle, in his autobiographic sketch, describes himself as a studious and good boy, notable only as unswervingly truthful, and taking his religion as a matter of course. Then suddenly, as has been told, during the great storm at Geneva, there came upon him the terror that he was not prepared for death, and the consequent pledge that, if his life were spared, he would seriously devote himself to the Christian life. The course of this resolve was typical, in that he first experienced the elation and joy of simple salvation; then followed a period of depression in which he contemplated suicide, when he imagined his sins too great to be forgiven; and lastly there came to him the realization that the religious life is a long and sober path to be followed to the end with the one purpose to save his soul. With no exaggeration, it can be said that from the day of his conversion his life was fixed in the determination to practise Christian piety; to study the Scriptures and the history of the Church Universal; and to consecrate his scientific labours for a witness to God's creation and governance of the universe.

Boyle used the leisure of his time in Florence in conversation and discussion with certain Rabbis to acquaint himself with the doctrines of Hebrew theology.[1] He also studied 'the new paradoxes of the great star-gazer Galileo.'[2] Of the practical influence of Romanism on the customs and morals of the Italians, his episode at Florence with the two lustful friars, and his observation at Rome of the (to him) idolatrous practices and cynical contempt for the hierarchy of the Papal Court deeply confirmed his boyish impressions of the evils which an undisputed authority of the Roman Church fastened on a people.

During his enforced stay of two years in Geneva, Boyle must have paid especial attention to the moderate form of Calvinism taught by Diodati. He was evidently sympathetic to much of that doctrine and, although he never wavered in his allegiance to the Church of England, he remained tolerant of the dissenters and joined with those divines who desired to broaden the Church to include nonconformists. It was not until he returned to an England convulsed with a civil war largely fostered by religious strife that he became bitter against a radical Protestantism; for to him the essence of Christianity was peace and charity.

Thus, at the age of seventeen Boyle had established the fundamentals of his religious faith, and he spent much of his decade at Stalbridge, until he finally devoted himself to science, in studying and developing his Christian philosophy. There is no doubt it was during this period that he read theology so systematically as to justify Bishop Burnet's comment: 'He had read so much of the Fathers, that he had formed out of it a clear judgement of all the eminent ones. He had read over a vast number of commentators on the Scriptures, and had gone with good exactness through the controversies of religion, and had a just idea of the entire body of divinity.' Nor did he make a casual selection of subjects for writing. Each of his early works bears strong evidence of having been composed to decide a particular phase of his own religious thought and to fix some principle in his mind. Thus, his tract against swearing related to his notable reverence for the name of God; his *Occasional Reflections* were an aid to encourage the habit, as did St. Francis, of finding a moral lesson in his every act and observation, and God's providence in everything; the *Seraphic Love* was a tract on how to lead the pious life in order to be rewarded by communion with the Saviour and the Saints after death; his *Theodora* aimed to strengthen his steadfastness in the faith of the early and uncorrupted Church; but of far greater importance, his tract on the *Style of the Scriptures* confirmed him in full agreement with the Anglican Divines who were developing that *via media* by accepting neither the Calvinistic dogma of the infallibility of the whole text, nor the Romanist's of the infallible interpretation by the Church. Nor would he agree with the 'witty cavillers' who could find no unified purpose running through the Bible's apparent diversities and contradictions.

For a man of Boyle's interest in religion, there are surprisingly few references to his relations with the Church and the clergy. Excepting his one reference to the fact that the churches of London were excellently supplied and but indifferently attended, there is scarcely a mention in his correspondence or works of church affiliation and attendance. However, Evelyn stated that Boyle was thoroughly contented with the services of the Anglican Church, and Bishop Burnet, in his funeral sermon on Boyle, mentioned that he was constant to the Established Church and went to no separate assemblies; that he hated all disputes and divisions on minor matters while the universally acknowledged truths were neglected; and that he was bitter against all severities and persecutions in the cause of the Christian religion.

An incident in this connexion is worth preserving on the authority of Sir Peter Pett. It seems that Boyle once went to Sir Henry Vane's house and there heard him preach a long sermon to a large audience on the text of Daniel. xii. 2. 'And many of them that sleep in the dust of the earth shall awake, some to everlasting life, and some to shame and everlasting contempt.' In his sermon, Sir Henry applied the text to doctrines of religion. At its conclusion, Boyle arose and said that, as it was proper in such private meetings for objections to be made, 'He thought himself obliged for the honour of God's truth to say, that this place in Daniel being the clearest one in all the Old Testament for the proof of the resurrection, we ought not to suffer the meaning of it to evaporate into allegory, etc.'

Mr. Boyle afterwards speaking of this conference to Sir Peter Pett, observed, that Sir Henry Vane at that time being in the height of his authority in the state, and his auditors at that meeting consisting chiefly of dependents on him and expectants from him, the fear of losing his favour would probably have restrained them from contradicting any of his interpretations of Scripture, how ridiculous soever: 'But I having no little awes of that kind upon me, thought myself bound to enter the lists with him, as I did, that the sense of the Scriptures might not be depraved.' [3]

Boyle's attitude towards the clergy and the priesthood is a problem serious enough to be discussed in considerable detail. He apparently regarded the priesthood as so exalted a profession, and the responsibility of the priest, as interpreter of God's word, as such a grave one, that ordinary men should hesitate to take orders; also, he believed the vows subscribed to by the priest would bias his judgement. So the influence of the free layman was often more effective than that of the clergy, who were dependent on their orthodoxy for their maintenance and were tempted to suppress their doubts and personal opinions.

This opinion is expressed several times in his writings; for example:

I fear there are too many, both commentators and other divines, that (though otherwise perhaps pious men) having espoused a church or party, and an aversion from all dissenters, are solicitous, when they peruse

the Scriptures, to take notice chiefly, if not only (I mean in points speculative) of those things, that may either suggest arguments against their
adversaries, or answers to their objections. But I meet with much fewer
than I could wish, who make it their business to *search the Scriptures*
for those things (such as unheeded prophecies, over-looked mysteries, and
strange harmonies) which being clearly and judiciously proposed, may
make that book appear worthy of the high extraction it challenges . . .
And indeed when I consider, how much more to the advantage of those
sacred writings, and of Christian theology in general, divers texts have
been explained and discoursed of by the excellent Grotius, by Episcopius,
Masius, Mr. Meade, and Sir Francis Bacon, and some other late great
wits (to name now no living ones) in their several kinds, than the same
places have been handled by vulgar expositors, and other divines.[4]

Or, again, when Boyle discourses on the veneration we owe to
God, he declares: 'It is not without some indignation, as well as
wonder, that I see many men, and some of them divines too, who
little considering what God is, and what themselves are, presume
to talk of him and his attributes as freely and as unpremeditately,
as if they were talking of a geometrical figure, or a mechanical
engine.' [5]

Perhaps Boyle's argument for the advantage of being a layman
when discussing religion is best expressed in his Preface to the
Christian Virtuoso.[6] He there sums up the reasons why, being a
scientist all his life, he has written so much on the Christian life
and religion. He had 'neither designed nor pretended to write a
body of natural theology, nor a demonstration of the Christian religion'; but to show 'that there is no inconsistence between a man's
being an industrious virtuoso, and a good Christian'; and that religion and science are compatible, although 'libertines thought that
a virtuoso ought not to be a Christian, and the others [learned
men], that he could not be a true one.' And for this purpose, he
adds:

I confess, I was somewhat encouraged to communicate my thoughts on
these subjects, by considering, that (though it ought not to be so, yet) it
is notorious, that, in the age we live in, there are too many persons, that
are like to be found more indisposed to be impressed on by arguments,
in favour of religion, from professed divines, how worthy soever, than
from such as I who am a layman, and have been looked upon as no un-
diligent cultivator of experimental philosophy.

If Boyle had doubts of the fitness of the average clergyman for his high office, he had no such feeling towards those leaders who were conducting the Church in the *via media;* with them, from the time of his migration to Oxford until his death, he was intimately associated; he learned from them the best thought of the time, and was regarded by them as an equal in theology. The chief members of his circle of friends at Oxford have been previously mentioned. Undoubtedly, he continued during his life to discuss problems of science and the affairs of the Royal Society with Seth Ward and John Wilkins; but we can be equally sure that, as both of them became influential bishops, matters of religion were also frequent in their conversation. The rigorous and unbending attitude of the former towards Nonconformists, he would surely oppose; on the other hand, there must have been an equally great sympathy with the scholarly, vivacious, and tolerant Wilkins, of whom Pepys noted: 'It is all the talk, I find, that Dr. Wilkins, my friend, the Bishop of Chester, shall be removed to Winchester, and be Lord Treasurer. Though this be foolish talk, yet I do gather that he is a mighty rising man, as being a Latitudinarian, and the Duke of Buckingham his great friend.' [7] One can also readily understand how immensely the contact with the group of Oriental scholars, to whom Boyle was a constant patron and friend, must have enlarged his textual and factual knowledge of the Scriptures.

Probably the most intimate of Boyle's clerical friends was Barlow, 'Bodley's Librarian,' and afterwards Bishop of Lincoln. From their correspondence we know what a high opinion Barlow had of Boyle's genius, whom he calls his confessor, as one 'who understands and loves our reformed religion.' They agreed in their fear of the Papacy and of the political intrigues of the Jesuits; and they disapproved of painting images of Apostles and Patriarchs on the walls of a parish church, 'as being an inlet to innovations dangerous to the Church of England and consequently to the Protestant cause.' We also learn that Boyle apparently accepted Barlow's thesis: 'That the souls of good or bad men departed this life, are not in heaven or hell (as the words are commonly understood) before the day of judgement, but in *Hades* (as the Greeks call it) or a middle state.'

Later, Boyle developed a friendship with the Cambridge Platonists, Ralph Cudworth and Henry More, which arose from their interest in the new science, and their defence of it against the materialistic atheism of Democritus, the Stoics, and the Epicureans. But above all else, they were united, with Ward, Wilkins, and Wallace, in their bitter antagonism against the atomic atheism of Hobbes; not even the peace-loving Boyle could refrain from constant attacks on that arch-heretic. A sample of More's admiration for Boyle has been previously cited; and Cudworth wrote to him:

I pray God continue your life and health; that you may still enrich the world with more. The writers of hypotheses in natural philosophy will be confuting one another, a long time, before the world will agree, if ever it do. But your pieces of natural history are unconfutable, and will afford the best grounds to build hypotheses upon. You have much outdone Sir Francis Bacon, in your natural experiments, and you have not insinuated anything, as he is thought to have done, tending to irreligion, but the contrary.[8]

To this list of Boyle's ecclesiastic friends and admirers, there are to be added the three distinguished Cambridge divines: Archbishop Tillotson, who was a Cromwellian and Presbyterian until the Act of Uniformity of 1662, and who devoted himself to the exact study of Biblical and patristic writers in order to attack atheism and the Papacy; Archbishop Tenison, bitter towards Rome, a member of the commission towards reconciliation of Dissenters, and a trustee of the Boyle Lectures; and Bishop Stillingfleet, probably the most learned and most skilful controversialist of the age against Nonconformism, Romanism, Deism, and Socinianism. And lastly, although there must have been others, Bishop Burnet should be mentioned. He was an intimate friend to Boyle, the dispenser of his great charities, and chosen to deliver the funeral eulogy which Evelyn remarked was notable in that in no way could it exaggerate the virtues of the deceased.

If one compares the writings of these and other leading Anglican divines with Boyle's, one is immediately impressed with their extraordinary congruence of purpose. They were united in their tolerance towards the radical Protestants on minor matters of church government, and in their opposition to the complete separation of church and state; they upheld a limited authority of a Catholic Church and 'departed from the Reformers of the Continent and from the Puritans at home in their rejection of what they regarded as an illegitimate extension of Scriptural authority.' But they enlisted all their profound erudition and rhetorical skill in combating the pretensions of the Church of Rome as infallible and as *the* Catholic and Universal Church; and they made the issue clear that their 'quarrel with Rome was because of her practice of extending the fundamentals of faith by increments on the warrant of her own inspired authority, and so of creating, as it were, instead of obeying tradition.'

In spite of Boyle's voluminous writings on religion, only *Protestant and Papist*,* is devoted to dogmatic theology. Unfortunately, the authorship of this short tract is in some doubt, as it was published anonymously and was not reprinted with the author's name, nor has it been included in any edition of Boyle's collected works. Yet its authorship is important, as on it must rest our explicit evidence of Boyle's reasons for his steadfast adherence to the Anglican Church as against the claims both of Romanism and of Puritanism. A careful comparison of this tract with his acknowledged religious convictions has removed my doubts as to his authorship. The opinions expressed in it are just those we should expect him to hold, and they are those of his intimate friends.

Paradoxically, the anonymity of the tract may be adduced as favourable evidence of Boyle's authorship. It will be remembered that his early works were composed during the troubled period of the Civil War; they were all of a religious tone quite out of sympathy with the times; they were, as he declared, written for his private edification and, although they were circulated amongst his friends who were in sympathy with his views, none was published until the Restoration had brought back civil and religious peace. There can be no reasonable doubt that this delay, so contrary to his usual haste in publication, was the result of his temperamental repugnance

---

* *Reasons why a Protestant should not turn Papist: or, Protestant prejudices against the Roman Catholic Religion;* propos'd in a letter to a Romish Priest. By a Person of Quality. London, for John Taylor, 1687. Dr. Fulton comments in his *Bibliography of Boyle:* 'This anonymous tract is not included in any of the collected editions of Boyle's works, and it is not mentioned in the biographies of Boulton, Birch, Masson, or in the *Term Catalogues.* The basis of its attribution to Boyle is evidently circumstantial. It is assigned to him by Halkett and Laing, and by the British Museum Catalogue, but evidence is not given. A perusal of the work, however, gives one no reason to doubt Boyle's authorship, for the style is most suggestive of him and the allusions are in many cases similar to those encountered in his other theological works.'

Dr. Fulton, when he most generously loaned me his own copies of this very rare tract, wrote to me: 'The authorship of *Protestant and Papist* has always worried me. So far as I know, there is no certain proof that it was Boyle, but it was attributed to him during his life-time and as far as I am aware he never denied authorship . . . I think Mr. G. L. Keynes is inclined to accept Boyle's authorship, but his evidence is no better than mine.'

against dispute and contention except when silence could not be avoided without reflection on his intellectual or moral integrity.

Protestant and Papist is an outspoken and vigorous polemic against the pretensions of Roman Catholicism, in the form of a letter addressed to a Romish Priest, which was in itself a favourite device of Boyle. In an *Introduction,* the author makes clear the necessity for his public confession as follows:

Sir, I know not well what you meant, when not long ago, after a free enquiry in a familiar converse about the right choice of religion, you was pleased to call me a *mere Christian,* but sure I am 'twas a better world when all such as really professed Christianity were but *mere Christians,* I mean, believed nothing more, under pain of eternal damnation, than what Christ and his Apostles had taught them: if this, Sir, was your meaning, I am indeed, and with the Grace of God ever shall be a *mere Christian;* and why should I find myself affronted by being so styled, since the Fathers of the primitive times were in the afore-mentioned sense *mere Christians,* as believing nothing to be articles of divine faith beyond what Christ and his Apostles had declared to be so . . . I shall revenge myself no otherwise, but by telling you, what I fancy you will readily grant, that you are something beyond a *mere Christian,* since neither the Scripture, nor the three Creeds, contain all the articles of your faith.

The author then states that he is now 'fulfilling the promise' which he had made, to give his reasons for remaining an Anglican.

That Boyle would write such a polemic as *Protestant and Papist* is conclusive proof to me of his having been challenged before witnesses on his beliefs, as is intimated in the passage cited, in such a way as to force from him a definite reply. His use of a thinly veiled anonymity, which did not deceive those he wished to influence but protected him from public criticism, would arise from the same cause which delayed his early publications; for the year 1687 was again a period of religious and civil strife—the final decision of England against Rome.

The author of the tract subscribes himself as *A Person of Quality,* who defends himself as a true adherent to the Primitive and Universal Church against the exaggerated claims of the *particular* Church of Rome. Is it not significant also that Boyle published the same year, and anonymously, his *Martyrdom of Theodora,* a manuscript written almost forty years previously? This romance has the same publisher; its author is now *A Person of Honour;* and its theme is indirectly the same, the author 'having had occasion many years ago to turn over a *Martyrology,* and some other books, that related to the sufferings of the Primitive Christians.'

Boyle (and, in the following discussion we assume him to be the author) bases his objections to becoming a Papist on the two false suppositions of the Church of Rome: its *pretended catholicity* or universality, and its infallibility:

The Church of Rome, whether it be the diocese of Rome, or all those persons who acknowledge the Pope as the supreme pastor, is only a particular church in exactly the same sense as is that of England, or of Greece, or of Abyssinia. The Roman Church in fact, comprises but the lesser part of the Catholic, or Universal Church, which is *the diffusive body of Christians in all ages under Christ as their invisible Head, and their respective Princes, Superiors, and Bishops, as their visible Governors.*

If one accepts that definition of *the Church,* it is easy, Boyle argues, to stop the mouths of Roman Catholics 'who raise so much dust among the unthinking multitude by this very word, *the Church';* and who frequently and unjustly charge all other churches with apostasy, heresy, or schism. One has merely to understand those terms to confute the charge: *

'Apostasy is an entire desertion of the Christian Faith.' But those dissenters from the Church of Rome are not apostates who retain the fundamental points of the Christian religion, and who reject only the later accretions declared to be fundamental on the assumption of infallibility.

'Heresy is an obstinate and wilful denial of what is held by the Universal Church.' What the Roman Catholics really mean is that all persons are heretics who do not believe the additional articles of the Church of Rome, grounded on the notoriously false supposition of infallibility.

'Schism is a causeless separation from any Christian church whatsoever.' Dissenters are not schismatics, since they had weighty reasons to separate from the Church of Rome—if for no other reason, the Roman church's taking away the Cup from the laity, against the universal practice of even their own Church for thirteen hundred years and more, and against the express command and institution of Christ.

* Boyle's definitions of these words agree with the definitions of the Oxford Dictionary if one applies the word *catholic* to the Universal Church and not to the Roman Church, which is, of course, the basis of his argument.

As Boyle points out, the validity of such charges against all the other Christian churches rests on the claim of the Roman Church to infallibility—a claim made by no other church, a claim denied to Rome by all other churches, and the one invincible barrier to a unanimity of faith. He states first: 'The Universal Church in this sense only may be called infallible, that notwithstanding all the efforts of the gates of hell to prevail against it, the true doctrine of Christ shall be still taught, and held in some part of the world by a particular providence of God over his Church.' He then declares flatly that the Roman doctrine is not only improbable, but really false and absurd as contrary to both reason and authority.

The doctrine of infallibility is certainly not self-evident, since a large majority of Christians reject it as false; and therefore it must be proved either by reason or by authority derived from the Scriptures. But, Boyle asserts:

I would then advise here the Roman Catholics, never to prove the infallibility of their Church by Scripture, this being undoubtedly their weakest side, because by this way of arguing, they are concluded in a circle, they could never yet get clear of, *whilst they must prove the infallibility of the Church by the Scripture, and the true sense of the Scripture by the very same Church,* which amounts to nothing more, but to your believing the Church upon her own word.*

Again, if the passages of Scripture cited by the Romanists were accepted as bestowing infallibility on any particular church, the Greek Church is the more ancient, and looks upon the Roman Church as schismatical; also she can prove an apostolic succession of Bishops more certainly than Rome, since there is no probable authority for her claim (the Scriptures being wholly silent on the matter) that St. Peter was ever at Rome or was Bishop of Rome.

Lastly, if the dogma of infallibility should be accepted, Boyle asks, where does the authority rest? The Church itself, he affirms, had never been able to agree whether the infallible, visible, judge was the Pope, or the General Councils, or both conjointly. (This question was, of course, decided finally in favour of the Pope by the Council of the Vatican, on 18 July 1870. However one may regard the validity of the action, it certainly was not taken even then without the bitterest opposition, nor could a unanimous vote be reached until a formidable, dissenting minority of members had

* Italics mine.

been granted a *leave of absence* by Pius IX and had absented themselves from the convocation.) Boyle then continues:

I am then upon another account quite out of conceit with the Church of Rome: her Transubstantiation I could never believe, and if I did, I should soon doubt of the confessed fundamentals of the Christian Religion: for I conceive not how a considering man can heartily believe Transubstantiation, and not doubt of all our chief mysteries, which I take to be the very existency of Christ in the world, his passion, his death, his resurrection and ascension, and all those wonderful works he did during his stay upon earth, in order to confirm mankind in the belief of his being God as well as man: now what proof have we of those primary articles, but the constant testimony of all men's senses?

If these things had not been *seen as they are,* no one would have believed them. Yet if he turn a Romanist, and sees, and touches, and tastes the bread and wine, he must believe what is evidently contradicted by his senses.

Enough has probably been given, without elaborating on his historical citations, to show why Boyle regarded such dogmas as Invocation of Saints, Prayers for the Dead, Purgatory, Adoration and Elevation of the Host, and such practices as service in an unknown tongue and denying the Cup to the laity, as unwarranted accretions to be accepted under pain of damnation. Protestantism, instead of being a schism from the Universal Church, he maintains is but a return to what 'was taught by Christ and his Apostles, and believed by the Primitive Christians, the standard of their belief being no other but the Apostolic Creed, and the Scripture, as interpreted by the Christians of the Primitive Church.'

Characteristically of the temper of the age, Boyle closes his polemic against Romanism by a declaration of loyalty to the state; and one must not forget that the year, 1687, witnessed the last open attempt of Rome to dominate England.

I was always loyal to the Royal Family, and with the Grace of God ever shall be, yet if I embrace the Roman Catholic Religion heartily, and with all its tenets, I know not but that I may begin to waver in this main point of my duty, by acknowledging another power upon earth above that of my own Prince . . . I pretend not nevertheless to say, that a Roman Catholic cannot be a good subject, God forbid I should think so; but I know so much of their religion, that I may safely venture to say, they owe their loyalty to their generous temper and good nature, rather than to the principles of the religion they profess . . . I am then quite out of conceit with your religion, since I cannot embrace it, without endangering my loyalty, in case I mind to live up to the pitch of its real principles: but 'tis all one to me, so long as I remain a Protestant, what religion my Prince is of, though I could wish he were of the same I profess, because his authority over me, and my indispensable obligation to submit to him, do not depend upon his opinion or religion, but upon his birth-right.

A very serious problem had been raised by the cultivators of the new inductive philosophy who had revived the atomic and mechanistic hypothesis as an explanation of natural phenomena and who, at the same time, would maintain their allegiance to the Christian religion; the problem was to define in terms of observation and reason the scriptural doctrine of the real existence of the soul and the resurrection of the body. They could no longer accept the naïve belief of the Middle Ages regarding the nature of the soul and the actual re-assembling of the material elements of the body; nor could they subscribe to the doctrine of the Epicureans, revived by Hobbes and regarded by them with horror as atheistic, which denied the reality of anything but bodies perceptible by the senses, and ascribed all phenomena to chance. The only contribution of Boyle, in this attempt to create a *via media,* was a short tract on *Some Physico-Theological Considerations about the Possibility of the Resurrection.**

Boyle first states he will not discuss the subject of resurrection as being brought to pass by merely physical agents and means, since the universal experience of the ages has afforded no instances of it. 'In fact,' he tells us, 'if God had not, in the Scriptures, positively revealed his purpose of raising the dead, I confess, I should not have thought of any such thing.' Thus the act is to be accepted as revealed: not one to be accomplished by any natural process, but by the omnipotent power of God. He will limit himself therefore to the discussion of the human body and its identity in relation to our ideas of nature.

First, he asks the very obvious question, what is meant by a man's body? And he revives the age-long controversy of the permanence

* *Works,* Vol. IV, pp. 192-202. 1675. This short tract was annexed by the publisher to a longer work on the *Reconcileableness of Reason and Religion* by an unknown layman, who signed himself, T. E. According to Dr. Fulton these works are unrelated. With this opinion I cannot quite agree, since both are examples of the constant effort of the age to prove that the essential characters of the Christian religion are not contrary to science, as was often asserted by those whom Boyle termed libertines and wits.

of Parmenides and the eternal flux of Heraclitus. He translates the *Rusticus exspectat dum defluat amnis* of Horace into: 'Thus the Thames is said to be the same river, that it was in the time of our forefathers, though indeed the water, that now runs under London Bridge, is not the same, that ran there an hour ago.' So an individual person preserves his identity although he is constantly receiving new matter and losing the old. Thus the resurrection of the body cannot mean, as was naïvely believed in the Middle Ages, the reassembling of the identical particles which at some one time formed it, and still less all the transient particles during life. As an *argumentum ad absurdum,* he adduces the quaint case of a man who had been eaten by a cannibal, 'for then the same flesh belonging successively to two differing persons, it is impossible that both should have it restored to them at once, or that any footsteps should remain of the relation it had to the first possessor.'

Although it would not be repugnant to the Scriptures, Boyle will not rely on the possible explanation that a small quantity of the matter of the body after death may, like the seed of a plant, have the power to grow. Nor will he discuss whether a plastic power in some part of the material of a dead body, being divinely excited, can repair and augment itself. And here to give an illustration, Boyle slips as he sometimes does into pure credulity. Two eminent persons of his acquaintance (one of them the witness; and the other, the experimenter) 'took some ashes of a plant, just like our English red poppy; and having sowed these alkalisate ashes in my friend's garden, they did, sooner than was expected, produce certain plants larger and fairer than any of that kind, that had been seen in those parts.'

Having thus cleared the way, Boyle proceeds to his purpose of showing that the resurrection is reconcilable with mechanistic philosophy. All philosophers with few exceptions, whether schoolmen, atomists, corpuscularians, or alchemists, agree that there is a *prima materia* which is absolutely permanent in quality and quantity; thus the variety of bodies is not caused by changes in the nature of matter but by changes in its attributes. Consider how the planning mind and the manipulative skill of the chemist can transform these attributes of the *prima materia;* is it then beyond reason to assume that God may do far more wonders with what he had created?

May not God in the Day of Judgement resurrect the body by reassembling the proper quantity of the *prima materia,* arranging and combining it to give the character of the person? We know that God has, in the past, altered the qualities of matter, as when he suspended the action of gravitation that St. Peter might, at the command of Christ, walk upon the sea. Nor, do we need to take the resurrected body in a literal sense. It may be that 'after death there shall be another state, wherein the soul shall no longer persevere in its separate condition, or, as it were, widowhood, but shall be again united, not to an ætherial, or the like fluid matter, but to such a substance as may, with tolerable propriety of speech, not withstanding its differences from our houses of clay, (as the Scripture speaks) be called a human body.'

The other works of Boyle that may be classed as religious were composed to counteract the cynical scepticism which had infected society after the Restoration, and especially to induce young gentlemen of high birth to substitute the serious joys of the Christian life for the frivolous amusements and dissipations of the Court; or to prove that the mechanistic philosophy, when derived from experimentation and as supported by the Royal Society, was a witness to God's purpose and laws, and was a most powerful antidote to the atheism of Hobbes.

In spite of Boyle's scorn of Aristotelian-scholastic science as being sterile because it was not based on observation, he acknowledged that his text for the *Usefulness of Experimental Philosophy*[9] was but an amplification of Aristotle's introduction to his *Metaphysics:* 'All men by nature desire to know.' And this love of knowledge arises from the delight we derive from our sensations; especially from the sensation of sight. He quotes many statements from classical and sacred writers to support this opinion. If the mere observation of nature gives such a pleasure—which often through custom we forget but is evident in the emotions of a girl, born blind, who having her sight restored, was ravished with delight at the appearance of the commonest objects—how much more will we be excited by the intelligent study of nature? For, as the understanding is our highest faculty, so its pleasures are the highest.

To the intelligent student even the most restricted subject, such as the rose, or a single metal, may require a whole treatise, as the adept, Basil Valentine, proved in his *Currus Triumphalis Antimonii.* Nor is there anything degrading in the study of such a humble object as a worm; quite the contrary, to the intelligent observer the beauty and complexity of such minute organisms as the cheese mite or vinegar wiggler are far more extraordinary than those of the elephant or the whale.

For my part, if I durst think my actions fit to be examples, I should tell you, that I have been so far from that effeminate squeamishness, that one of the philosophical treatises, for which I have been gathering experiments, is of the nature and use of dungs. And though my condition does (God be praised) enable me to make experiments by others' hands; yet I have not been so nice, as to decline dissecting dogs, wolves, fishes, and even rats and mice, with my own hands.

And Boyle also would rate the 'divine science' which is concerned with divine objects (now made perfect by the Incarnation) as a far nobler delight than the science of nature. And the highest advantage

the knowledge of nature brings to the minds of men, is, that therein it excites and cherishes devotion; which when I say, Pyrophilus, I forget not, that there are several divines (and some of them eminent ones) that out of a holy jealousy (as they think) for religion, labour to deter men from addicting themselves to serious and thorough enquiries into nature, as from a study unsafe for a Christian, and likely to end in atheism . . . If this apprehension were well grounded, I should think the threatened evil so considerable, that instead of inviting you to the study of natural philosophy, I should very earnestly labour to dissuade you from it. For I, that had much rather have men not philosophers than not Christians, should be better content to see you ignore the mysteries of nature than deny the author of it.

To the enquiring mind, the creation of the universe, probably, and of the earth and conspicuous stars, certainly, was for the manifestation of God's own glory and for the good of men. 'To which purpose we may observe, that though man was not created, till the close of the sixth day (the resident's arrival being obligingly suspended till the palace was made ready to entertain him) yet, that none of God's works might want intelligent spectators and admirers, the angels were created the first day.' Even the pagan philosophers, excepting the Epicureans and other classic atomists, testified to the existence of a creator. Aristotle, who was generally hesitant in his belief regarding God's interest in his creatures, states that what the pilot is to the ship and the general to the army, such is God in the world, save that he performs without labour or trouble. And Seneca nobly declares: *Haec qui contemplatur, quid Deo praestat? ne tanta ejus opera sine teste sint.*

As Newton, in the *Principia,* came to the conviction that the orderliness of motion in the vast cosmic system presupposes the planning mind and creative power of a Creator, so Boyle cites instance after instance of the adaptation of the various parts of animals and plants, especially of the eye, to their needs and uses, as a convincing proof of the wisdom and beneficence of God. One example of his curiosity may be cited: to confute those who claimed that the habits of insects were imitations, and not the result of innate or seminal impressions endowed by God, eggs of the silk-worm were imported from Italy, and the worms hatched from them in nowise differed in their actions although there was no example for them to imitate.

If, as Boyle believed, experimental science is limited to the investigation of efficient causes, can the study of natural phenomena throw any light on the Divine Purpose, creating and guiding the universe? And he answers in one of his most important works, written in his full maturity when his intellectual powers were at their height: 'If we neglect this enquiry, we live in danger of being ungrateful, in overlooking those uses of things, that may give us just cause of admiring and thanking the Author of them, and of losing the benefit, relating as well to philosophy as to piety, that the knowledge of them may afford us.' *

In Boyle's discussion, he had to consider chiefly two schools of philosophy which denied that the naturalist should busy himself about final causes. Epicurus and most of his followers, excepting especially Gassendi, held that the universe is a matter of chance and so no ends or purposes of things can be imagined. The world of Epicurus, as a product of atoms and chance motions, has been 'disallowed by almost all other sects and has been confuted by others'; so he will pass by that school. But the Cartesians, who accept God as an omniscient agent, regard it as rash and presumptuous for men to think they may know, or can investigate, his purpose or ends; this argument, because it was so prevalent among learned men, he will answer.

Boyle suggests that Descartes may have been brought to this extreme view of rejecting the consideration of final causes by the scientist, because the School-Philosophers rashly assumed that all creatures were designed solely, or at least chiefly, for the service or

---

* *A Disquisition about the Final Causes of Natural Things.* 1688. *Works,* Vol. v, pp. 392-452. Written at the request of Oldenburg, Secretary of the Royal Society, and laid aside at the time of his death in 1677.

benefit of man; in fact he himself can cite the presumptuous expressions of a certain famous writer who, in a treatise on divinity, to support his opinion that the universe would be annihilated in the Day of Judgement, argued that since it was made for man in his travelling condition (*hominis viatoris causâ*), when once the final doom was pronounced, there would be no further use for the world. Such an opinion might well disgust Descartes, but such indiscretions should not prejudice truth; so he (Boyle) will consider the subject on its merits and will propose four distinctions in regard to 'the ends, which nature, or rather the author of nature, is said to have in things corporeal.'

First; the grand and general ends of the whole universe, which display the Creator's power, wisdom, goodness.

Secondly; the sun, planets, fixed stars, and perhaps the two great divisions of the earth's surface, may be permanent parts necessary to the universal ends of creation.

Thirdly; the ends which concern the structure and parts of animals and plants and are designed for the welfare, and existence, of the whole organism.

Fourthly; human ends, mental and corporeal, and how far nature may have framed things for man's use and benefit.

Boyle first discusses the general Cartesian principle with an argument to prove that the Cartesians themselves consider final causes.

It is a known principle of the Cartesian philosophy, that there is always just the same quantity of motion in the world at one time that there is at another: of which assertion this reason is given, that there is no cause, why God, who is immutable, should at the beginning of things, when he first put matter into motion, have given it such a quantity of motion, as would have to be afterwards augmented or lessened. But I see not how, by this negative way of arguing, those, that employ it, do not (implicitly at least) take upon them to judge of the ends, that God may have proposed to himself in natural things. For, without a supposition, that they know what God designed in setting matter a-moving, it is hard for them to show, that his design could not be such, as might be best accomplished by sometimes adding to, and sometimes taking from, the quantity of motion he communicated to matter at first . . . And particularly it seems not clear, why God may not as well be immutable, though he should sometimes vary the quantity of motion, that he has put into the world; as he is, though, according to the opinion of most of the Cartesians themselves, he does daily create multitudes of rational

souls, to unite them to human bodies . . . I say not this, as if I absolutely rejected the Cartesian doctrine, about the continuance of the same
quantity of motion in the whole mass of matter; for, whether or no it
be a truth, I think it no unuseful nor improbable hypothesis; and I have
not so much argued against it, as upon the grounds on which they argue
for it.

In conclusion, Boyle pays a sincere compliment to Descartes: he
declares that it troubles him to oppose so vigorously some of the
opinions of that philosopher from whom 'I am not forward to dissent: and this I the rather declare to you, because I am not at all of
their mind, that think M. Descartes a favourer of atheism, which,
to my apprehension, would subvert the very foundation of those
tenets of mechanical philosophy that are particularly his.' One may
infer that he had Henry More especially in mind.

Boyle then discusses each of his four varieties of final causes in
great detail and with a wealth of interesting and apposite illustrations; his conclusions may be briefly summarized as follows: While
the orderliness of the heavenly bodies does not contradict their des-
ignation for the use of man, it is too much to suppose such a vast
system (even though he doubts the vastness of it as supposed by
the Copernicans) was created solely for that purpose, or to illumi-
nate our tiny world. The stars give no such clear evidence of wisdom and design as do the bodies of animals and plants; for to him
there is more admirable contrivance in a man's muscles than in the
celestial orbs; and the eye of a fly exhibits a more curious work-
manship than the body of the sun. In this opinion, Boyle differs
from Newton, to whom the orderliness of the solar system was the
convincing proof of the existence of a final cause; but, it should be
remembered that Boyle probably had not read the *Principia,* which
had been published only a year previously, and he was not a
mathematician.

As for such bodies as stones, metals, etc., whose matter seems not
organized, it is not absurd to think them to be the result of chance
aggregations of parts of the universal matter. Nor can we discover
much about the purpose of the material bodies of the earth, except
to say that intelligent man has found uses for them. But we know
nothing of the nature of the earth a mile below the surface, and it
may contain fossils and other creatures not even discoverable; how
then, can we assume them to have been made for the use of man?

But the study of the parts of animate bodies gives convincing proof of their design for the use of the whole organism. One illustration from the many will suffice:

When I asked our famous Harvey, in the only discourse I had with him, (which was but a while before he died) what were the things, that induced him to think of a circulation of the blood? he answered me, that when he took notice, that the valves in the veins of so many parts of the body were so placed, that they gave free passage to the blood towards the heart, but opposed the passage of the venal blood the contrary way; he was invited to imagine, that so provident a cause as nature had not so placed so many valves without design; and no design seemed more probable than—that the blood should be sent through the arteries, and return through the veins, whose valves did not oppose its course that way.

Boyle also discovers in the remarkable instincts of animals, and particularly of insects, clear evidence of design; and he has dwelt long on his third proposition because it is 'a duty our reason owes to its Author, to endeavour to vindicate his manifold wisdom, in this libertine age; wherein too many men, that have more wit than philosophy or piety, have upon Epicurean (and some also even upon Cartesian) principles, laboured to depreciate the wisdom of God, and some of them presumed to censure the contrivances of these living *automata,* that (in their protoplasts) were originally his.'

The final conclusion of this notable treatise is: we must not assume that we have found, or ever can find, all the destinated uses and motives of the parts of animals, etc., but the naturalist should not permit the search for, or discovery of, a final cause of nature's works, to make him undervalue or neglect the studious investigation of their efficient causes.

Boyle frequently expressed the opinion that the layman had more influence with the public than the professed clergyman, and gave several reasons to support his opinion; but he neglected the most cogent, which came from the spirit of an age captivated by its discovery of observation and reason and by its desire to rationalize religion. And the age thought it had found in the work of Boyle, Locke, and Newton, the foundation for a Deism in which the existence of God could be proved as rigorously as a problem of geometry, and his nature and purpose made evident from a knowledge of the laws and phenomena of nature. Boyle and Newton had provided the data and laws of the world machine, and 'Locke, in particular, has been described as "the writer whose influence pervades the eighteenth century with an almost scriptural authority." ' [10]

There is no doubt in my mind that those three intimate and sympathetic friends were the dominating force of the age; they were the creators of modern mechanistic empiricism; they certainly were the source from which Deism flowed; and they were professing members of the Church of England. How can such apparent contradictions be reconciled? As for Locke, if the two following statements can be taken at their face value, his Christianity seems to sink to a system of conventional morality. Revelation to him was the reason of the scientist: 'Whatever God hath revealed is certainly true; no doubt can be made of it. This is the proper object of faith; but *whether it be a divine revelation or no, reason must judge.* ' [11] And of the Bible: 'It is a collection of writings, designed by God, for the instruction of the illiterate bulk of mankind, in the way of salvation.' [12]

It is quite impossible to give a clear idea of Newton's theism,* because of his distaste for any public expression of his personal beliefs; it is certain, however, that he was a theist, believing in a personal and spiritual God, and that he thought God was best revealed in the laws of nature. He even doubted whether the cosmic system could continue to operate without at least divine control and adjustment—a control 'not blind or fortuitous, but very well skilled in mechanics and geometry.' It is also certain that he was a Unitarian; for he privately denied the divinity of Christ and the doctrine of the Trinity as inexplicable, although he conformed publicly to the usages of the Church of England. There is very little in either his published works or in the *Portsmouth Collection* of his papers regarding God's government of the animate world. There is in one place a vague query whether vital actions could not be explained by a very subtle and mechanical æther; but since he could not express them in quantitative and mathematical laws, he simply excluded them from his cosmic system. As for sensation, the translation of an external mechanical stimulus into subjective impression, of sound into tone, or of light into sight, was accomplished in an unknowable way by the soul, which included the will and intellect, and was located in the *sensorium,* somewhere in the brain.

* The religious beliefs of Newton are discussed at length in my *Life of Newton,* Chap. XVI. There were rumours of his heterodoxy during his life. Bishop Horsford and Brewster suppressed the evidence on this point, lest it influence others.

Although Boyle's work has always been cited as a support for Deism, it should be remembered that general term embraced widely differing opinions. A study of his principles should be convincing that he himself was not a Deist except as were the leading divines of the seventeenth century, or in fact as are those Protestants in general who place the ultimate responsibility of decision in matters of faith on the individual rather than on the infallible authority of a church. Unlike Newton, he published his religious doctrines openly, and he was considered to be an orthodox Anglican. He accepted without reserve the fundamental principle of *the* Universal Church; he subscribed to the Apostles' Creed, and he acknowledged the doctrine of the Trinity, 'not as some schoolmen explicate, or rather darken it, but as the Gospel delivers it.'[13] And again: 'I shall not name for proof of this [revelation] the adorable mystery of the Trinity, wherein it is acknowledged that the most soaring speculators are wont to be posed, or to lose themselves.'[14]

Boyle described himself as a mechanist; but he was quite vague about what corpuscles were or how they acted to form bodies, except that they were a more rational *prima materia* than mercury, or sulphur, or salt; and a mechanical motion was a more effective agent than the formal causes of the Schoolmen. He was not a mathematician and made no attempt to express corpuscular actions and motions in quantitative laws. Newton had not yet disclosed the law of gravitational force as a cause of motion, and the best explanation of the communication of motion from one body to another was by impact, which Descartes had made the basis of his hypothesis of cosmic vortices.

Everywhere in the universe, Boyle found the divine plan operating on the materials created by divine power; he was thus particularly antagonistic to the Epicurean philosophy of chance, and caught in the dilemma of mechanistic chance and teleologic purpose, he welcomed the abortive attempt of Gassendi to reconcile those two irreconcilables. Although he believed the material parts of the universe operated according to mechanical laws, he opposed those Deists who held that they were self-acting, and he differed from Newton, who thought God's action was limited to repairing the machine. He was much closer to the Cambridge Platonists, since he believed that actions occur 'as if there were diffused through the universe an intelligent being, watchful over the public good of it, and careful to administer all things wisely for the good of the particular parts of it, but so far forth as is consistent with the good of the whole and the preservation of the primitive and catholic law established by the supreme cause.'* Both Boyle and Newton believed that God miraculously superseded physical law; and since they both were alchemists and searched for the philosopher's stone, they believed also that man could within fixed limits control chemical operations.

The impression which many historians of metaphysics and of science (Professor Burtt's *Metaphysical Foundations of Physics* may be cited as typical) have given to us of the universe as conceived by the mechanists of the seventeenth century is of a vast and complex machine, invented and fashioned we know not how—a remorseless Juggernaut grinding its way through the ages. Man, seemingly endowed with a rational soul as a sort of fantastic cog, looks on for a brief time as a helpless spectator impotent to affect its actions, until he is finally obliterated under its inexorable wheels.

Such a picture is a strange perversion of fact. Even Newton, who is regarded as the supreme exponent of such a universe, had no such idea of man. In the first place, he regarded life and its phenomena as incapable of expression in the mathematical formulæ of mechanical actions, exactly as physicists and chemists of today find it to be; and it was necessary for him to exclude it from his mechanical system, just as the physicist distinguishes the fields of light, electricity, and heat as separable subjects, or the biologist divides plants and animals, although he knows that the subjects are mutually related. Furthermore, there is no statement in his works which implies that man is a passive spectator; rather he is like a skilful chess player who is bound by certain rules of motion impressed on his pieces, but if he obeys those rules he has great freedom of action.

As for Boyle, the following quotation from one of his most mature and important works is sufficient proof that he had no such conception of even the physical world:

* *Works,* Vol. ii, p. 39. Professor Burtt, in his *Metaphysical Foundations of Physics,* p. 192, says of this passage: 'Nowhere is there any clear attempt to reconcile this with the position that the laws of motion and the phenomena of gravitation represent quite self-sufficient mechanical operations.' He, himself, seems to show a very considerable ignorance of the then state of Physics. The laws of motion were but imperfectly known and very limited in their application; the weight of the air was in dispute; heat and cold were generally believed to be bodies; Newton's *Principia* had not been published, and it was not until a century later that Laplace claimed to have proved 'the phenomena of gravity represent quite self-sufficient mechanical operations' to account for the stability of the solar system; and today no physicist would admit that claim as true.

When I consider the nature of brute matter, and the vastness of the bodies that make up the world, the strange variety of those bodies which the earth does comprise, and others of them it may not absurdly be presumed to contain; and when I likewise consider the fluidity of that vast interstellar part of the world wherein these globes swim, I cannot but suspect there may be less of accurateness, and of constant regularity, than we have been taught to believe, in the structure of the universe, and a greater obnoxiousness [i. e. amenableness] to deviations than the schools, who were taught by their master Aristotle to be great admirers of the imaginary perfections of the celestial bodies, have allowed their disciples to think.[15]

As for the frequent criticism, that the seventeenth-century philosophers took man out of the universe, in which the mediævalists had comfortably placed him as its master under God, and left him in the impossible situation of being no part of it; there is no doubt that scientists have since then ceaselessly tried to absorb him in it, and with no conspicuous success, for he still presents himself as an unique phenomenon. Biologists, psychologists, anthropologists, and a host of other exponents of new and dubious sciences, have endeavoured to prove that the essence of life is but a complex chemical molecule; thought and sensation but shifting patterns of such molecules composing the brain. In their scheme, all that is, is body. Do they not overlook the fundamental attribute of body that it is only expressible in terms of space and time? Yet, if there be any certainty in the sciences of physics and chemistry, on which mechanistic biology depends, it is that life and thought are not body in that respect, and to regard them as such would wreck the science of mechanics. Furthermore, since the time the modern hypothesis of universal mechanism was first advanced by Spencer and Huxley, additional knowledge has steadily increased the gap between physics and biology, and between biology and psychology. Perhaps, the seventeenth-century philosophers were merely expressing a fundamental truth when they postulated the existence of three entities— body, life, and soul, each with its distinct qualities and each subject to its own discipline. If so, then the attempt to create a universal science of mechanics is but an unfortunate dream.

It was, in fact, just the fear lest his reputation as an experimental philosopher and his advocacy of a corpuscularian hypothesis might cause people to think that he was a Deist of the radical type, or that he had revived the atheism of Epicurus, or still worse of

Hobbes, which induced Boyle to publish one of his most important tracts: *The Excellency of Theology, Compared with Natural Philosophy*.[16] He tells us that he had gone into the country to escape the Great Plague of 1665 and had written the work while visiting in several places; but he suppressed its publication till 1674:

Whilst he feared it might be misapplied by some enemies to experimental philosophy, that then made a noise against it, without suffering these papers to come abroad, till the addresses and encomiums of many eminent foreign virtuosi, and their desire to be admitted into the Royal Society, had sufficiently manifested, how little its reputation was prejudiced, or like to be endangered, by the attempts of some envious or misinformed person.

Also many might think that, as his scientific work had been so well received, he should stick to it; but being neither a lecturer, nor a professor of physics, he felt free to do what he pleased.

The study of the nature and attributes of God is, to Boyle, the noblest aim of life. As a consequence, he declares: 'The vastness, beauty, orderliness, of the heavenly bodies; the excellent structure of animals and plants; and the other phenomena of nature justly induce an intelligent and unprejudiced observer to conclude a supremely powerful, just, and good author.'[17] While observation and reason should induce in the minds of all men a conviction of a Creator, there is for the Christian a much stronger conviction of the existence of God, of his Incarnate Son, and of their relation to man, which is not rational but revealed in the Bible and which discloses more of the attributes of God than does the book of nature. The mysteries of divine things, which are essential to salvation and are revealed in the Bible, are beyond our knowledge; but so also is the knowledge of the nature of body and of our sensations. We know by experience that a hearty endeavour to understand divine things brings a greater reward than is the case with other kinds of endeavour: 'The patient chemist, that consumes himself and his estate in seeking after the philosopher's stone, if he miss of his idolized elixir, had as good, nay better, have never sought it.' How have the labours of the greatest geometricians been received; and 'their successor, Mr. Hobbes, after all the ways he has taken, and those he has proposed, to square the circle, and double the cube, by missing of his end, has, after his various attempts, come off, not only with disappointment, but with disgrace'?[18]

'Is it wise to dispute anxiously about the properties of an atom, and be careless about the enquiry into the attributes of the great God, who formed all things; to investigate the spontaneous generation of such vile creatures as insects, than the mysterious generation of the adorable Son of God?'[19] The study of physics may be delightful, if we engage in experimental philosophy instead of in the barren and empty disputes of the Schoolmen; but it is so laborious and perplexing as to lead to discouragement; and even if one be lucky enough to make a real discovery, the pleasure may be great, yet it is impaired by doubt and anxiety. 'So that, if knowledge, as some philosophers have styled it, is the aliment of the rational soul, I fear I may too truly say, that the naturalist is usually fain to live upon salads and sauces, which, though they yield some nourishment, excite more appetite than they satisfy, and give us indeed the pleasure of eating with a good stomach, but then reduce us to an unwelcome necessity of always rising hungry from the table.'[20]

Boyle next discusses the claim so frequently made by scientists that their results are clear and positive, while opinions on theological matters are mere words and have no end. But he will not admit such an accusation and goes so far as to assert that, if a rational and cogent proof of any article of religion cannot be given, it is *ipso facto* not necessary to be believed. Any other conclusion would be to impute folly to an all-wise and impotence to an all-powerful God, who sent not only his prophets and his apostles, but even his only Son, to promulgate the Christian religion; they have caused it to be written that it may be understood, and have altered the course of nature by numerous miracles that it might be believed. Would God defeat his own purpose by declaring such matters as are necessary to salvation so obscurely that they cannot be understood?

And then Boyle turns the tables on the scientists in regard to their knowledge of the nature of body and of sensation. Such knowledge is the very starting point for science,

and yet the notion of body in general, or what it is, that makes a thing to be a corporeal substance, and discriminates it from all other things, has been very hotly disputed of, even among the modern philosophers . . . But though we do not clearly understand the nature of body in general; yet sure we cannot but be perfectly acquainted with what passes within ourselves in reference to the particular bodies we daily see, and hear, and smell, and taste, and touch; yet we know very little of the manner, by which our senses inform us . . . Now, according to Descartes, a man's body being but a well organized statue, that, which is truly called sensation, is not performed by the organ, but by the mind, which perceives the motion produced in the organ . . . But now, Sir, give me leave to take notice, that this union of an incorporeal, with a corporeal substance (and that without a medium) is a thing so unexampled in nature, and so difficult to comprehend, that I somewhat question, whether the profound secrets of theology, not to say the adorable mystery itself of the Incarnation, be more abstruse than this.[21]

Alas, these questions of the translation of an objective motion of body into a subjective sensation, of the *location* of the mind, of the *union* of life and body, which so puzzled Boyle, have perplexed men from time immemorial and they are still as inexplicable as they ever were. So beyond our comprehension are they that we have not even been able to invent words to express such ideas, but must clothe them in concrete metaphors. We first define *body* as that only which has motion and location, and then speak of the *location* of sensation and of mind; we talk of the *union* of soul and body, and of their *separation* after death. Aristotle once declared that there are other differences between a live ass and a dead one than physical and chemical changes; everyone knows it to be true; but neither he, nor anyone else, can say what the other changes are.

Those things which appeal to our senses, especially of sight and touch, are so insistent that we are thoughtlessly prone to assert that only such things as bodies endowed with spatial and temporal qualities can have reality—all else is but an accident of body.

So the modern biologist, with his repugnance to any form of vitalism, has striven to explain all the activities of the living organism in terms of physical and chemical activities of body, and he has woefully failed. The physicist or chemist, who has observed certain activities which he terms mechanical, has of necessity postulated the entity, body, as that which so acts, because man cannot think except in the sentence or combination of a noun and a verb. The biologist observes certain activities of the living organism, such as growth, propagation, etc., which do not occur in the dead body; he too must and does, however reluctantly, in his thought and speech postulate the entity, life, and for the same necessity that he postulates the entity, body. He thus labours under the dilemma of privately thinking of life as an entity, and of professionally proclaiming it an accidental quality of body.

Boyle devotes the last section of his tract to the comparison of science and theology as subjects worthy to satisfy the ambition of the student. In an amusing manner he portrays science as a fickle and litigious taskmaster. The difference in temperament of Boyle and Newton cannot be better illustrated than by comparing the manner in which Boyle, with urbane sarcasm, describes the disappointments of the ambitious scientist who can never satisfy himself nor avoid the jealousy of stupid and carping critics, and Newton's bitter cry of disgust: 'I have made myself a slave to philosophy, but if I get free of Mr. Linus's business I will resolutely bid adieu to it eternally, excepting what I do for my private satisfaction, or leave to come out after me; for I see a man must either resolve to put out nothing new, or to become a slave to defend it.' [22] After all, Boyle slyly remarks, an ambitious man 'who values and enquires into the mysteries of religion, may also attain to an eminent degree in the knowledge of those of nature.' In proof, he calls to mind many ecclesiastics, then living in England, who were notable for their scientific attainments; and he lists a number of the most eminent scientists, such as Copernicus and Gassendi, who were churchmen; also he mentions himself quite modestly as having some reputation in both fields. As a last argument for the excellency of theology:

It will contribute to the credit, which theological discoveries and illustrations may procure a man, that the importance of the subjects, and the earnestness, wherewith men are wont to busy themselves about them, some upon the score of piety, and others upon that of interest, some to learn truths, and others to defend what they have long or publicly taught for truth, does make greater numbers of men take notice of such matters, and concern themselves far more about them, than about almost any other things, and especially far more, than about matters purely philosophical, which but few are wont to think themselves fit to judge of, and concerned to trouble themselves about.[23]

With Boyle's conclusion that 'upon the whole matter, we have no reason to despond, or to complain of the study of theology, for but making us decline an empty and transitory fame for solid and eternal glory,' we may close this study of his religion, and turn to a discussion of his achievements and failures in science.

X

ALCHEMY AND MEDIÆVAL SCIENCE

THE opinion is generally accepted, that the seventeenth century brought the pseudo-science of the Classic and Middle Ages to an end, and instituted what we believe to be the modern method which has since then flourished so fruitfully as to tag our day the Age of Science. In England, at least, and without much opposition elsewhere, Robert Boyle is held to be one of the chief innovators of this revolution in natural philosophy—a revolution so complete that it requires even a new nomenclature to express its ideas and methods; for example, the old alchemy became the new chemistry, and physics replaced physiology, which became restricted to the study of living bodies. Before discussing Boyle's philosophy and scientific work, and his connexion with the New Inductive Philosophy, a chapter will be devoted to a review of mediæval alchemy, its accomplishment and failure.

There is a mass of evidence that the theoretical philosophers and experimental scientists of the seventeenth century firmly believed they had overthrown an outworn era and had ushered in one which would lead to Truth. To find a parallel to this confidence we should have to cite the biologists of the last half of the nineteenth century who proclaimed with equal assurance that evolution, by natural selection and the survival of the fittest, would disclose to us all the mysteries of life. They relied on Spencer as their predecessors did on Bacon for a philosophy; on Huxley, instead of Boyle, as a propagandist; and on agnosticism, or humanitarianism, for a creed in place of Deism.

In following the sonorous precepts of Bacon and the diligent practices of his child, the Royal Society, these earlier scientists were certain that the hitherto untried inductive method would not only dissipate the fog of mysticism and reveal the divine orderliness of Nature, but would also teach us God's purpose and his plan of salvation. By the middle of the century, their hopes were expressed by proclaiming Boyle to be the Father of Chemistry; and by the end of the century, on the appearance of the *Principia* of Newton, their conviction of success was summed up by Pope's couplet:

> Nature and Nature's laws lay hid in night;
> God said 'Let Newton be,' and all was light.

In Professor Whitehead's opinion, 'The seventeenth century had finally produced a scheme of scientific thought framed by mathematicians, for the use of mathematicians. The great characteristic of the mathematical mind is its capacity for dealing with abstractions; and for eliciting from them clear-cut demonstrative trains of reasoning, entirely satisfactory so long as it is those abstractions which you want to think about.'[1] And Professor Burtt takes the much exaggerated view that 'It was of the greatest consequence for succeeding thought that now the great Newton's authority was squarely behind that view of the cosmos which saw in man a puny, irrelevant spectator (so far as a being wholly imprisoned in a dark room can be called such) of the vast mathematical system whose regular motions according to mechanical principles constituted the world of nature.'[2]

What makes the seventeenth century so interesting and so instructive to us is just the fact that the attempt was made, and believed to be successful, to cultivate simultaneously the irreconcilable mechanistic science and the Christian religion. Boyle and Newton could be confirmed believers, at once, in mystical alchemy and in immutable laws of chemistry; in unchangeable laws of Nature and in the omnipotent Christian God. And not only could they hold to both views, but they could also keep our regard for Nature and God in an equal balance. 'Bacon was pleading for science in an age dominated by "religion"; Browne is already—at least in the *Religio Medici*—pleading for religion in an age which was beginning to be dominated by science.'[3]

Mr. Willey, to illustrate this double purpose of the age, selects Sir Thomas Browne as the 'type of the scientific man who yet retains a religious faith, . . . an enthusiasm for verified truth with a constantly "marvelling temper."' Then, he sums up the spirit of the age:

[Browne] was himself his own 'great amphibium,' living simultaneously in divided and distinguished worlds; or perhaps we may say his own Janus, the double-faced divinity he so often uses as a symbol of paradox. Perhaps no writer is more truly representative of the double-faced age in which he lived, an age half scientific and half magical, half sceptical and half credulous, looking back in one direction to Maundeville, and forward to Newton. At one moment a Baconian experimentalist and herald of the new world, at another Browne is discoursing of cockatrices and unicorns and mermaids in a tone which implies that though part of him is incredulous, the world is still incalculable enough to contain such marvels. At one moment he confesses himself a follower of Hermes Trismegistus, and feels, pantheistically, 'the warm gale and gentle ventilation' of the world-soul; at another, he accounts the world 'not an Inn, but an Hospital; a place not to live, but to die in.'

Any revolution, whether of thought or of action, must first assume that the previous ideas, which directed the search for truth, had been false, or at least inefficient. It must also propose a new philosophy which will convince the general public that its leaders have found a new key to truth so effective as to make it abandon old and familiar habits, and to venture fearfully in new and untried paths. In both aspects, the seventeenth century was happy in finding a leader in Francis Bacon, who not only convinced his contemporaries that the past had failed, but also that he had discovered an untried and all-powerful philosophic discipline, whose conclusions following from observation and reason were not only incontrovertible, but would produce useful fruits. He also was endowed with a gift of language, sonorous and compelling to the spirit of the age. As Aristotle was the originator of the classical and deductive philosophy, and had dominated later thought, so he, Bacon, had conceived a new instauration of learning to guide the future. For the outworn *Organon* in the Greek tongue, the language of the few, he offered a *Novum Organum* in the Latin vernacular, accessible to the many.

It is the fashion of scientists today to regard Bacon as a doctrinaire metaphysician, and to exclude him from the rôle of creative scientists. The gravamen of this charge rests on the fact that he, the proponent of the experimental method, has no experimental discoveries to his credit; that he himself actually retarded the New Philosophy by rejecting the Copernican system; and that he was as credulous as the mediæval Schoolmen in believing in magic, in mysticism, and in a personal God who interfered with natural law to reward or to punish individual human beings.

Such criticism is quite irrelevant. It cannot be denied that Bacon formulated modern scientific method; that he was the model for the seventeenth-century experimentalists, such as Boyle, Newton, and Hooke, who began to cultivate science for its fruits; that he advocated the open exchange of ideas and communities of researchers, instead of the solitary *adeptus* who concealed his results from the vulgar in an esoteric language. To exclude the name of Bacon from the list of great creative scientists is to ignore the function of the critic and theorist. One may as well exclude the preacher, the teacher, the mathematician, and the philosopher, all of whom are to be judged by their ideas and not by their practices.

When seeking the causes and results of the scientific revolt of the Renaissance, we should keep in mind that it was confined primarily to the physical sciences, and owed its success to an extraordinarily coherent and able line of mathematical physicists beginning with Copernicus and ending with Newton. And we must also remember that during the Middle Ages those sciences were related mostly to astrology and alchemy, in which the useful investigations of the phenomena of the stars and of the compositions of bodies had been confused with an inextricable mess of natural and supernatural agents, and of formal and animistic causes. They had also been rendered almost unintelligible by a mystical nomenclature and a religious symbolism. As for the biological sciences, they scarcely existed, interest in them being confined to husbandry and medicine as arts. The only question at issue in the minds of the reformers of science was whether reliance for our knowledge of physical phenomena was to be placed in a progressive acquisition of data of observation and in their rational interpretation; or whether the canon had been established by the Church which relied on a fixed knowledge handed down principally from the Hebrews and Greeks.

A better understanding of the classical and mediæval science has proved to us that the seventeenth century was in error in assuming it to have been fruitless because it had been based on a purely deductive method. If the inductive philosophy is inconclusive and impossible to practise, and if observation and reason are not the key to certainty of knowledge, in what did the break with mediæval scholasticism consist, and why may modern science be dated from it?

The awakened interest in science was but one phase of the broad movement, which we call the Renaissance, that sought to establish a more even balance between our relations to worldly and other-worldly affairs. By a return to the classical goal of balance, moderation, and measure, the dignity of human nature would be restored and we could enjoy again the legitimate delight we take in knowledge derived from our sensations.

The first effects of the new freedom are to be seen in the fields of art, literature, and religion. It was not until the seventeenth century that belief in rigorous natural phenomena and laws became prevalent, with a corresponding discredit of magic and mystic agents. In philosophic terms, science began to seek efficient, rather than final, causes; to limit its enquiry to find *how,* rather than *why,* nature operates. Instead of exclusiveness, its scientists, and particularly Boyle, advocated a clear style and an exact nomenclature in order that science might be widely known and its fruits be applied to benefit the conditions of life. In these changes lay the germ of our industrial and scientific age.

It is impossible now, and probably always will be, to give an accurate review of the rise and development of the science of alchemy. All alchemists were convinced that their subject had its roots in the earliest times of mankind and that they were the humble followers of mighty magicians endowed with mysterious powers by God or by the devil. And each author added to this tangled forest of mystical legend till it became quite impenetrable. As a result, most scientists now, and I think erroneously, ignore the value of alchemy as a precursor to their work.

Our knowledge of alchemy, from historical documents, goes back to the fourth century. But very few original manuscripts relating to the subject in the Greek, Syriac, and Arabian tongues have been preserved, if there were ever many; and what there are lie buried in the libraries of Europe, because the interest of scholars has not been great enough to overcome the difficulties of a decipherment made doubly difficult by an abstruse language and subject.

So far as we are concerned, we depend on Latin texts beginning about the tenth century and continuing to the eighteenth century in increasing numbers. While they become successively clearer in purpose and in exposition, they all reproduce the same symbolic style, the same pretensions of a mystical source, the same falsification of records, and the same deliberate purpose to conceal knowledge except to the initiated adepts of the *arcana majora.*

Thus, there must always remain the doubt whether there was a continuity of knowledge passed from generation to generation by oral and secret tradition, or whether the consistent symbolism was an attempt to conceal knowledge from the generality, or to conceal the alchemists' own ignorance and their failure to discover the philosopher's stone. Again, we cannot be sure who many of the alchemists were, or whether the treatises bearing their names were not written by someone else. In modern times, an author may be trusted to sign his work with his own name to enhance his reputation; but in the Middle Ages, it was the desire to give weight to the work which led authors to subscribe the name of a distinguished authority. This habit accounts for the many spurious treatises attributed to the Arabian Jaber; of many others to Albertus Magnus, who was a favourite target for legends of magic, and who probably was not an alchemist; even some of the most celebrated alchemists, as Basil Valentine, are now supposed to be fictitious persons.

A few quotations from Louis Figuier's *L'alchimie et les alchimistes* will be sufficient to convince any one of the hopelessness of obtaining any accurate knowledge of the processes of alchemy when the alchemists, bewildered themselves, purposely bewildered every one else.

Artephius boldly justifies deception: 'Poor idiot, are you so simple as to believe that we shall teach you openly and clearly the greatest and most important of secrets.' And Salmon: 'It is only in apparent contradictions and lies that we find the truth.' Basil Valentine, on the other hand, reproaches himself severely for the clarity of his writings—those who have wrestled with his celebrated work, *Currus Triumphalis Antimonii,* will exonerate him from at least transparent clarity.

To illustrate the cryptic language and the lack of any clear knowledge of what occurred during their chemical manipulations, any and all the alchemists could be cited; the following are but examples: The early Byzantine, known as Pseudo-Democritus and who also is probably apocryphal, advises us how to solidify mercury: 'Take some mercury and solidify it with magnesia, or with sulphur, or with the foam of silver, or with chalk, or with alum, or with what you wish.' The Arabic *magister,* Rhasis, is even more catholic in his recipe for making alcohol: '*Recipe aliquid ignotum, quantum volueris,*'—'Take as much as you wish of something unknown.' As late as the seventeenth century, George Ripley, Canon of Bridlington and contemporary of Boyle and Newton, was regarded as a supreme authority, and yet his followers must ravel such mystic mazes as this, found in his *Twelve Gates:* 'Begin with the setting sun, then the Red husband and the White wife join in the spirit of life to live in love and tranquillity, in the exact proportion of water and earth. From the West advance across the shadows towards the North; alter and dissolve the sea and the woman between winter and spring, etc.'

Possibly, the widest gulf which separates chemists and alchemists was their conviction that chemical actions would not prosper without the aid of magic, nor unless the adept led a pious life. Even Paracelsus, the great innovator and iconoclast, whose motto was *'Qui suus esse potest non sit alterius,'* believed that his power lay in his piety and prayer, and yet he held fast to the efficacy of magic: 'If you do not understand the usages of the cabbalists and the ancient astrologers, God has not created you to be a spagyrist [alchemist], and Nature has not chosen you for the work of Vulcan.'

Until nearly the close of the nineteenth century, knowledge of alchemy and of the alchemists was derived from enthusiasts who, attracted to mystical cults, regarded obscurity as a proof and measure of profundity; or from historians of science who, convinced that truth was restricted to observation and reason, argued that experimental science began with the seventeenth century; that the Middle Ages were a sterile period because the Church persecuted all those who attempted such work; and that Greek natural philosophy was but a set of formulæ spun from the imagination. Fortunately, during a voyage in 1869 to Egypt, the eminent chemist Berthelot became deeply interested in the work and philosophy of the alchemists.

On Berthelot's return, his interest did not diminish. He set himself the task of searching the libraries of Europe and disclosed an unexpected wealth of manuscripts. Some of these he, with the aid of linguists, deciphered and translated. He mastered the nomenclature of the alchemists and interpreted their chemical work. In many articles and in three treatises,[4] he published the results of his research, which entirely changed our opinion of these early scientists and made him the authority on their work.

Berthelot's conclusion is best expressed in his own carefully chosen words:

I have found not only the thread of ideas which led them [the Greek alchemists of Byzantium and Alexandria] to pursue the transmutation of metals; but also the theory, the philosophy of nature which served them as guide; theory founded on the philosophy of the unity of matter and as plausible fundamentally as the most respected of modern theories of today. This theory, advanced by the Greeks, was adopted by the Arabs and by the scholars of the Middle Ages, and was accompanied by a steadily growing industrial practice. But in this field of ideas, the Middle Ages were no more creative than they were in that of physics or of the natural sciences. It is common knowledge, how sterile that epoch was in scientific interest.[5]

As would be expected Berthelot was interested chiefly in the early history of alchemy as a science; it is fortunate that the mystical and religious aspects of the subject have been seriously investigated by A. E. Waite, one of the greatest of living scholars in those fields.[6]

The thesis of Waite, himself a sceptic as regards the existence of so-called secret sciences, is:

The secret theosophies, like Kabalism and one at least of the secret sciences, were perpetuated *ex hypothesi* by reception; in other words, by transmission from one person and generation to another. They suppose therefore custodians, without which such transmission would be impossible. On the face of alchemical literature the claim of this custody is plainly written: possibly it is the only thing which is plain or demonstrable concerning it. It forms part of a considerable body of evidence that certain knowledge—whether actual or fanciful does not signify at the moment—was handed down from an early period and through the Middle Ages to later times. Such knowledge was sometimes concerned with matters of research belonging to the domain of physics, as in the case of alchemy; at others it transmitted old ideas of philosophy: Cornelius Agrippa had claims on the past in this respect, and even Paracelsus . . . confesses to something brought down. In yet other cases religious practices, connoting religious beliefs of antiquity, under one or other guise and amidst inevitable mutations, have been apparently handed on. So far as the West is concerned, the literature of alchemy is in the main a Latin literature, and it rose up in Europe about the beginning of the tenth century.[7]

However confused the minds of the alchemists may have been by their belief in magic and supernatural powers, and however lacking their knowledge of chemical compositions and their skill in experimental manipulation, they practised many of the analytic and synthetic methods in use today and accumulated a respectable quantity of experimental data which was used in the arts and manufactures. Their practical work was centred in the problems of the nature and use of metals, probably the most important substances in the economy of nature, and especially in that of gold, the most perfect and the most precious of all.

While the practical work of the alchemists has been so built upon and increased by the accumulation of later knowledge that it has now only historical interest, the philosophy of nature which guided them—and in fact alchemy was a philosophy—is essentially the same as that subscribed to by the most modern chemists and physicists.

If I am correct, alchemy was a rational explanation, based on the fundamental postulate that there exists in fact a single basic element, that the various bodies are merely different combinations, or arrangements, of this element. Thus, since one body differs from another only in accidental qualities, it may be changed from one kind to another by altering them; and it was the function of the alchemist to recognize and to manipulate such changes.

This philosophy of the alchemists was more strictly logical than is ours today, because of the passion for logical accuracy of the Middle Ages and because they were less distracted by an accumulated body of facts. It never, from its beginning to its maturity, relied on the miraculous, however much its adepts may have resorted to magic and to spiritual help to accomplish what their philosophy predicted and what constantly eluded their efforts.

The search for a fixed principle in the inextricable flux of phenomena has haunted men's minds, as though possessed by a 'demon of the absolute,' ever since it was first explicitly stated by Thales to be 'water.' It permeated all of classic metaphysics, changing only its protean name: the atom of Democritus, the four elements of Empedocles, the *nous* of Anaxagoras, the living fire of Heraclitus, the geometric triangle of Plato, the *hyle* of Aristotle, the metaphysical *something* of the Stoics and Epicureans which, as Lucretius puts it, must remain immutable lest all things be utterly reduced to the void.*

This demonic idea was forgotten with the collapse of the classic civilization, but it reappeared as an obsession of the mediæval al-

---

* *Immutabile enim quiddam superare necessest. Ne res ad nilum redigantur funditus omnes.* Lucretius, Bk. 1, 1. 790.

chemists as a new *prima materia,* under the name of philosophic
mercury. In the seventeenth century, the demon masqueraded as a
corpuscle; as an atom during the two succeeding centuries; and in
the twentieth, it is now a brood of electrical ions, a quantum of
energy, or a bundle of vacuous waves. And in all its forms, this
'demon of the absolute' has remained as a fiction of the mind, without substance, and impelling man, as one possessed, to incalculable
labour.

When we turn from the general philosophic principle that there
is a single, immutable, element and that all sensible bodies are
transmutable one into another, we find the main practical purpose
of the alchemists to be the transmutation of metals. The cause of
the existence of metals and of gems, which were hardly distinguished in primitive times and which lie hidden in the earth, usually disguised in ores and matrices, fascinated the imagination. And
it is not surprising that great honour was paid to the metallurgist
who extracted the metal from the ore, and to the artisan who
worked it into articles of use and ornament. Nor is it surprising
that such a transformation of the dull ore seemed mysterious and
to require the use of magic.

The first principle regarding the nature of metals, universally
accepted with only minor divergencies of opinion, was that they
were alive and grew from seeds somewhat like plants. Nature always attempted to produce silver and gold, which were held to be
noble and perfect because they were usually found together and in
their pure state and were less subject to acids or other agents. Thus,
the formation of all other metals was something like an abortion,
caused by an accident to nature or by a disease contracted from a
foul matrix.

Again, it was believed that the growth of each metal was fostered
by an effluvium from its guardian planet; and, to the ancient mind,
there was great significance in the fact that seven metals and seven
planets were known. So, by the laws of astrology, the stars affected
not only the lives of men but also all the operations of chemistry.
It is not difficult to guess why the yellow sun was assigned to gold,
and the white moon to silver, as the sovereigns of the heavens and
of metals. And probably a fancied relation between the attributes
of the god and the uses of the metal made them assign Mars to iron,

Saturn to lead, Venus to copper, Mercury to tin, and Jupiter to electrum, an alloy of gold and silver; later electrum was dropped and
Jupiter was given to tin, and quicksilver to Mercury, or Hermes.
So close was the relation that the symbols of the planets were used
to designate the metals.

The astrological aspect of alchemy was especially cultivated by
the Jewish and Arabian adepts. On the other hand, the Latin
writers turned more to Greek practice and they more and more forsook astrology, for it had never struck its roots deeply into Greek
philosophy. With the exception of Paracelsus, the only other two
important Latin adepts who took magic and astrology seriously
were Arnold de Villanova (thirteenth century) and Basil Valentine
(sixteenth century).

While the alchemists believed that metals grew from seeds by
natural processes, yet such production was thought to be exceedingly slow, so slow that centuries would be needed for any large
accumulation of gold. What nature could accomplish only slowly,
the alchemists supposed might be done quickly by the rational mind
and manipulative skill of man; and the great endeavour for centuries was to create gold in the laboratory, just as in modern times
it is the object of the biochemist to reproduce synthetically the
chemical products of the living body.

The alchemists accepted unreservedly the four primal elements—
earth, water, air, and fire—and their mutual transmutation by the
active agents, heat and cold, moisture and dryness, as taught by
Aristotle. They also accepted his category of causes. His formal
cause became the specific attributes of the metal and, of these, colour
was the most important criterion. The efficient cause as motion they
rejected as part of the Democritean principle of chance; in its place,
as the cause of chemical combination they substituted the vitalistic
principle of love and hate, first proposed by Empedocles, and which
lingers in our own nomenclature as 'chemical affinity.'

While the belief in the four Aristotelian elements as transmutable
manifestations of the *hyle* persisted till it was replaced in the eighteenth century by a revival of the hypothesis of the mechanical atom,
yet there seemed to be a need for an immutable element especially
pertinent to the transmutable metals. For some reason, some unknown alchemist chose mercury as the metallic *prima materia*—not

the hydrargyrum or quicksilver of commerce, but its essential principle, or what came to be named philosophic mercury.*

Philosophic mercury, as the *prima materia* appears in the early history of alchemy. Although the method of transmuting metals by its aid was confused by the Oriental writers with magic and occult rites, it had, even in the early Latin literature, become standardized in form and logical in procedure. The Latin treatises of Geber,† according to Waite, mark a new epoch in alchemy. In his opinion, Geber's *Summa perfectionis magisterii* is the supreme authority of the alchemists:

There are no important texts of alchemical literature which can compare with the *Summa* for the complete absence of any spiritual motive or recognition of things divine, save only the other texts of the Latin Geber and of his Arabian *alter ego*. The conclusion of this chapter [on early Latin literature] follows from its entire content: the early Latin literature is that of pure physicists, expounding the principles and practice of a purely physical work.[8]

The general theory of transmutation is simple and logical. From any metal, remove one by one its specific qualities, or formal causes; for example, its colour, hardness, etc. When these are carried out successfully by chemical operations, one will have reduced it to the *prima materia*. Then, one has only to add the qualities appropriate to the desired metal, and the metal has been transmuted. The theory is simple enough, but the difficulty lay in recognizing the *prima materia*. It was believed that this philosophic mercury could be most readily obtained from metallic mercury: to do so, first abstract from it all of its earthy principle, and then the water or fluid element; to fix it, remove the air or volatile principle; finally, to give it the desired qualities, treat it with pure sulphur or, as some said, with arsenic.

* One may hazard the guess that mercury was selected because of its ability to liquefy gold and silver. The names given to the metal suggest that it was believed to have mysterious powers. As mercury, it symbolized the quick and faithful messenger of the gods; as quicksilver, the power of motion and of life, and the essential colour of silver; as hydrargyrum, its name first known from Pliny, signifying its ability to turn the noble metals to water: and water was the name used as a symbol of life and of divine power in the Scriptures, and in the *Timaeus* of Plato, an unquestioned authority for the neo-Platonists and for the Arabian alchemists.

† These manuscripts, of the twelfth or thirteenth century, purport to be translations from the Arabic treatises of the supreme alchemist, Sheik Abu Moussa Jaber, Latinized as Geber, who lived at the end of the eighth century. As will be seen later, Berthelot insists that these texts are original documents by an unknown European alchemist who ascribed them to Jaber, or Geber, to give them greater authority, a not uncommon device.

Although mercury continued to be the *prima materia* of metals, the conviction gradually grew that metals were not merely varieties of a single element but were compound bodies; to satisfy this hypothesis sulphur was selected as an ancillary element, though some chose arsenic; and later, salt as a component was added. In the end, the hypothesis was accepted that these three elements in different proportions were the components of all the metals. Mercury accounted for their lustre and fusibility; sulphur, for colour and combustibility; and salt was the *caput mortuum* or earthy matter.

Each alchemist devised his own practical recipes for transmutation, or attempted to copy the obscure practices of some former adept. One cannot but admire the enthusiasm of these early scientists, who worked with excessive labour on this impossible task only to find, after a life spent on the work, that their great hope was a dream; the real and useful chemical results which they had achieved, and which form the basis of our chemistry, they had deemed worthless.

In order to accomplish transmutation practically, the alchemists relied almost entirely on long and repeated heating, and on dissolving the metals by different agents, or *menstrua*. They also resorted to repeated distilling. In judging the success or failure of their successive operations, they regarded colour as the chief formal criterion; they believed that, if the colour of gold or silver were exactly duplicated, the product was true gold or silver. There is evidence that the practical metallurgists of ancient Egypt were very skilful in making imitation gold and silver articles by tingeing the surfaces of other and cheaper metals. It is supposed the earliest alchemists inherited some of their recipes and were deceived into thinking an actual transmutation had been achieved. In course of time it came to be the highest purpose of alchemy to tinge metals so that they would have the essential principle of gold, and not merely its surface colour.

In order to illustrate the purely physical operations of the alchemists and their dependence on colour as the final criterion of transmutations, two examples will be sufficient.

The first is taken from Geber's *Summa,* as given by Berthelot:

It was by submitting metals to prolonged oxidation and calcination, by reducing them again to the metallic state, and by repeating these operations, that Geber sought to remove their specific qualities: for example, by this means tin is deprived of its 'cry,' its fusibility, and its softness, the qualities which distinguish it from silver; it is then hardened and fixed by repeated regenerations to the metallic state. The same is true for lead, which Geber states is easily changed to silver: he confesses that lead which he calcined and regenerated twice did not harden.[9]

The second illustration is taken from *La bibliothèque des philosophes chimiques* of the adept William Salmon:

The philosophic mercury, which is named the female, is added to and amalgamated with gold, the male, which must be very pure and supplied in leaves or in filings. The amalgam is placed in a philosopher's egg (a small, oval *matras,* hermetically sealed to prevent exhalations from escaping). The egg is next placed in a bowl full of ashes and introduced into the furnace. Then this mercury, by the heat of its included sulphur excited by the fire beneath it which is kept at a proper heat; this mercury, I say, dissolves the gold quietly and reduces it into atoms. At the end of six months a black powder is obtained, which is the *raven's head,* or *Saturn,* or *cimmerian darkness*. If the action be further prolonged, it becomes white, and it is now the *white tincture* or the *little philosopher's stone* which will transmute metals into silver and manufacture pearls. If, lastly, the fire is increased, the matter melts, becomes green and finally changes to a red powder. This is the true *philosopher's stone* which, thrown on a base metal in a state of fusion, will instantly transform it into gold.[10]

The constant failure to achieve the perfect transmutation to gold must have induced serious questioning why, when an universally accepted philosophy had been followed so exactly, the practical results should fail. In an age of more simple piety than ours, when a too great reliance on one's intellectual powers was condemned as a sin of the pride of the intellect, it was inevitable that failure should be regarded as the displeasure of God. Such would seem to be the reason why all the adepts assert that chemical work must be preceded by prayer, and also that the essential qualities of character for anyone devoting himself to this work were the love of God, unselfishness, charity, and detachment from worldly interests and pleasure. Paradoxically, the alchemists, who apparently were seeking untold wealth, must devote themselves to a life of poverty and humility. The enthusiast can always solve such problems by imagining, as will be shown later, other benefits which would outweigh the certain evils.

If then transmutation was beyond the reach of man's unaided efforts, God had provided a means of success which he would disclose to the pious seeker. Even as early as in the collection of the Greek alchemists,* references are made to the existence of a mystical body which, if merely placed in contact with a base metal, would by 'projection' instantly change any amount of it into pure gold. Thus arose the legend of the mysterious 'philosopher's stone,' that will-o'-the-wisp pursued so ardently, so heart-breakingly for centuries, and so conducive to charlatanry. The amount of gold projected by the philosopher's stone, or by the grand magister, or by any of the many other names it passed under, was at first moderate; but, as time went on, the claims became more and more extravagant, until to project a million times its weight seemed to be no exaggeration. Raymond Lully probably was never outmatched when he boasted: 'Mare tingerem, si mercurius esset.'

Naturally, such an instrument of unbounded wealth excited the cupidity of the powerful ecclesiastic or nobleman, who would engage an alchemist as a member of his retinue and frequently kept him in durance under threat of torture until he should deliver the goods. On the other hand, the rôle of the alchemist was a tempting inducement to the clever rascal, and the tales are many of the tricks practised on the unwary employer. Commercialized transmutation became a recognized profession which did much to discredit the serious work of honourable alchemists.

However, there are too many statements of thoroughly reputable scientists who had obtained an object, or a powder, which to their conviction produced small amounts of gold or silver for us to doubt their word or the result. The account of Robert Boyle's degradation of gold to silver will be given later in detail; his word is to be trusted with any man's. Also Van Helmont, the greatest chemist of his day, stated: 'I have seen and handled the philosopher's stone. It has the colour of powdered saffron; it was heavy and brilliant as broken glass.' This description is unusual only in that most adepts declared it to be insignificant in appearance. The small quantities of gold or silver which they found in their crucibles at the conclusion of their chemical manipulations were often genuine

* This collection, if we omit later additions, was formed during the eighth or ninth century at Constantinople, and our oldest known manuscript belongs to the end of the tenth. The alchemists referred to in the collection are quoted as being of the third or fourth century.—Waite.

enough: the error lay in the fact that the base metals they used contained traces of the gold or silver which they had unwittingly separated out in their ignorance of chemical reactions.

The distinctions between animals, plants, and chemical bodies were less clear in the Middle Ages than they are even today in spite of our belief in evolution. As late as the seventeenth century, Boyle cited many transmutations between any two of the three kingdoms. When metals were thought to grow as plants, it was only natural to endow the Stone also with perfect medicinal properties. The Stone, as the grand elixir, the quintessence, or the tincture, would cure all maladies and prolong life indefinitely. It was the custom for insincere or fanatic alchemists, as a proof of their success, to assert that they had discovered and used the elixir, and were in consequence centuries old. Isaac of Holland, whom even Paracelsus held in esteem, assures us that, if one takes a little of the philosopher's stone each week, he will always be well and live till the last hour assigned to him by God. Boyle also, when he hesitated to publish his work on transmutation for fear of its harmful effect on society, hoped that the benefit as a medicine would outweigh the danger of unlimited wealth.

According to Figuier,[11] the belief in the efficacy of the Stone as a sovereign remedy for all diseases did not originate till the thirteenth century. He cites the opinion of Boerhaave that the Latin writers were brought to this belief by taking literally the figurative language of the early Oriental masters. To illustrate this opinion he cites a saying of Jaber: 'Bring me the six lepers, that I may cure them,' by which he meant that he would transmute six metals into gold. Figuier is undoubtedly wrong in assigning so late a date, and the evidence of Boerhaave is not satisfactory. The belief in effluvia from gems and minerals as of great efficacy in medicine goes back to primitive times. As soon as the doctrine of the philosopher's stone was accepted, and it antedated the twelfth century, its medicinal power would be accepted immediately. Boerhaave's explanation is more ingenious than reliable, since the Latin writers were too used to the figurative language of the Arabians to be so easily misled. Also, the citation is of doubtful origin, since most sayings attributed to the Arabian Jaber are from the writings of the unknown Latin Geber.

However the idea of the elixir of life arose, and to me it would inevitably follow from the combined physical and spiritual powers of the Stone, it became one of the chief tenets in alchemy. For Paracelsus, that strange combination of charlatan and of genius, of bombast and of great achievement, the elixir was the ultimate goal.

In order to prepare the elixir, the first essential was to find a menstruum, or special solvent. In his *De viribus membrorum,* Paracelsus mentions his discovery of such a solvent: 'There is a liquor, the alkahest, which acts most efficaciously on the liver; sustains it, fortifies it, and preserves it from the maladies which attack it . . . All those who practise medicine should know how to prepare the alkahest.' [12] With this as a hint, Van Helmont expanded the alkahest into an universal solvent with magic properties. He lists all sorts of materials which immediately succumb to it. Although it was above human ability to make, he possessed some which had been given to him by an unknown stranger, but he could not preserve it. The alkahest excited profound interest, and there was much speculation as to the meaning of the name, for Paracelsus had the habit of coining words which concealed anagrammatically a key. Many accepted Glauber's suggestion, that it was potash, or *alkali est;* others that it was hydrochloric acid. It was not until the middle of the eighteenth century that the derivation for alkahest was given by Kunckel in his *Laboratorium chymicum* as *Alles Lügen heisst.* As he caustically remarks, no one could have an alkahest for, if it dissolves all substances, it would dissolve any vessel which contained it. But, by this time, chemistry had begun a soberer career and, except for visionaries, the Stone and the elixir ceased to be objects of search.

There is another aspect of alchemy of great interest and value which should be discussed briefly, although it lies somewhat outside the purpose of this essay.

Alchemy was not only a natural philosophy and a rudimentary science of chemistry; it also became a religious cult, disguising the Christian sacraments and rites with the symbolism of chemistry and *vice versa.* The belief in a substance which would change the nature of material bodies—the mystic Stone which was not a stone, the magic Stone mean and insignificant in appearance—was similar to the figurative description of Christ as the Stone rejected by the builder; the doctrine of the transmutation of metals was similar to the mystery of transubstantiation; the cycle of a metal and its oxide to the spiritual resurrection of the body: all these were too apparent to be missed. The verbal analogy between the material and spiritual worlds once thus visualized, it was certain that every phase of the one could, and would, be expressed in terms of the other.

According to the temperaments of the alchemists, some would be interested only in the material problems, and some in the spiritual phase; and though their words might sound the same, their significance to the two classes of minds would be quite different. But we can be sure that the great majority carried on the two trains of thought and purpose without much consideration whether they were really concordant or discordant. Is it not true that many scientists can follow without discomfort a purely materialistic philosophy during the week and a Christian theology on Sunday?

The strictly scientific work of the alchemists was permeated from its earliest beginning with the prevalent belief in magic and mysticism. When Europe became Christianized and developed a philosophy which conflated the religious life of Christ with Platonic idealism, pagan mysticism was fused with the belief in the possibility of union with the Divine Nature by means of ecstatic contemplation. Nor did the Christian religion escape, from its beginning, an infusion of the extravagant mysticism of the neo-Platonic, the Manichæistic, and Gnostic cults, which, though finally pronounced heterodox, lingered at all times and became strong during periods of stress and anxiety. As an illustration, there is even today a definite recrudescence of occultism together with a general lack of interest in orthodox religion, and with a corresponding absorption in material values.

As has been mentioned before, the legends of many early peoples assigned mysterious properties and powers to metals, and endowed with magic skill the metallurgists who extracted the metal from the ore and the artisans who fashioned it. These legends were particularly rife in Egypt. The Egyptians were famed for their knowledge of metals, gems, glass working, and of dyeing and tingeing materials. They were also expert counterfeiters of gems, and of gold and silver articles, by superficial tingeing of glass and metals. Apparently, these trades were under the exclusive control of the priests, and the recipes for the workmen were jealously kept secret. The patron divinity of these crafts was the god Thoth. Under the Greek influence, the Egyptian god was translated to Hermes, Latin Mercury, the reputed inventor of the sciences. Thus came into existence the semi-divine Hermes Trismegistus, the threefold great, and the final authority on all alchemy.

In order that the alchemists might be blessed by an actual message from their founder and saint, a pious alchemist wrote the famous *Tabula Smaragdina* of Hermes, 'and this has been of highest and indeed supreme authority among alchemists from the time when it became known to them, somewhere in the thirteenth century.' * To make the work impressive, it was claimed that the original had been engraved on a huge table of emerald by Hermes himself, and had once been in the possession of Alexander the Great.

Although it was the habit of the alchemists, without exception, to assume that their divine science originated in ancient Egypt, there is no evidence of a belief in transmutation in any hieroglyph yet discovered. Our earliest documentary evidence is that it owed its inception and first development to the Greeks of Constantinople in the third or fourth century, A.D. Our present collection of Greek alchemists was written during the eighth or ninth century and all of them cite the authors of the earlier period.

These documents give convincing proof that the Byzantine school of alchemists, from the author of earliest known text extant, Zosimus the Panopolitan, were practical workers and sought for the transmutation of metals. Also, for all of them, it was a secret science and a divine theosophy to be transmitted to masters only who possessed purity of character. The symbolic nomenclature, so characteristic of alchemy, had been developed; and the primitive legends had been fused with Gnosticism and the neo-Platonism of Alexandria to produce a mystic and incomprehensible Christian cult.

Berthelot has offered an ingenious explanation of the source from which the Greek alchemists derived their belief in transmutation, and which has the authority of his profound study of their works. There is a Greek papyrus manuscript in Leyden, absolutely authentic and referable to the third century, which was found in a tomb at Thebes. The manuscript is an unsystematic compilation, and is, in Berthelot's opinion, the notebook of an Egyptian artisan in metals. It comprises seventy-five metallurgical formulæ, for making alloys, the surface colouring of metal, assaying, etc., and fifteen

* Waite: *Secret Tradition*, p. 53. The text is in Latin and no trace of a Greek original remains. It was first printed in 1541 at Nuremberg, with the Latin works of Geber.

processes for producing gold and silver letters, which are described in simple and plain words such as an artisan would jot down to aid his memory. They include tingeing to counterfeit gold, surface colouring of copper for the same purpose, gilding silver, tincture by varnishing, etc.

Berthelot maintains that the Leyden Papyrus is proof that, when alchemy began in Egypt, it was merely the art of adulterating and imitating gold, silver, and gems. 'It bears witness to a science of alloys and metallic tingeing which was very skilful and much advanced, a science which had for its object the fabrication and falsification of articles of gold and silver.' Also, he found that, 'not only is the notion analogous, but the practices exposed in this Papyrus are the same as those of the oldest Greek alchemists, such as pseudo-Democritus, Zosimus, Olympiodorus, and pseudo-Moses.'

The first step towards the developed philosophy of alchemy was taken when the Egyptian artisans, doubting their skill to accomplish their work, invoked the aid of a god; or, fearing punishment for their fraudulent practices, inserted propitiating prayers. Next, the Greek commentators, ignorant of science, obscured and neglected such practical recipes; misunderstood the falsification of gold as a true transmutation; and interpreted the individual prayers as a general need of divine help, which God had provided in the form of a mystic body, the philosopher's stone, as he had given his Son for man's spiritual redemption. According to Berthelot, the same fraudulent recipes are to be found in the Byzantine writers, but A. E. Waite thinks they recognized the purpose of the Papyrus and endeavoured to improve the process into a real transmutation.

If Berthelot's ingenious hypothesis be correct, then the science and the religious cult of alchemy were founded on fraud and flourished on a mystical misconception of a practical art. It is not, of course, the only religious cult which arose from a perversion of facts, but it is probably a most notable example. It is, however, subject to doubt whether the Byzantine writers were acquainted with the Leyden Papyrus or other similar texts; and, if the recipes are given in such a matter of fact manner, why were they deceived?

The intermediate history of alchemy, till it reached Latin Europe, was by way of Syriac to Arabic adepts. Our knowledge of Syriac alchemy is derived from two manuscripts in the British Museum and one in Cambridge. They comprise a translation of pseudo-

Democritus and a later text of the same school. Our known Arabic treatises include the *Book of Crates,* the *Book of El-Habib,* the *Book of Ostanes,* and the genuine works of Abu Moussa Jaber— not to be confused with the later and unknown writer who adopted the same name in the Latinized form of Geber.

According to Berthelot, the Syriac texts are a collection of practical recipes, jumbled with mystic and magic formulæ, and too mutilated for serious criticism. In contrast to the unadorned style of those texts, the Arabic treatises are grandiloquent, visionary, and so prolix that their alchemy is buried in a mass of speculation on all possible subjects. The Syriac and Arabic writers added so little to scientific alchemy, and so confused its spiritual aspect, that they are of interest only to the historical specialist.

Before Berthelot gave to the world his researches in alchemy, it was generally accepted that the Latin treatises of Geber (twelfth or thirteenth century) were mere translations from the Arabic of Jaber, who lived at the end of the eighth century and to whom were attributed more than five hundred works. Of the three treatises of Geber which have been published, the *Summa perfectionis magisterii in sua natura* is the masterpiece, and was held to be an absolute authority. It marks, according to Berthelot, a new epoch in alchemy by its clear logic and plain statement of facts. The known chemical operations such as volatilization, distillation, etc., are evidence of a true science of chemistry:

These operations are given by the Greek alchemists; but Geber presents them with a clarity and method lacking to them, and which make the older authors more intelligible.

Then, there follows a scientific description of the metals analogous to that of a modern treatise. But he adds to this information on the nature of the metals, recipes for methods of manufacturing them for all purposes. Geber states that metals are composed of sulphur, mercury, and arsenic; a theory originating with the Greek alchemists and continuing to the Middle Ages. Gold, in particular, is formed from purified mercury with the addition of a small quantity of pure sulphur. The pure sulphur, mercury, and arsenic are quintessences, more subtile than the ordinary substances of the same names. He, who is able to isolate them, can manufacture and transform the metals at will. The mercury which gives perfection to metals is not quicksilver but the essence extracted from it: the gross earthy element and the superfluous fluid element must be removed.

Similarly for sulphur and arsenic the earthy element and the fiery element, its inflammability, must be withdrawn.

It is, in brief, by subjecting a metal to prolonged oxydation and calcination, and then by reducing again to the metallic state, that Geber seeks to transmute their qualities.[13]

Since the works of Geber, and especially the *Summa,* were accepted as giving a true account of the chemical theory and practice of the Arabians as early as the eighth century, the Arabians were cited in chemical textbooks (and are yet) as creative chemists, whom later alchemists followed with little improvement. But, if Berthelot's conclusions are correct, no such credit should be assigned to them, and the science of chemistry owes its real beginning to the Latin alchemists.

Berthelot, to prove his argument, translated with collaborators the six known Arabic manuscripts in the Paris and Leyden libraries. He found them to be quite different in character from the Latin texts of Geber. While he was not certain that they were the works of Jaber, they could be definitely assigned to a date between the ninth and twelfth centuries, and thus ante-dating the Arabic influence on Europe.

The Arabic manuscripts were found to differ in style completely from the *Summa.* They are vague and allegorical, giving no accurate details of chemical practices but are pious exponents of Islam. They contain no reference to the elements, mercury, sulphur, and arsenic; and they are astrological. Though A. E. Waite believes Berthelot may be overconfident in his conclusion, he agrees that the styles are different; that the *Summa* denies the influence of the stars; and that it is a purely scientific text. But, his own statement of the work seems to me to agree with Berthelot: 'There are no important texts of alchemical literature which can compare with the *Summa* for the complete absence of any spiritual motive or recognition of things divine, save only the other tracts of the Latin Geber and of his Arabian *alter ego.*'[14]

In spite of the fact that alchemy towards the end of the sixteenth century and the first half of the seventeenth became a mystical religious cult, so long as it followed the *Summa* as its guide and Geber as its master, its purpose was to investigate material rather than spiritual problems; thus, whatever its nomenclature may have been, it was a science.

It is significant on another account, that the *Summa* is contemporaneous with the great religious revival of the twelfth and thirteenth centuries, when all men's thoughts and occupations were saturated with religion and were expressed in spiritual terms. The familiar criticism that the Church crushed science and persecuted scientists is contradicted by the fact that no opposition was made to alchemy, except to the use of magic or fraud; on the contrary, the alchemists were often monks or clerks, or they were unknown men who gave weight to their treatises by using the names of distinguished churchmen. By this supposititious method the title of adept in the *arcana majora* was given to the mysterious Raymond Lully, Doctor Illuminatus and Missionary to the Moors; to Albertus Magnus, Doctor Universalis; and to Thomas Aquinas, Doctor Angelicus.

So far as I can discover, the only actions taken by the Church against science were to forbid the study and teaching of the materialistic theory of atoms during a short period in the thirteenth century, and the Copernican theory in the seventeenth—in both cases as heterodox. The Church undoubtedly discouraged any ardent pursuit of science, lest it should usurp devotion to spiritual welfare. The neglect of science during the Middle Ages must be attributed to that 'Climate of Opinion' which placed the value of life on spiritual pursuits rather than, as now, on material power and comfort. Thus men of education and of intellect chose the field of religion rather than of science. We can thus safely assume that the conflation of spiritual and material ideas and the use of a mystic nomenclature were not only natural, but were also a safeguard to the alchemist and an aid to alchemy.

The large number of alchemistic works extant, and the many which did not survive, give the impression that a considerable number of alchemists contributed to our knowledge of experimental chemistry. The converse is true: A. E. Waite [15] lists the following few names as those who made real contributions to the science of chemistry from the time of Geber to the seventeenth century: Roger Bacon, Arnoldus de Villanova, and the pseudo-Lully, in the thirteenth; Ferrarius, Bonus, and Johannes de Rupecissa, in the fourteenth; Basil Valentine, Isaac the Hollander, Trevisan, Norton, and Ripley, in the fifteenth; Paracelsus, Denys Zachaire, and Heinrich Khunrath, in the sixteenth century. The rest of the large literature on alchemy he classifies as:

(1) works of commentary; (2) the theoretical works; (3) a large class of either undeclared authorship or of writers about whom little or nothing is known; (4) a doubtful class, put forward in the name of the mastery but carrying no authentic marks; (5) testimonies to the fact of transmutation by persons of consequence who had no claim on knowledge; (6) works presenting or believed to present a spiritual side of the subject.

Until the sixteenth century, however much alchemy may have been obscured by an infusion of religious mysticism and made abortive by a fantastic nomenclature, the alchemists as a body were endeavouring to discover the properties of metals by scientific method; nor were they fraudulently exploiting their work for illicit wealth. But in that turbulent century, there developed a radical and twofold change in the aspect of alchemy, which caused its efflorescence in the next century as a social and religious menace, and its collapse in the eighteenth century. As a social evil, the transmutation of metals was exploited by individuals, and even by governments, solely as a means of securing unlimited wealth; as a mystic cult the science degenerated into a grotesque allegory of the sacraments, and of the redemption of man, by an almost blasphemous identification of Christ with the philosopher's stone.

The opinion of such an authority as A. E. Waite on the final state of alchemy is enlightening. He writes:

As regards the spiritual side it seems to have later records, the last apparent testimony coming from a hidden Temple of the Rosy Cross on the eve of the French Revolution. On its origin we may glean a little light by recurring once more to the parlous condition of Alchemy at the end of the sixteenth century, when it had become a commercial venture, so far as the literature is concerned. The pretended adepts were everywhere, above all in Germany, and their books in all the booths. No one held the key which might unlock their meaning, and none could distinguish therefore between purely fraudulent wares and those which might count as serious. The operators also were on all sides, with a thousand processes, not one of which led anywhere except to ruin. There is no question that when Jacob Boehme arose he became a great light in the eyes of occult schools, though he was cast out of Lutheran churches, and perhaps because of his expulsion. He was in particular a light unexpected—indeed after the manner of revelation—to hosts of earnest students who had sat in darkness and in the shadow of death among 'the blind work in metals,' pinning their unprofitable faith to 'the narrow name of *Chemia.*' [16]

How an eminent modern psychologist explains the tangled riddle of spiritual and material alchemy on purely scientific grounds is seen in the chapter on alchemy in Dr. Carl Jung's recent book, *The Integration of the Personality*. Dr. Jung's knowledge of alchemy, as he states, may be recent, but he made a thorough examination of the original texts, because to his surprise and satisfaction he found alchemy to be the most convincing example of the projection of the chaotic unconscious into the centralized conscious ego; he also found it to be the bridge between Greek Gnosticism and modern psychology.

Dr. Jung's thesis is: 'The conscious mind is based upon, and results from, an unconscious psyche which is prior to consciousness and continues to function together with, or despite consciousness.' As a scientific definition, this leaves much to be desired; it first supposes that those two states can be clearly and definitely distinguished, or even be defined; also, it assumes that we know the rational mind is but an evolution of animal instincts, which is a pure guess, since *homo sapiens,* as distinguished from the animal *homo,* is defined as the unique possessor of a rational mind whose attributes have never satisfactorily been deduced from animal instincts; lastly, the doctrine of evolution precludes a development from unconsciousness to consciousness.

If one is able to accept psychology in general as an objective science, and, in particular, Dr. Jung's thesis, he will be interested in two pronouncements on alchemy, which he, happily, can dismiss as a rational science and can find in it only an upsurge of the chaotic unconscious. 'There is no hope of an approach to the subject if it is considered from the standpoint of modern chemistry, and it appears hopeless when one first tries to understand it psychologically. But my patience has been richly rewarded. I am now satisfied that alchemy is the requisite mediæval exemplar of this concept of individuation.' Again: 'The heavy darkness that covers the chemical operation comes from the fact that the alchemist actually takes little interest in the purely chemical side, and uses it only to devise a new nomenclature for the psychic transformations that hold a real fascination for him.'

Against these assertions must be placed the direct statements of Figuier and Berthelot, both able chemists, that alchemy was a science in both theory and practice, and that it was the foundation of modern chemistry. Also the evidence of such a student of mysticism as A. E. Waite must be weighed. He states that from the time of Geber to the seventeenth century the alchemists sought metallic transmutation, and not spiritual redemption, however much they may have confused their scientific practice by a mystical nomenclature; and that the Stone was to them a physical object expressed in mystical imagery, and not the mystic Stone of the Church disguised in chemical terms. If words have any explicit meaning, the language of the alchemists expressed a fervent interest in the chemical operations which would transmute metals into gold.

BOYLE AS ALCHEMIST

IT is generally known that Robert Boyle was an alchemist; that he accepted, theoretically and practically, the doctrine of the transmutation of the elements; and that he was convinced he had solved the problem. But, unless his two neglected tracts on the subject, and the scattered references to it throughout his works, are collected and studied, one is apt to overlook what an obsession it was.

In February 1675/6, Boyle sent a paper to the Royal Society with the title, 'An experimental discourse of quicksilver growing hot with gold.'[1] This article excited wide interest among the members because, while the author did not claim to have accomplished the 'projection' of gold, he boldly asserted he had so purified quicksilver into an essential mercury that it approached the hermetic *prima materia,* and consequently he was in sight of solving the coveted problem of transmutation. Such a confident assertion by Boyle, whose reputation was challenged only by that of Paracelsus and Van Helmont, carried great weight.

Boyle stated in this paper that as early as 1652 (that is, it should be remembered, when he was living in Stalbridge) he had, by God's blessing, obtained a mercury from quicksilver which, when mixed with pure and pulverized gold in the palm of his hand, quickly became appreciably hot. This incalescence, as it was called, was generally regarded as a fundamental quality of the essence or soul of mercury. But he confessed that he had not attained to pure 'projection,' * since he had had to use almost equal quantities of gold and his mercury. But he emphasized its intense activity:

That, which makes this incalescence the more considerable is, that being willing to husband my mercury, a great part of which had been, as I guessed, stolen from me before I employed it, I made these trials but

---

* The alchemistic term for the use of a minute quantity of the transmuting agent which would change great quantities of metals suddenly into gold and, like a catalytic agent, could be used repeatedly, as it experienced no change.

with a drachm at a time, which scarce amounts in quantity to the bigness of half a middle-sized bean; whereas, if I could have made the experiment with a spoonful or two of quicksilver, and a due proportion of
gold, it is probable the heat would have been intense enough, not only
to burn one's hand, but perchance to crack a glass vial.*

The reasons Boyle had concealed so important a discovery for
twenty-four years were that he wished to make sure of it by repeated trials and by constantly improving his processes, and that
he feared its effect on society if it were divulged.

Thus: One of the chief reasons, that makes me backward to have the
foregoing observations communicated to the curious, is that I fear, we
may thereby procure divers queries and perhaps requests, (relating to
this mercury) which I would by all means avoid, for divers reasons, and
particularly for this, that a great weakness of that part disables me to
write with my own hand [his paralysis], and I know, you will not think
it fit I should, about such a subject, employ an amanuensis.

Like all alchemists, Boyle did not publish his method of preparing this mercury either because, as may be possible, he had secret
doubts of its success, or because he wished to enjoy the usufructs
of his discovery, or because he feared a convulsion consequent in
society. As for the third reason he, like Paracelsus, thought that what
the philosopher's stone 'may do in physic, is likely much to exceed
the political inconveniences, that may ensue, if it should prove to
be of the best kind, and fall in ill hands. The knowledge of the
opinions of the wise and skilful about this case will be requisite to
assist me to take right measures in an affair of this nature. And, till
I receive this information, I am obliged to silence.' †

Newton, also at the time an ardent alchemist, was so excited by
the publication of Boyle's 'incalescing mercury' that, for the first
and only time in his life, he ventured an enthusiastic criticism of
the work of another man. In a letter to Oldenburg he wrote:

Sir,   Cambridge, April 26, 1676.
    . . . Yesterday I, reading the two last *Philosophical Transactions,* had
the opportunity to consider Mr. Boyle's uncommon experiment about

* Boyle was pursued by ill-luck: ignorant servants threw away his important products
or they were stolen; notes and manuscripts were mislaid, destroyed, or stolen; and twice
his only reliable operator died suddenly at a crucial time.
    † It is impossible to know what this purified quicksilver was, for amalgams of gold and
mercury produce but very little heat. Perhaps, some corrosive agent was not completely removed and caused a sensation of heat to the hand.

the incalescence of gold and mercury. I believe the fingers of many will itch to be at the knowledge of the preparation of such a mercury, and for that end some will not be wanting to move for the publishing of it, by urging the good it may do in the world; but in my simple judgement the noble author, since he has thought fit to reveal himself so far, does prudently in being reserved in the rest. Not that I think any great excellence in such a mercury, either for medical or chemical operations . . . [In explanation of this opinion, he argues that the metalline particles impregnated in Boyle's mercury may not have a peculiar and subtile quality; but because, being grosser than the particles of mercury, they may give a greater shock and motion to the particles of the gold, and so heat it. If so, then the action of Boyle's prepared mercury is merely similar to the heat caused by a corrosive liquor, such as aqua fortis.] . . . If this analogy of these two kinds of liquors may be allowed, one may guess at the little use of the one by the indisposition of the other, either to medicine or vegetation. But yet because the way, by which mercury may be so impregnated, has been thought fit to be concealed by others that have known it, and therefore may possibly be an inlet to some thing more noble, not to be communicated without immense damage to the world, if there should be any verity in the Hermetic writers, therefore I question not but that the great wisdom of the noble author will sway him to high silence till he shall be resolved of what consequence the thing may be, either by his own experience, or the judgement of some other, that thoroughly understands what he speaks about, that is, of a true Hermetic philosopher, whose judgement (if there be any such) would be more to be regarded in this point than that of all the world beside to the contrary, there being other things beside the transmutation of metals, (if those great pretenders * brag not) which none but they understand. Sir, because the author seems desirous of the sense of others in this point, I have been so free as to shoot my bolt; but pray keep this letter private to yourself.

Your servant
Is. Newton.[2]

Newton's character is in contrast with that of Boyle in this letter. While Newton uses the language of the alchemists, his essentially critical nature makes him first seek an explanation in the ordinary reactions of chemical agents. Nor does he believe that Boyle has obtained valuable results but, since alchemists claim to know great secrets, they may now be induced to publish them; till then, it is

---

* It should again be pointed out that his use of the word 'pretenders' did not imply that he considered them to be imposters, as Brewster alleged. On the contrary, it was used at that time as equivalent to our professor of chemistry.

wise for Boyle to preserve a 'high silence.' And lastly, there is that characteristic and exasperating touch, so persistent in Newton's secretive character, of requesting his opinion be kept private. No one acquainted with Oldenburg's garrulous and even meddlesome disposition, and his intimacy with Boyle, will believe for a moment that he did not communicate this letter. Miss Masson states in her *Life of Boyle* that: 'Newton's "bolt" took effect, though it must have cost Boyle something to give up that little bit of research.'[3] The 'bolt' was too caustic, and too sound, not to have chilled the enthusiasm and confidence of Boyle. But it is easy to prove that, far from giving up that 'little bit of experiment,' which was in reality as great a prize in chemistry as was gravitation in physics, he cultivated it doggedly during the rest of his life.

The immediate effect of the 'bolt' was that Boyle, instead of being angry at the presumption of a young man who had thus confidently reversed the role of Mentor to him, then at the height of his reputation, must have sought an interview and asked for Newton's opinion on the corpuscularian hypothesis in general and of transmutation in particular. There is no other way to account for the extraordinary letter— extraordinary in length and in freedom from restraint—which Newton wrote to him on 28 February 1678/9.[4] In this letter, after apologizing for engaging in speculations which were mere guesswork and not science, he explains in detail the hypothesis that many of the phenomena of light, of most chemical operations including Boyle's incalescence of gold, and even of gravitation, were caused by a universal æther.

We have no knowledge of Boyle's reaction to Newton's letter, since his answer, if he made one, has not been found; but the hypothesis was so consonant with his own, that its influence can be traced in his later speculations. There is no evidence of further meetings or correspondence between the two men. Newton, during his rare visits to the Royal Society, may have met Boyle, and probably did, but when he went to live in London, Boyle had been dead for some years.

But Newton's warning was in vain: so difficult, so very difficult, it is to wean the affection of a doting father from these children of his mind. Within two years of his 'bolt' and in the same year as his letter on the æther, Boyle published in 1678 a short tract with the title, *An historical account of a degradation of gold, made by an anti-elixir: A strange chymical narrative.*[5] The work, like so many others by Boyle, is written as a philosophic dialogue and, although he published it anonymously, the use of the name Pyrophilus as the chief speaker easily identified the author. One would wish that Boyle had never published this paper, for it descends to the tricks and mystifications of the charlatan. Perhaps he himself was a bit ashamed of it; or perhaps he feared another 'bolt' from Newton.

Pyrophilus introduces the dialogue with the apology:

I cannot remove all your doubts and objections, or my own, by being able to affirm to you, that I have with my own hands made a projection, (as chemists are wont to call the sudden transmutation made by a small quantity of their admirable elixir) yet I can confirm much of what hath been argued for the possibility of such a sudden change of a metalline body, by a way, which, I presume, will surprise you; for, to make it more credible, that other metals are capable of being graduated, or exalted into gold, by way of projection, I will relate to you, that by the like way gold has been degraded, or imbased.

The company having expressed a proper surprise, Pyrophilus proceeds to tell them that a stranger, meeting him in the lodging of a virtuoso, entertained him with tales of the wonders he had met with in many foreign lands. Pyrophilus asks him whether he had met with any chemists in the eastern parts:

He answered me, that he had; and that though they were fewer, and more reserved than ours, yet he did not find them at all less skilful. And on this occasion, before he left the town to go aboard the ship he was to overtake, he in a very obliging way put into my hands, at parting, a little piece of paper, folded up, which he said contained all that he had left of a rarity he had received from an eastern virtuoso, and which he intimated would give me occasion both to remember him, and to exercise my thoughts in uncommon speculations.[6]

In the packet of paper, there was discovered about an eighth of a grain of a *darkish red powder* (note this red earth,* as it will turn up later under different circumstances, as a coveted product of Boyle's own making). Having begun with all the trappings to excite and to deceive the credulous, Pyrophilus *then* takes every precaution to have unbiased witnesses to his experiments and to use scrupulous care. Two drachms of refined gold were melted in a new crucible without the use of borax and then, with his own hands,

---

* This red earth is perhaps the oxide or sulphide of mercury.

the magic powder was introduced. Finally, he poured the well-melted gold into another crucible and he

was somewhat surprised to find, when the matter was grown cold, that though it appeared upon the balance that we had not lost anything of the weight we had put in, yet, instead of fine gold, we had a lump of metal of a dirty colour, as it were overcast with a thin coat, almost like half vitrified litharge; and somewhat to increase the wonder, we perceived, that there stuck to one side of the crucible a little globule of metal, that looked not at all yellowish, but like coarse silver.[7]

The company of course is convinced that Pyrophilus's magic elixir actually degraded pure gold into true silver; and he closes the dialogue with this cryptic and tantalizing sentence. 'As extraordinary, as I perceive most of you think the phenomena of the lately described experiment; yet I have not (because I must not do it) as yet acquainted you with the strangest effect of our admirable powder.'

Boyle was undoubtedly credulous; or, perhaps, we should say, as did Herschel, that he had an 'undistinguishing appetite.' He would readily believe in transmutation and would search for the philosopher's stone as eagerly as another—not, probably, to acquire wealth, because he had a sufficiency all his life, but for the mystery and excitement of the chase. There was for him, however, a strong, practical reason to solve the problem, dear to his heart, and that was its supposed benefit to medicine. Paracelsus had proclaimed the discovery of an alkahest, a liquid more potent than the philosopher's stone which would dissolve gold and would be of marvellous excellence as a medicine.* For that reason, Boyle had been willing to publish the recipe for his incalescing mercury, if he were advised to do so, because its blessing as an universal nostrum would outweigh any possible disturbance to society.

Besides these two works, specifically on transmutation, there are numerous references to the subject scattered throughout his writings. Like all renowned alchemists, Boyle had compounded his own wonder-working agent, which he had named a *menstruum pera-*

* This belief in the alkahest of Paracelsus was general, and Van Helmont had elevated it into an universal solvent, revealed by God to the elect only.—Nor was it questioned till Kunckel in his *Laboratorium Chymicum* killed the idea by the obvious statement that such an alkahest could not be found because it would dissolve any vessel in which it was made. He added that Paracelsus was said by some to have coined the name as an anagram from *alkali est;* others, that he derived it from *der all Geist;* by still others, from *alles ist.* 'But, I say the alkahest Is *alles Lügen heisst,* or *alles Lügen ist';* for it is all a lie.

cutum. As early as 1666, in his important treatise on *The Origin of Forms,* he gives its recipe and examples of its potency: 'Made by pouring on the rectified oil of the butter of antimony as much strong spirit of nitre, as would serve to precipitate out of it all the *bezoarticum minerale;* and then with a good smart fire distilling off all the liquor that would come over, and (if need be) cohobating it upon the antimonial powder.'[8] Then he proceeds:

Having then provided a sufficient quantity of this liquor (for I have observed that gold ordinarily requires a more copious solvent than silver) we took a quantity of the best gold we could get, and melted it with three or four times its weight of copper, which metal we choose rather than that which is more useful among refiners, silver, that there may be the less suspicion that there remained any silver with the gold after their separation: this mixture we then put into good aqua fortis or spirit of nitre, that all the copper being dissolved, the gold might be left pure and finely powdered at the bottom; this operation with aqua fortis being accounted the best way of refining gold that is yet known, and not subject like lead, to leave any silver with it, since the aqua fortis takes up that metal. And for greater security we gave the powder to an ancient chemist to boil some more of the menstruum upon it, without communicating to him our design. This highly refined gold being by a competent degree of heat brought, as is usual, to its native colour and lustre, we put to it a large proportion of the *menstruum peracutum* (to which we have sometimes found cause to add a little spirit of salt to promote the solution) wherein it dissolves slowly and quietly enough; and there remained at the bottom of the glass a pretty quantity (in show, though not in weight) of white powder that the menstruum would not touch; and, if I much misremember not, we found it as indissolvable in aqua regia too.

Then Boyle fluxed the powder, and obtained a white metal, which he confirmed, to his satisfaction, to be true silver.* He did repeat the experiment once, and again obtained the white powder, which he washed and laid on a white paper to dry: 'Being suddenly called out of my chamber, an ignorant maid, that in the meantime came to dress it up, unluckily swept this paper, as a foul one, into the

---

* In modern terms, Boyle's menstruum was impure aqua regia with an excess of nitric acid, since to increase its action on gold he often added hydrochloric acid. The reaction: Butter of antimony is its chloride, and adding to it nitric acid, the basic salts of antimony, and probably some of its acids, will be precipitated, i.e. the *bezoarticum minerale;* the liquor distilled off is a mixture of nitric and hydrochloric acids. While Boyle was acquainted with aqua regia he would not know that it could be obtained in this manner. The white powder was probably the chloride of the silver originally alloyed with the gold or copper.

fire; which discouragement, together with a multiplicity of occasions, have made me suspend the pursuit of this experiment till another opportunity.'

This is an apparently straightforward account of a scientific experiment, in which the agents and processes are detailed, and the error lay only in the false identification of the residual white powder as being silver; or, if it was silver, and Boyle seems to have been content with very superficial tests, then it must have been originally present as an alloy of the gold or copper. No one can believe that he permitted the accident of an ignorant servant (such accidents are astonishingly frequent in the work of the alchemists) to stop further work with his anti-elixir. And the fact that he continued to work on the degradation of gold to silver, and to believe that he had achieved the ambition of the ages, is proved by his paper on *The Degradation of Gold* mentioned above, published twelve years later.

Also Boyle, as a consequence of being a corpuscularian, would regard transmutation as a fundamental principle of nature. He had achieved a great victory in replacing the scholastic doctrine of substantial forms, as it was superficially understood in the seventeenth century, by a mechanistic cause. His corpuscular hypothesis, like all its variants from the atom of Democritus to the electron of today, is simple in statement and yet exasperating in results. All the different qualities of bodies are assumed to be merely the effect of different geometric patterns of aggregations of identical corpuscles; and every chemical analysis, or synthesis, is thus only a mechanical rearrangement of one pattern into another. If so, was it to be doubted that a chemist, with his planning mind and manipulative skill, could discover a chain of actions by which he would rearrange the pattern which was, for example, lead, into the pattern which is gold?

Boyle was even receptive to the idea that special patterns of corpuscles were also the stuff of life. In this belief, he anticipated by two centuries Herbert Spencer, who imagined the beginning of life on the earth as merely a chance aggregating of atoms into an unusually complicated pattern, and all the subsequent varieties of life as shifts in their geometric arrangement. The only difference was that Boyle believed the cause of such variations to be the inscrutable hand and mind of God; and Spencer, that it was an inexorable law of mechanics, instituted we know not how, but apparently only as a result of chance.

Thus Boyle, to substantiate his hypothesis, was eager to collect evidences of transmutation of all sorts by personal experimentation and observation, and from reports of others. It will suffice to give an account of his experimental proof of water changing into an earth, and two or three reports of transformations of animals and plants, taken from his monograph on *The Origin of Forms and Qualities*.[9]

Boyle was first led to investigate (or indagate, as he would say) the artificial transmutation of water into earth,[10] after he had been consulted 'by an ancient chymist but not at all a philosopher' who, having evaporated a great quantity of putrefied rain-water, obtained from it much less what he looked for, but a great deal of a whitish excrementitious matter deposited in the vessel. Boyle, being interested, placed a quantity of distilled rain-water in a new and clean glass vessel and redistilling it, found, to his joy and surprise, 'the bottom of the glass covered over with a white (but not so very white) substance, which being scraped off with a knife, appeared to be a fine earth, in which I perceived no manifest taste, and which, in a word, by several qualities seemed to be earth.'

By chance, Boyle mentioned this experiment to a very ingenious person well versed in chemical matters, and was pleased to learn that he, too, had redistilled rain-water in clean glass vessels, 'and near two hundred times, without finding that his liquor grew weary of affording him the white earth.' This confirmation convinced them of a true transmutation. And was this opinion not justified, granting their postulate that glass was insoluble in water, and that they had no test for, or knowledge of, silica?

So great was the influence of Boyle, and so authoritative his treatise *On the Origin of Forms,* that the transmutation of water into earth by repeated distillation was undisputed for a century. It was not till Lavoisier established the balance to be the ultimate test of the conservation of mass in chemical reactions that the correct answer to this problem was given. In 1770, he demonstrated that the weight of a sealed glass vessel and the water it contained remained the same however long the water was boiled. By long protracted boiling he obtained a considerable amount of the 'white earth,' and then he proved by careful weighing that its weight was equal, within the limits of error, to the weight lost by the vessel;

while the weight of the water remained constant. From this he inferred that the earth was matter dissolved from the vessel, and not transmuted water.

It should be noted that disproof of such transmutations must rest on the absolute agreement of repeated weighings. And the paradox is unavoidable; that the more delicate the balance, and the more carefully the observations are made, the greater will always be the discrepancies between successive weighings of the same object. Lavoisier's experiment is a striking illustration of the faith which a scientist must repose in fundamental postulates and dogmas—a faith so unquestioning that he habitually changes his observations to conform to it.

The following illustrations of transmutation were cited by Boyle as collected by him from strange tales of wonderful animals and plants in foreign lands, the farther from home, the better. And, in those days of imagination, he accumulated a rich harvest.

For coral, to pass by all other plants of that kind that may be mentioned to the same purpose, whilst it grows in the bottom of the sea, is a real plant, and several times (which suffices for my present scope) hath been there found by an acquaintance of mine, as well as by other enquirers, soft and tender like any other plant: nay, I elsewhere bring very good and recent authority to prove that it is oftentimes found very succulent, and does propagate its species as well as other shrubs; and yet coral being gathered and removed into the air, by the recess of its soul, no new lapidific form being so much as pretended to, turns into a concretion, that is by many eminent writers, and others, reckoned among lapideous ones.[11]

Of transmutation of animals into stone, Boyle quotes this example from an eyewitness of authority: 'I saw in a small fresh-water and shallow lake of the island Hainan (which belongs to China) crabs or craw-fishes, which, as soon as they were drawn out of the water, did in a moment lose both life and motion, and became petrified, though nothing appeared to be changed either in the external or internal figure of their bodies.'[12]

Two examples of transmutations between animals and plants may also be cited: 'The industrious Piso, in his excellent history of Brazil vouches a multitude of witnesses (not having an opportunity to be one himself) for the ordinary transformation of a sort of animals (not much unlike grasshoppers) into vegetables, at a certain season of the year.' And the following from an eyewitness, Sir James Lancaster, in his own words, is even more pertinent:

Here (says he, speaking of the coast of Sombrero) we found upon the sand by the sea side a small twig growing up to a young tree; and offering to pluck up the same, it shrunk down into the ground, and sinketh unless you hold very hard. And being plucked up, a great worm is the root of it: and look how the tree groweth in greatness, the worm diminisheth. Now as soon as the worm is wholly turned into the tree, it rooteth in the ground, and so groweth to be great. This transformation was one of the greatest wonders I saw in all my travels. This tree being plucked up a little, the leaves stripped off, and the peel, by that time it was dry, turned into a hard stone, much like white coral. So that this worm was twice transformed into different natures: of these we gathered and brought home many.[13]

This last example of transmutation so impressed Boyle that he transmitted it to the Royal Society with the request it be investigated. They, in turn, invited the English Agent in Sumatra to report on its truth. The Agent, after some delay, wrote that he had not found any one who had himself seen the shrub, but he had met several who knew persons that had seen it: and there the investigation seems to have ended.

There is no doubt that Boyle, after he left Oxford for London, continued to work on his 'mercury' and his 'red earth' in connexion with the multiplying of gold and with ever increasing hope of success. Besides his lodgings and his personal laboratory in Pall Mall, he also maintained another place in the city, to which he occasionally retired when distracted by visitors; and he owned and operated a large commercial laboratory. The prints of this laboratory, which have fortunately been preserved, show that it was well equipped with apparatus and workmen. Boyle seems to have conducted the business as a company, manufacturing and selling the commercial products in use, and enjoying a monopoly in making phosphorus; here, also, were carried on his attempts to multiply gold.

Boyle became so confident of success in transmutation that he petitioned Parliament, and succeeded in having the act of Henry IV against 'multipliers of gold' repealed in 1689. The clause of the act repealed was: 'That none from thenceforth should use to multiply gold or silver, or use the craft of multiplication; and if any the same do, they should now incur the pain of felony.' The new act provided that all gold and silver extracted by melting and refining of metals and *otherwise improving of them and their ores* shall be used only for increasing money and be deposited at the royal mint in the Tower of London. It finally provided that no mine of copper, tin, iron, or lead, shall be reputed to be a royal mine, even though gold ore be extracted from it.[14]

Some further knowledge of Boyle as a 'multiplier' is obtained, in an unexpected way, from correspondence between John Locke and Newton.* After Boyle's death, his manuscripts and notes on chemistry were entrusted to Locke, who was, himself, an able chemist. He evidently found amongst them Boyle's recipes for his 'mercury' and his 'red earth.' Doubtful of their meaning or of their value, he wrote to Newton for advice. A month after Boyle's death, Newton replied: "I understand Mr. Boyle communicated his process about the red earth and mercury to you as well as to me, and before his death, procured some of that earth for his friends.' And again the following month: 'Mr. Pawling told me, you had writ for some of Mr. Boyle's red earth, and by that I knew you had the recipe.'

What Boyle wished Locke to do with the recipe is not known; but Locke, who was then editing Boyle's *General History of the Air,* evidently began to work on the recipe, for Newton wrote to him a long letter of advice. This extraordinary account of the whole queer proceedings is quoted at large.

August 2d, 1692.

Sir,

I beg your pardon that I sent not your papers last week; the carrier went out a quarter of an hour sooner than I was aware of. I am glad you have all three parts of the recipe entire; but before you go to work about it, I desire you would consider these things, for it may perhaps save you time and expense. This recipe I take to be the thing for the sake of which Mr. Boyle procured the repeal of the Act of Parliament against Multipliers, and therefore he had it then in his hands. In the margin of the recipe was noted, that the mercury of the first work would grow hot with gold, and thence I gather that this recipe was the foundation of what he published many years ago, about such mercuries

* Lord King's *Life of John Locke,* Vol. 1, pp. 388-423. Their correspondence began in 1688, and the first letter of Newton's is a proof, different and simpler than the one in the *Principia,* that the planets, because of gravity towards the sun, may move in ellipses. Most of the letters are on Biblical interpretation or personal matters; only three refer to Boyle. Although we have only the letters by Newton, it is not difficult to guess Locke's questions.

as would grow hot with gold, and therefore was then known to him, that is, sixteen or twenty years ago, at least; and yet, in all this time, I cannot find that he has either tried it himself, or got it tried with success by any body else: for, when I spoke doubtingly about it, he confessed that he had not seen it tried; but added, that a certain gentleman was now about it, and it succeeded very well so far as he had gone, and that all signs [of transmutation] appeared, so that I needed not doubt of it. This satisfied me that mercury, by this recipe, may be brought to change its colours and properties, but not that gold may be multiplied thereby; and I doubt it the more, because I heard some years ago of a company, who were upon this work in London, and after Mr. Boyle had communicated his recipe to me, so that I knew it was the same with theirs. I enquired after them, and learnt that two of them were since forced to other means of living; and a third, who was the chief artist, was still at work, but was run so far into debt that he had much ado to live; and by these circumstances, I understood that these gentlemen could not make the thing succeed. When I told Mr. Boyle of these gentlemen, he acknowledged that the recipe was gone about among several chymists, and therefore I intend to stay till I hear that it succeeds with some of them.

But, besides, if I would try this recipe, I am satisfied that I could not, for Mr. Boyle has reserved a part of it from my knowledge. I know more of it than he has told me; and by that, and an expression or two which dropped from him, I know that what he has told me is imperfect and useless without knowing more than I do: and, therefore, I intend only to try whether I know enough to make a mercury which will grow hot with gold, if perhaps I shall try that . . . In dissuading you from too hasty a trial of this recipe, I have forborne to say any thing against multiplication in general, because you seem persuaded of it; though there is one argument against it, which I could never find an answer to, and which, if you will let me have your opinion about it, I will send you in my next.

[Is. Newton.] [15]

What became of this red earth and the recipe, so cherished by Boyle that he had laboured on them for almost forty years, we shall probably never know and really care little; but we would give much to discover Newton's unanswerable argument.

Boyle's motives for surrounding his work with secrecy were probably mixed. He might hesitate to disturb society by the creation of unlimited wealth, even though he might balance that danger by the benefit of a universal panacea. But he must have been disturbed by secret doubts of his success which caused him to consult Newton and give him a sample of his red earth and its recipe. And yet, jealous of the result, he withheld an essential part.

There were persistent complaints by Boyle of plagiarism of his writings, of misfortunes to his operations, and especially of the loss and theft of his manuscripts. One would expect plagiarism of a popular writer, as it was a common practice of the age; also accidents and misfortunes are frequent in chemistry; but an author's notes and manuscripts are not usually of enough value to excite temptation.

Is it not possible, and even probable, that rumours were widely spread of Boyle's possession of a recipe which would turn base metals into gold? Such a prize would certainly tempt the cupidity of assistants and visitors, who might hope to find it included amongst manuscripts they could pilfer. Some such explanation seems necessary to account for an extraordinary advertisement about his loss of manuscript, addressed to J.W. and published in two pages in folio. As this advertisement appeared in 1688, the year before he succeeded in having the Act against Multipliers repealed, the coincidence is very striking. The portion pertinent to this guess is as follows:

In the month of May 1688, I thought myself obliged to give notice to the public, that I had, partly by some men's fraud, and partly by mischance, lost so many of my essays and other tracts, and had so many of my remaining papers endamaged by corrosive liquors, that the curious were not thenceforth to expect from me any thing but imperfect and mutilated. And yet since that time all my care and circumspection has not hindered me from losing six centuries of matters of fact in one parcel, besides so many papers of lesser bulk, that I am reduced to remind the curious of my former advertisement; not for any pleasure I take in complaining, or troubling others with my misfortunes, but to render a reason of the course I am by these misadventures driven to, though otherwise I should not think it eligible. This is to secure the remaining part of my writings, especially those that contain most matters of fact, by sending them maimed and unfinished, as they come to hand, to the press.

Being wont, when I first turned writer, to set down, as others use to do, my thoughts and observations on papers bound up into books, I was quite discouraged from that practise, by the losses I made at several times of manuscripts, which I strongly suspected to have been surreptitiously conveyed away by some, that though they expected to find valuabler things than I supposed they met with, would not probably have stolen away those papers, if their bulk had not been a main temptation to the theft.

Wherefore I afterwards resolved to write in single sheets, and other loose papers, that the ignorance of the coherence might keep men from thinking them worth stealing. And though I could not, by so doing, prevent the losing sometimes a paper or two by chance, or other men's fraud, yet I thought such inconveniences (which I could sometimes easily repair out of my memory) much inferior to those of losing an entire discourse, or a whole discourse at a time . . .[16]

The remainder of the advertisement deals with the widely prevalent vice of plagiarism, and methods of prevention. However one regards it, the incident discloses an amazing state of affairs, and an equally amazing remedy. One would suppose some simpler method of safeguarding Boyle's papers could have been devised if, as is suggested, he knew that they included such tempting materials.

Boyle, as a chemist, seems to have been an object of constant wonder; to the virtuosi, because he eschewed the purposely obscure, pedantic, and bombastic style of the alchemists; to the general public, because he chose to adopt the simple life of a scientist rather than to enjoy the social rewards of wealth and high position. He also thought, as the following letter to a friend indicates, that he should justify his motives for cultivating science as a profession, and for restricting himself to luciferous, rather than lucriferous experiments—his equivalent for our snobbish distinction between pure and applied science. He would also prove that his avoidance of difficult and abstruse problems was from choice, and not because he could not match the virtuosi with his knowledge and skill of the *arcana majora*.*

[Circ. 1689.]

Sir,

I confess you are not the only person among my friends, to whom it hath seemed somewhat strange, that I, who have spent many of my thoughts, some of my money, and, what I value far more, of my time too, upon chemistry, as well as divers other parts of learning, have not been taken notice of to have found any *particulars,* as chemists speak, or other lucriferous experiments upon metals and minerals, nor have pretended to be possessor of those difficult and compounded experiments, that are magnified by chemists as excellent Hermetic Arcana.

* *Works,* Vol. 1, p. cxxx. This collection of difficult chemical processes was never published. Birch states it was not to be found amongst his manuscripts when he published his first edition of Boyle's Works in 1744.

But, Sir, since I find you in the list of those that have made the newly-mentioned reflection, I am content to give you such a summary account of my comportment, as may at least lessen your wonder at it. I must inform you then, that when, among other studies, I applied myself to the cultivating of natural philosophy, I soon perceived, that some insight into chemical operations was, though not absolutely necessary, yet highly conducive to the true knowledge of nature, and especially to the indagation of several of her most abstruse mysteries. On this score I was induced to make a nearer inspection into chemistry than virtuosi are wont to think it worth while to do; and I did not repent me of my labour. But as I cultivated chemistry, not so much for itself, as for the sake of natural philosophy, and in order to it, so most of the experiments I devised and pursued, were generally such as tended not to multiply processes, or gain the reputation of having store of difficult and elaborate ones; but to serve for foundations, and other useful materials for an experimental history of nature, on which a solid theory may in process of time be superstructed. For this purpose I judged, that plain and easy experiments, and as simple, or as little compounded as may be, would, *caeteris paribus,* be the fittest, as being the most easy to be tried (and, if need be, repeated) and to be judged of, both in relation to their causes, and to their effects. And for these reasons, though I had by me a not inconsiderable number of more compounded and elaborate processes, some of which I had made, and others I received as great secrets from noted artists; I purposely forbore to mention any number of them in my writings about physics, being desirous rather to increase knowledge, than make any ostentation of any that I thought would puzzle most readers more than it would instruct them.

This, Sir, I hope, will appear to you a fair account of your not finding my physical discourses larded with long and intricate processes, some of which may, I willingly grant, produce notable effects, and for that reason are valuable, but are less fit than far more simple ones to discover the causes of things, which yet is the chief scope of a naturalist, as such. And to those that think it strange, that among my other experiments about metals and minerals, I have not produced those gainful ones, that chemists call *particulars,* it may, I hope, suffice to represent, that being a bachelor, and through God's bounty furnished with a competent estate for a younger brother, and freed from any ambition to leave my heirs rich, I had no need to pursue lucriferous experiments, to which I so much preferred luciferous ones, that I had a kind of ambition (which I now perceive to have been a vanity) of being able to say, that I cultivated chemistry with a disinterested mind, neither seeking nor scarce caring for any other advantages by it, than those of the improvement of my own knowledge of nature, the gratifying the curious and industrious, and the acquist of some useful helps to make good and uncommon medicines.

If I may be allowed to judge of courses by the success, the entertainment, that the public has been pleased to give my endeavours to serve it, will not make me repent of the way I have made choice of to do it in. But, however, since I find myself now grown old, I think it time to comply with my former intentions to leave a kind of Hermetic legacy to the studious disciples of that art, and to deliver candidly, in the annexed paper, some processes chemical and medicinal, that are less simple and plain than those barely luciferous ones I have been wont to affect, and of a more difficult and elaborate kind than those I have hitherto published, and more of kin to the noblest Hermetic secrets, or, as Helmont styles them, *Arcana majora*. Some of these I have made and tried; others I have (though not without much difficulty) obtained, by exchange or otherwise, from those that affirm they knew them to be real, and were themselves competent judges, as being some of them disciples of true adepts, or otherwise admitted to their acquaintance and conversation. Most of these processes are clearly enough delivered; and of the rest there is plainly set down, without deceitful terms, as much as may serve to make what is literally taught to be of great utility, though the full and complete uses are not mentioned, partly because, in spite of my philanthropy, I was engaged to secrecy, as to some of these uses, and partly because I must ingenuously confess it, I am not yet, or perhaps ever shall be acquainted with them myself. The knowledge I have of your great affection for the public good, and your particular kindness for me, invites me, among the many virtuosi, in whose friendship I am happy, to intrust the following papers in your hands, earnestly desiring you to impart them to the public faithfully, and without envy, *verbatim,* in my own expressions, as a monument of my good affections to mankind, as well in my chemical capacity, as in the others, wherein I have been solicitous to do it service. I am, with sincere respect,

    Sir,

        Your most faithful and most humble servant,

                                    Robert Boyle.

With this review of Boyle's interest in alchemy and his explanation of his purpose in cultivating science, we are prepared to discuss his transition from an alchemist to a chemist.

XII

BOYLE AS THE SCEPTICAL SCIENTIST

IT is difficult for us to appreciate the commanding influence
which Boyle exerted on the thought of his day; an influence
only little short of that of the 'incomparable Newton.' There
is no doubt that, more truly than any other man, he was regarded
as the creator of modern chemistry and of science as a profession,
the first fruits of the New Learning; yet there are no great and
fundamental achievements attached to his name, if we make the
possible exception of the discovery that the air was a body and had
weight; and even this was but imperfectly developed, for his law of
pressure was inaccurately determined, the effect of temperature was
neglected, and its chemical properties were not investigated.

To account for the reputation of Boyle during his lifetime, we
must look rather to the indirect benefits which he contributed by
expounding the new scientific discipline and philosophy clearly and
simply, by exhibiting experiments in public which excited widespread interest, by insisting on the useful applications of science to
industry and the arts, and by beginning the accumulation of data
and recipes which has gradually developed into those useful ad-
juncts, specialized journals and reference tables. To effect the profound change from scholastic to modern natural philosophy, those
accomplishments were as essential as were the isolated discoveries
of a Galileo or of a Newton; for such will remain fruitless unless
a public is educated to receive and appreciate their value, as is so
well illustrated by the genius of a da Vinci, which ripened out of
season.

With those necessary requirements for guiding an interested and
discriminating public, Boyle was eminently gifted; and that such
was his reputation can be best verified by the references to him by
poets, who are accurate mirrors of social trends and philosophy.
Thus, we find that Davenant and Cowley, himself the author of a
plan for the Royal Society, ranked him among the first men of his

age in copiousness of conversation and wit. Thomson in the *Seasons* applauds him:

> Why need I name thy Boyle whose pious search
> Amid the dark recesses of His works
> The great Creator sought?

And Cowper terms him:

> Sagacious reader of the works of God,
> And in His Word sagacious.

It was inevitable that the reputation of Boyle, which had been exaggerated, would suffer an eclipse when later discoveries and inventions were made with an ever increasing rapidity, sweeping his own contributions into the limbo of forgotten things. The history of science has as yet, for the most part, confined itself to a chronicle of the outstanding and lasting discoveries and applications of natural phenomena, and to the tabulation of the data of observation. It has given correspondingly little attention to the mutual influences of the sciences and the humanities on each other, or to those pioneers whose new philosophy of ideas directed the future course of science. And, it is just in these two respects that the seventeenth century was pre-eminent; for it expressed clearly and emphatically the principles of experimentation, even if it did not originate the distinction between an organized laboratory and the indiscriminate observations of individuals; it also developed an empiric philosophy which, at first limited to the phenomena of the realm of material bodies, has spread far beyond that limit until it now dominates the fields of life and of the spirit. Since it was Boyle's connexion with this philosophy which makes him such an important figure, emphasis in the following critique of his scientific work will be given to his ideas rather than to his experimental industry.

The examination of Boyle's scientific work and influence is made extremely difficult because of its diversity: questions of religion, of philosophy, of the practical and theoretical relations of all the sciences are so interwoven as to require his biographer to follow his example in being conversant with the whole trend of the age. He, even more clearly than his contemporaries, realized that science is not an isolated discipline which can be pursued without profoundly affecting the whole welfare of society. The outstanding advocate of scientific research, he repeatedly emphasized the truth that the search for character was more important than the attainment of knowledge of, and power over, natural phenomena; so that natural philosophy, as he defined it, should be, if not the handmaid of moral philosophy, at best a lady of lower degree of nobility. With anxious care, he defended the new mechanistic philosophy as being, when rightly understood and applied, not only not subversive, but in fact a support of the essentials of the Christian religion; he would have repudiated with scorn the prevalent attitude of scientists of today that, since they are disinterested seekers after the truth, they are in no way responsible for the results which the publication not only of their observations and laws, but also of their guesses and hypotheses, may have. If he could have foreseen the fatal effect on religion which the mechanistic philosophy has had by enlarging it to include non-material phenomena, he would have deplored its application to such phenomena as error.

Even when the examination, as in the present chapter, is confined to Boyle's specifically scientific work, the critic is puzzled by the problem of determining exactly how much was his personal contribution. So catholic was the range of his science, so astonishing was the mass of observations and experiments, of reports collected from written and oral sources, of suggestions for further work, and of arguments for and against the mechanistic philosophy which were published over his name, that he should be classed as an institution rather than as an individual worker. Not even a robust man, undisturbed by other interests, could have accomplished such a colossal work; much less he, afflicted by weak eye-sight, early paralysis, and a multitude of ills; distracted by the obligations of a large fortune and a high social position; and frequently on the move because of troubled times and of many visits to relatives and friends. And we have frequent confirmation of the fact that he employed many assistants, experimenters, secretaries, and collectors; that he maintained well-equipped laboratories and had devoted proof-readers and editors for his publications.

The impression made on the casual reader of Boyle's scientific work is that he was led by his insatiable curiosity to try every experiment which came to his mind and to make a memorandum of everything he read or heard, and then to publish it all indiscriminately. But verbose as Boyle's works may be, a comparison with earlier treatises shows he was one of the first scientists to recognize that the advancement of science depends on a discriminating accumulation of the data of observation, and that the statement of such scientific knowledge should be expressed in a clear and simple style.

He almost always referred to his treatises as histories, for he was convinced that the prevalent habit of explaining phenomena by hypotheses led only to confusion and error, unless they were generalizations made from an adequate body of previously known facts; and, in spite of centuries of labour, there were no such sufficient data. Yet, although Boyle modestly called himself a recorder of science, there is no subject he discussed, and he touched on all, which he did not enrich with significant discoveries. If his experimental work had been critically excerpted and tabulated to separate the permanent from the temporary, as is the custom in modern times, he would be found to rank as one of the eminent chemists of all time. Also, he deserves great credit because there seems to be little doubt that Newton and Locke built their philosophy of mechanistic empiricism on the foundation of his two guiding principles, that the ultimate element of body is the imperceptible corpuscle, and that experimental data are the criteria with which laws of phenomena and hypotheses of causes must conform. There is abundant evidence, also, that he had perfected the transition from mediæval to modern science.

During a period of thirteen years, from 1660 to 1673, most of Boyle's significant scientific work was published. Before then, he was the apprentice; and after that period, while he was living in London and afflicted with paralysis, his numerous publications were amplifications of his earlier work in religion and science, gleanings from his notebooks, or delayed manuscripts.

Criticism of natural philosophy had arisen in the sixteenth century as the result largely of the work of Copernicus, Kepler, and Galileo. But it was Boyle who first conceived the idea of devising and executing an elaborate series of experiments to prove that the four Aristotelian elements of the Schoolmen, the mercuric *prima materia* of the Alchemists, and the three principles of the Renaissance Chemists, or Spagyrists, as they had been named by Paracelsus, had merely a verbal agreement with the substances whose names they bore; and that even as symbolic essences, they were inadequate to account for the variety of observed phenomena. As a substitute, supported or at least not contradicted by his experiments, he advocated a return to a corpuscularian hypothesis. As to the success of his effort there is no gainsaying, for by the end of the century the earlier hypotheses had passed into oblivion and his corpuscularian hypothesis was firmly established.

It is not definitely known when Boyle was converted to the atomic and mechanistic philosophy of the Epicureans; nor when he conceived the original and critical plan of ending the interminable verbal controversy of the Schools by submitting the rival hypotheses to the test of experimental evidence, as Galileo with the telescope had tested the Copernican and Ptolemaic cosmic systems. He stated in the Preface to his *Style of the Scriptures* that he was a corpuscularian in 1661;[1] but since he wrote the book some ten years previously, there remains the question, when did he write the Preface? Evidence will be given, even though it be more or less indirect, that he had been converted to that hypothesis while he was living in Stalbridge, and that he removed to Oxford as the best place in which to test it experimentally.

The opinion which is often held, that Boyle first became interested in philosophy after he settled in Oxford, rests on his statement that he had deliberately refrained from reading philosophy because he was interested only in experimentation; and that it was not until 1657/8, or three years after he went to Oxford, that he reluctantly put himself to read the *Novum Organum* of Bacon, the *Syntagma Epicuri Philosophiae* of Gassendi, and the *Principia Philosophiae* of Descartes; he found in those authors, 'less a complete body of physiology, than general principles to aid man to explain the phenomena of nature.'* And to this apparently clear statement must be added Anthony à Wood's note that Sthael taught him the Cartesian philosophy. But, such statements by Boyle are capable of a different interpretation: because of his modesty, he habitually understated his accomplishments and they should rather be interpreted to mean that he then first made a *systematic study* of those authors.

This is not the only case where Boyle's modesty has deceived his critics. In an otherwise very instructive essay on Boyle,[2] Professor Wiener not only repeats the opinion that Boyle 'never studied Bacon's works until he was thirty,' forgetting, apparently, that he had been an ardent member of the Invisible College of Baconians since the age of seventeen; but he also makes the astonishing accusation:

* *Works*, Vol. 1, p. 306. Physiology was the term used for all physical phenomena.

'All the evidence of Boyle's own writings indicates that he had no true appreciation of Scholasticism; first, because *he had not read their Latin writings;* and, secondly, because he identified their views with those held by the shallow self-styled Aristotelians around him . . . In the first place, *he expressly declares that he had forgotten even while young most of his early Latin instruction.*' Ergo Boyle could not understand Scholasticism, because he knew little Latin, and much less Greek!

The question now is not whether Boyle misunderstood Scholasticism, but, whether he could not understand it because he did not read Latin. In support of his opinion, the author refers to Boyle's *Autobiography* * where it is stated: 'He forgot much of that Latin he had got' while at Eton. On the same page, however, Boyle relates that at Stalbridge, under the tutelage of Mr. Douch, he renewed his acquaintance with Latin so thoroughly 'he could readily enough express himself in prose, and began to be no dull proficient in the poetic strain.' The reader will recall his conviction of the necessity of knowing the classic and oriental tongues, and Bishop Burnet's statement that he could quote practically all the New Testament in Greek, and that he had read the Church Fathers and History copiously. But, really, there is no need to cite evidence that Boyle, who was esteemed one of the most learned men of his day, could read Latin fluently and probably speak it, because the language was the common vehicle for both science and theology. He emphasized his acquisition of the Oriental languages because that was rare; he mentioned Greek, because that was not generally cultivated; but it would not occur to him to mention Latin, because his knowledge of that language would be taken for granted.

As another instance of misinterpretation of Boyle's work, I confess that I, also, was for a time deceived by some of Boyle's statements, by some of his critics, and by the diversity and apparent lack of integration in his writings, into thinking that he lacked a definite and unified purpose and had accomplished no permanent results to justify his inclusion amongst the very few creators and pioneers of science. It was only after Boyle's scientific work had been re-read and pondered over as a whole in preparation for this chapter, that I altered my opinion.

When did Boyle acquire his natural philosophy? His letters, from

* *Works,* Vol. 1, p. xviii. Boyle at the time was about fourteen years old.

the time he first reached London till he went to Oxford, are frequent in their reference to the delight he found in his intimacy with the members of the Invisible College, which was founded and continued for the sole purpose of advancing the Baconian philosophy. He refers to their conversations as going far beyond the philosophy taught in the Universities and as embracing all the new ideas which had created the Renaissance. There can be no doubt, on the one hand, that he took part in the discussions by the best scholars of England about scholasticism, alchemy, and the chemistry of the Spagyrists; and on the other hand, that there would be even more eager talk of the new physics and astronomy of Copernicus, Kepler, and Galileo; the new magnetism of Gilbert, the new physiology of Harvey; the endeavour of Bacon and Descartes to find a new philosophy fitted to the new life; and lastly, the revival of the atomic theory of Democritus and Epicurus by Gassendi.

We, today, have become so dependent upon the written word for knowledge, that we make reading and learning almost synonymous. Such was not the case in the seventeenth century. There were few libraries—even the Bodleian was an infant; books were comparatively scarce and expensive, and very few people had large collections. The coffee-houses were the common centres for the exchange of news and ideas. In them groups of men met, assorted according to their tastes, and passed a large part of the day in conversation. The early meetings of the Royal Society were often held in a tavern; in another coffee-house occurred the famous discussion of Wren, Halley, and Hooke on the problem of gravitation, which was to lead to the *Principia*.

This opinion, at least, solves many otherwise puzzling questions in Boyle's life. During his early years at Stalbridge he was equally interested in theology, literature, and chemistry. By nature, he was inquisitive and fascinated with observing and experimenting; though he was encouraged by the Invisible College to choose natural philosophy as a vocation, he would be advised against being a practical chemist. That subject was not regarded as a science, but as an art fit to be followed by a jeweller or druggist. It was an old subject, whose philosophy had become inextricably infused with magic, which was beginning to be ridiculed, and whose practice had garnered a chaos of recipes of little intelligibility or usefulness. Neither could it be allied to geometry or algebra, under whose guidance physics and astronomy were making such noteworthy advances.

But Boyle, like his father, was obstinate and independent, and he continued his chemical experiments as a gentleman amateur, free from the necessity of seeking a livelihood from them. He had listened to the arguments for and against the various causal hypotheses of natural phenomena, which had been discussed for centuries and with no apparent conclusion. May we not suppose that the idea came to him to accept literally what the Baconian philosophers claimed to be the scientific method, and for the first time to subject hypothesis to the test of agreement with experimental data rather than to anyone's *ipse dixit?*

Unless Boyle, a rather apprehensive valetudinarian, had determined on some such ambitious plan, it is difficult to understand why he forsook the comforts of his Stalbridge manor and the easy pleasures of a wealthy country squire for the restricted accommodations of an Oxford lodging house for fourteen years. But, if he had made such a decision, Oxford was the place best suited to the purpose, for it had become the flourishing centre of the new philosophy, and there he would find advice and sympathy. It would also explain why he, so prolific a writer afterwards, served so long an apprenticeship as six years without publishing anything. He would require time to assemble a large staff of assistants and to equip laboratories, which Anthony à Wood tells us he did on a lavish scale. He would also need to study systematically the various philosophies; to prepare himself to be a skilful experimenter; and to provide himself with an impressive accumulation of experimental data.

And just such an apprenticeship Boyle served from 1654 to 1660, and then during the next thirteen years he published in quick succession a series of monographs in which he compared critically the classical, the mediæval, and the renaissance hypotheses of the nature and activities of bodies; and—what was original and profoundly important—he subjected their claims to the test of their agreement with the evidence given by an extraordinary number of pertinent experiments.

Although the first monograph [3] Boyle published when his apprenticeship was finished does not form an integral part of his specific plan, it is important in itself and it has an indirect bearing on his subsequent work. In the first place, he adopted an original form of scientific exposition; instead of the customary long and obscure narrations, he merely described his apparatus, the new air-pump, and then followed with the results of forty-three experiments, arranged in sequence according to topic and expressed as simply and clearly as he could. In the second place, he proved, by the mere force of experimental evidence, that the air had weight which could be measured on a pair of scales against a lump of iron or lead; and that it had also an expansive force which resisted pressure. As a result, his conclusions were universally accepted, disregarding the objections of Linus and Hobbes, and he was immediately proclaimed as the highest authority in science—the honourable heir of Galileo.

Boyle had made a devastating assault on the stronghold of the mysticism of Scholasticism by proving that air, or gas as we now term it, was only one of the three distinctive states of bodies. From classical times, air was regarded as an essential element and, except for fire, it was the most active and most mysterious in the economy of nature. As breath, it was symbolic, and hardly distinguishable from life; and as spirit, from the soul, and even from the Trinity. Endowed with the will to levitate and to penetrate into the most minute of openings, it was the most effective agent to prevent a vacuum. And to us, it is difficult to appreciate the horror of a vacuum which obsessed the mediæval mind. To prevent such a catastrophe all nature would come to the rescue, or as Boyle puts it:

'These experiments may teach us, what to judge of the vulgar axiom received for so many ages as an undoubted truth in the Peripatetic schools, that nature abhors and flieth a vacuum, and that to such a degree, that no human power (to go no higher) is able to make one in the universe; wherein heaven and earth would change places, and all its other bodies rather act contrary to their own nature, than suffer it.'[4] Then, he cautiously explains that if a vacuum were to mean a space absolutely devoid of any substance, there may be none; but the Plenists mean by *horror vacui* that, for example, mercury or water contrary to its nature rises in a barometer tube and a subtile air penetrates through glass and the fluid into the space above the column to prevent the catastrophe of a vacuum.

By proving experimentally that the barometric column was pushed upwards and maintained solely by the weight of the outside air, Boyle had forced the issue with the Aristotelian schools. And the publication of his experiments dates the beginning of an ever-increasing reliance on mechanical, rather than on animistic, causes as truly as the publication of the *De revolutionibus* by Copernicus began the new physics.

In addition to his experiments on the weight and expansion of air, Boyle also was equally interested in the effects of air on combustion and respiration. In this, and in his subesquent papers, for the subject fascinated him all his life, he proved not only that air was necessary for both, but also he suspected that the active principle was a special ingredient of the air. Unfortunately, he did not, or could not, follow up that suspicion, and so the capital discovery of oxygen was left to Priestley and Lavoisier.

Historians of science have attributed to Dr. John Mayow [5] the credit of announcing that the air contains a substance necessary for combustion and respiration. It is, however, now known that this is a legend started by someone and amplified by others who did not bother to examine the facts.*

A few quotations from Boyle's work will show how closely he came to a knowledge of, and yet missed, the true function of air in respiration and combustion. In the first place, to prove that air which has been repeatedly breathed, or, as he expressed it, 'too much thickened (and as it were clogged) with steams, is unfit for respiration,' he placed a small bird in a closed, small, glass receiver, and noted: 'Though for a quarter of an hour he seemed not much prejudiced by the closeness of his prison, he afterwards first began to pant very vehemently, and keep his bill very open, and then to appear very sick; . . . as being just ready to die. We perceived, that . . . he had so thickened and tainted the air with the steams of his body, that it was become altogether unfit for the use of respiration.' [6]

Boyle also placed all sorts of animals in his receiver and, in every case, he found that they suffered and died when the air was sufficiently exhausted by the pump; and he questions whether, 'if a man were raised to the very top of the atmosphere, he would be able to live many minutes.'

* Cf. *John Mayow in Contemporary Setting.* By Professor T. S. Patterson, *Isis,* xv, 47-96: 504-46. The author proves without doubt that historians had not examined the facts critically; that Mayow's ideas were not original and were taken largely from the observations of Boyle; and that 'Mayow's so-called "discovery of oxygen" was not forgotten; it was never made.' p. 538. In an excellent review of Boyle's work, Dr. J. F. Fulton (*Isis,* Vol. xviii, pp. 77-102, 1934) adds to, and substantiates, this opinion.

The chemists of his time were quite unable to deal with the nature of gases; but Boyle did venture to guess:

That there is some use of the air which we do not yet so well understand, that makes it so continually needful to the life of the animals. Paracelsus, indeed, tells us, 'that as the stomach concocts meat, and makes part of it useful to the body, rejecting the other part; so the lungs consume part of the air, and proscribe the rest.' So that according to our Hermetic philosopher . . . there is in the air a little vital quintessence (if I may call it so) which serves to the refreshment and restauration of our vital spirits, for which uses the grosser and incomparably greater part of the air being unserviceable, it need not seem strange, that an animal stands in need of almost incessantly drawing in fresh air. But though this opinion is not (as some of the same author) absurd, . . . it should not be barely asserted, but explicated and proved.'[7]

In addition to his pioneer work on respiration, Boyle performed many experiments on combustion and found the necessity of air for its action. He had become suspicious of the distinction made between the element of pure fire and the ordinary flame of combustion, and of the assertion that fire was the only active agent in chemical changes. He was also fascinated by so apparent a similarity in the effects of the air on life and combustion:

I might compose hymns to the wise author of nature, who, in the excellent contrivance of the lungs, and other parts of (those admirable engines) animals, manifests himself.[8] . . . Wherefore I have sometimes been inclined to favourable thoughts of their opinion, who would have the air necessary to ventilate and cherish the vital flame, which they do suppose to be continually in the heart. For we see, that in our engine [the pump] the flame of a lamp will last almost as little after the exsuction of the air, as the life of an animal.[9]

Boyle kept the problem of combustion and respiration in his mind and frequently returned to it. While he was conscious that he was unable to recognize the chemical constitution and function of the air, his remarks as quoted below, make it evident how close he had come to discovering oxygen and carbon dioxide.

Besides the four first qualities of the air, (heat, cold, dryness and moisture) that are known even to the vulgar; and those more unobvious, that philosophers and chemists have discovered, such as gravity, springiness, and power of refraction [on] the beams of light, . . . I have often suspected, that there may be in the air some yet more latent qualities or

powers differing enough from all these, and principally due to the substantial parts or ingredients, whereof it consists. And to this conjecture
I have been led, partly (though not only, or perhaps chiefly) by considering the constitution of that air we live and breathe in, which to avoid
ambiguities, I elsewhere call Atmospheric air. For this is not, as many
imagine, a simple and elementary body, but a confused aggregate of
effluviums from such differing bodies, that, though they all agree in
constituting, by their minuteness and various motions, one great mass of
fluid matter, yet perhaps there is scarce a more heterogeneous body in
the world.[10]

The difficulty we find of keeping flame and fire alive, though but for a
little time, without air, makes me sometimes prone to suspect, that there
may be dispersed through the rest of the atmosphere some odd substance, either of a solar, or astral, or some other exotic, nature, on whose
account the air is so necessary to the subsistence of flame; which necessity I have found to be greater, and less dependent upon the manifest
attributes of the air, than naturalists seem to have observed.[11]

There is no doubt that Boyle had made an immense advance in
knowledge of the air; he had taken from it most of the mysterious
qualities assigned to it and had reduced it to the status of a body;
but in calling atmospheric air a heterogeneous body, he thought of
it as a homogeneous air mixed with various foreign steams or effluvia, which were if corpuscular of a different nature from those
of pure air. That such was Boyle's belief seems evident from the
following quotation:

It is proposed as one of the considerable uses of the air in respiration, that, being drawn into the lungs, it serves to carry off with it, when
it is breathed out again, the recrementitious steams that are separated
from the mass of the blood in its passage through the lungs; from which
fuliginous excrements, if the blood were not continually freed by the
help of the air, after nature had been accustomed to that way of dis-
charging them, their stay in the body might have very great and de-
structive operations on it.*

Although Boyle connected the phenomena of respiration and
combustion, he conceived the function of the air to be quite different in the two cases. In respiration, it served only to carry off noxious

---

* *Experiments concerning Respiration, Philosophical Trans. of the R. S.,* 1670. *Works,*
Vol. III, p. 383. Conclusion: experiments to prove, that it was neither want of coldness nor
hot exhalations from their bodies which made mice and birds suffer and die when kept in
closed vessels, at atmospheric pressure.

steams generated in the body; but combustion was caused by the action of a special *form* of corpuscles existing in the atmosphere:

Supposing, upon the grounds there laid, that flame may act upon some bodies as a menstruum, it seems no way incredible, that, as almost all other menstruums, so flame should have some of its own particles united with those of the bodies exposed to its action; and the generality of those particles being (as it is shown in the paradox about the fuel of flames) either saline, or of some such piercing and terrestrial nature, it is no wonder, that being wedged into the pores, or being brought to adhere very fast to the little parts of the bodies exposed to their action, the accession of so many little bodies, that want not gravity, should, because of their multitude, be considerable upon a balance, whereon one or two, or but few of these corpuscles, would have no visible effect.[12]

Enough has been given to prove that chemistry had still a long, painful, and devious path to traverse before it could shake itself clear of relying on especial effluvia for every action. But, after all, the purpose of Boyle's *Spring and Weight of the Air* was to put to a practical test the Baconian philosophy; and in that respect, it was eminently successful. The tract was designedly so experimental that the author practically ignored the cause of the phenomena. The weight of the air, shown to be a gross body, is merely the property of gravity—a tendency, in the scholastic sense, to move towards the centre of the earth. As for the spring, or elasticity, of the air, Boyle suggested it may be caused by corpuscular motions; but, believing that cause to involve difficulties, he was content to picture the air as like a mass of coiled springs, or of wool, reacting against the pressure of its weight.*

Boyle was so encouraged by the enthusiastic reception given to his treatise on air that he decided to proceed with his plan of making an experimental science of chemistry. And like a wise reformer he wished to proceed cautiously: to cultivate his garden first by ridding it of weeds, lest by a rasher method he should destroy the

---

* It should be noted, however, that Boyle ventured a possible explanation of the spring of the air in terms of an atomic hypothesis in his *Defence against the Objections of Linus,* which was published as an appendix to the second edition of the *Spring and Weight of the Air,* 1680. To show that Linus is at fault, he supposes that the particles of air may be like tiny, coiled watchsprings, each having a complicated and innate circular motion. And he concludes: 'So then, by granting Epicurus his principles, that the atoms or particles of bodies have an innate motion; and granting our supposition of the determinate motion and figure of the aerial particles, all the phenomena of rarefaction and condensation, of light, sound, heat, etc., will naturally and necessarily follow.' (*Works,* Vol. I, p. 180.) But Boyle is here matching a fantastic objection in kind.

profitable plants which had been sown there in the past. He would be a reformer rather than a revolutionary, and avoid the disasters which had taken place in the field of religion.

With this plan in mind, Boyle published in March 1661 a collection of *Essays*,[13] largely gleanings from his experimental notebooks. In addition to the experiments, he pleads for a wider cultivation of chemistry as a science, delightful in itself and useful in its applications. He gives hints on the proper method of experimenting and, in a semi-humorous way, the lessons to be learned from unsuccessful attempts. He also gives some specimens of experiments on saltpetre, and on fluidity and hardness, with which to illustrate the corpuscular philosophy and 'the desirableness of a good intelligence betwixt the corpuscularian philosophers and the chemists.' Though these essays were well received and increased his authority, their influence was almost immediately overshadowed by the appearance of his *Sceptical Chymist* in August of the same year.

The *Sceptical Chymist* * is undoubtedly the most famous of Boyle's works. It might almost be said to be the only one still alive —or rather it is the one known by title by most scientists; few have read it, for the mistaken notion has been early fixed in their minds that the study of the great classics of science is of little value in their education. It is unfortunate that such should be the case, for the *Sceptical Chymist* is usually misrepresented as the first modern treatise on chemistry, which it certainly is not, and as containing his celebrated and original definition of a chemical element, which actually first appears in the second edition some twenty years later.

* *Works*, Vol. 1, pp. 458-586; Appendix, pp. 587-661. According to Dr. Fulton (*Bibliog.*, p. 34) there is much confusion in bibliographic details and the only account of the editions 'without error is that of Tenney L. Davis (*Isis*, Vol. VIII, pp. 71-6).' The first edition, London, 1661, is a rare book, of which only eleven perfect copies have been found; of a supposed Oxford imprint of 1661, none are known. 'There is a general title-page in red and black, bearing Robert Boyle's name, and a second title-page, also in red and black, inserted between pp. 34 and 35, from which his name is omitted.'

The title, important in giving the author's purpose, is *The Sceptical Chymist: or Chymico-Physical Doubts and Paradoxes, Touching the Spagyrist's Principles Commonly call'd Hypostatical*, etc., London, 1661.

The title for the second edition, Oxford, printed in 1679 and exposed for sale in 1680, has the important change, after 'Paradoxes,' to read: 'Touching the Experiments whereby Vulgar Spagyrists are wont to Endeavour to Evince their Salt, Sulphur and Mercury, to be the True Principles of Things.' To this edition was appended 'Experiments and Notes about the Producibleness of Chymical Principles.' It is important to note that his 'celebrated definition of a chemical element' first appears in this Appendix.

The *Sceptical Chymist* has now been made accessible to the general public by the reprints of Dent and Sons, London, and Dutton and Co., New York, 1911; and in Ostwald's *Klassiker*, No. 229, 1929.

As interesting and as important as it may be, the *Sceptical Chymist* is surpassed in value by his later and more mature treatises to which it is propædeutic.

Boyle himself is quite explicit about his purpose in writing the *Sceptical Chymist*. He had successfully demonstrated his experimental powers in his tract on air, and had proved that the 'inductive philosophy' of Bacon had a practical as well as a theoretical value. He had astonished the scientific world by a further collection of experiments such as had not previously been attempted. Now, he would consider critically and sceptically the natural philosophies from the earliest classic times down to his own tentative corpuscularian hypothesis. He would not examine them to see whether or not their conclusions followed logically from the postulates which had been assumed as true; but he would test their postulates and conclusions in regard to their consonance with the then-known experimental facts. The reader is not to expect positive decisions, 'if you remember, that it is a sceptic speaks to you, and that it is not so much my present task to make assertions as to suggest doubts, I hope you will look upon what I have proposed, rather as a narrative of my former conjectures touching the principles of things, than as a resolute declaration of my present opinions of them.' [14]

And Boyle, who had professed himself to be a corpuscularian, confesses: *'That it may as yet be doubted, whether or no there be any determinate number of elements; or, if you please, whether or no all compound bodies do consist of the same number of elementary ingredients or material principles.'* *

Boyle is more explicit in his doubt of the two systems of natural philosophy most in vogue: 'And (concludes Carneades smiling) it were no great disparagement for a sceptic to confess to you, that as unsatisfied as the past discourse may have made you think me with the doctrines of the Peripatetics, and the Chemists, about the elements and principles, I can yet so little discover what to acquiesce in, that perchance the enquiries of others have scarce been more unsatisfactory to me, than my own have been to myself.' [15]

In order to assume the rôle of the impartial and impersonal critic, Boyle adopts the dialogue form, which had been used so effectively by Galileo. The chief speaker is Carneades, a corpuscularian, who can occasionally quote a Mr. Boyle as an authority; the others are

* *Works,* Vol. 1, p. 560. The italics are Boyle's.

a Peripatetic, a Spagyrist or modern Chemist, and an inquisitive guest.* And the discussion is to be conducted as among gentlemen, and in 'no litigious humour of loving to wrangle about words, or terms, or notions as empty,' but 'to insist rather on experiments than on syllogisms. For I, and no doubt you, have long observed, that those dialectical subtleties, that the Schoolmen too often employ about physiological mysteries, are wont much more to declare the wit of him that uses them, than increase the knowledge, or remove the doubts of sober lovers of truth.'

No, Boyle will remain the sceptic, loyal to the motto of the newly founded Royal Society, whose members will not be slaves to any philosophic system: 'Because I seem not satisfied with the vulgar doctrines, either of the Peripatetic or Paracelsian Schools many of those that know me have thought me wedded to the Epicurean hypothesis (as others have mistaken me for an Helmontian) yet if you knew how little conversant I have been with Epicurean authors, and how great a part of Lucretius himself I never yet had the curiosity to read, you would perchance be of another mind.' [16] He will admit only in the most general sense that, he has 'suspected the principles of the world, as it now is, to be three, matter, motion, and rest.' He is first of all an experimenter and knows the value of the experimental work of the Spagyrists, disputing only their dogmatic hypotheses. It is unfortunate, he thinks, that beginners in chemistry are enslaved in judgement by being at once required to give their allegiance to a hypothesis, but he was trained differently: 'I, who had the good fortune to learn the operations from illiterate persons, upon whose credit I was not tempted to take up any opinion about them, should consider things with less prejudice.'

The dialogue is opened by Themistius, the Peripatetic, with a eulogy glorifying that admirable philosophy which needs, accord-

* The principal natural philosophies then in vogue were: the Peripatetic, based on the metaphysics of Aristotle; according to which all bodies were a mixture of four essential *elements*—earth, water, air, and fire. They were mutually transmutable by the active agents of heat and cold, dryness and moisture. To these, the Alchemists had added an essential mercury as a *prima materia* for metals.

In the sixteenth century, the school of the Chemists, or Spagyrists, had been founded by Paracelsus; according to which all bodies were compounds of three hypostatic principles—salt, sulphur, and mercury—and the reduction of a compound body to its principles was by fire alone. An Iatrist was a chemist interested in medicine.

Of late, the atomic hypothesis of Democritus, as developed by the Epicureans, had been revived by Gassendi and Boyle, as a corollary of Cartesianism; and, to indicate that the taint of atheistic chance had been removed, the atom was changed to a vaguer corpuscle.

Lastly, it might be mentioned, Van Helmont had proposed the fantastic doctrine that all things were water fructified by seeds of various tendencies.

ing to him, only to be known to be accepted: 'I should almost as little doubt of making you [Carneades] a proselyte to those unsevered teachers, Truth and Aristotle, as I do of your candour and judgement.' [17] To be convinced, you have only to consider how Aristotle, 'the greatest master of logic that ever lived,' built up a philosophic system whose parts are so coherent that, like an arch of nicely fitted stones, each opinion supports and solidifies the whole fabric. The keystone of this arch is the doctrine of the elements: consider how harmoniously it agrees with 'his other principles of philosophy; and how rationally he has deduced their number from that of the combinations of the four first qualities, from the kinds of simple motions belonging to simple bodies, and from I know not how many other principles and phenomena of nature, which so conspire with his doctrine of the elements, that they mutually strengthen and support each other.' Although it is sufficient that his philosophy thus conforms with reason, it also agrees with the testimony of experience. Yet you must be aware of the fact 'that if men were as perfectly rational, as it is to be wished they were, this sensible way of probation would be as needless, as it is wont to be imperfect . . . And therefore the Peripatetics have not been very solicitous to gather experiments to prove their doctrines'; but rather to illustrate them, as the following example amply demonstrates:

If you but consider a piece of green wood burning in a chimney, you will readily discern in the disbanded parts of it the four elements, of which we teach it and other mixed bodies to be composed. The *fire* discovers itself in the flame by its own light; the smoke, by ascending to the top of the chimney, and there readily vanishing into *air,* like a river losing itself in the sea, sufficiently manifests to what element it belongs, and gladly returns. The *water,* in its own form, boiling and hissing at the ends of the burning wood, betrays itself to more than one of our senses; and the ashes by their weight, their fieriness, and their dryness, put it past doubt, that they belong to the element of *earth*.

Nor has an hypothesis, so deliberately and maturely established, been called in question, till in the last century Paracelsus and some few other sooty empirics, rather than (as they are fain to call themselves) philosophers, having their eyes darkened, and their brains troubled with the smoke of their own furnaces, began to rail at the Peripatetic doctrine, and to tell the credulous world there were only three ingredients in mixed bodies—salt, sulphur, and mercury—to which they gave the canting title of hypostatical principles.

Such was the understanding of the seventeenth century of Aristotle's philosophy of chemistry, as interpreted by the Schoolmen; how accurate this understanding was will be discussed in the following chapter. Now, Carneades answers that he has listened to a harangue which, for the most part, needs no answer. The discussion is on the question whether the four elements, or the three hypostatical principles, actually explain the analysis of all compounds into simple *primae materiae,* or whether they are mere names, signifying nothing, and could be called by any other words. Also, the question is to be answered, whether fire is the one and only agent to accomplish such analyses, which is held to be true by Aristotelians and Paracelsians alike.

In the illustration given, both assumptions are, according to Carneades, more than doubtful. 'In Themistius's analysed wood, and in other bodies dissipated and altered by the fire, it appears, and he confesses, that, which he takes for elementary fire and water, are made out of the concrete; but it appears not, that the concrete was made up of fire and water. Nor has either he, or any man, for aught I know, of his persuasion, yet proved, that nothing can be obtained from a body by the fire, that was not pre-existent in it.'

It is really difficult to determine the effects of fire, and chemists are very lax in stating how the fire is used; nor does it seem to act differently from any chemical *menstruum* which changes one compound body into other compounds; even mere cold will freeze out the aqueous from the spirituous parts of wine and beer. How can such facts be ignored as that no degree of fire applied to gold, a mixed body, will give any one of the elements, or salt, sulphur, or mercury; or when fire sublimes camphor, the sublimate is identical with the original camphor?

But, Themistius's own illustration may be cited to show how vaguely fire is used, and how its effects differ according to the way it is used: 'Guaiacum (for instance) burnt with an open fire in a chimney, is sequestered into ashes and soot, whereas the same wood, distilled in a retort does yield far other heterogeneities (to use the Helmontian expression) and is resolved into oil, spirit, vinegar, water and charcoal; the last of which, to be reduced into ashes, requires the being farther calcined than it can be in a closed vessel.'[18] Where are the four elements, and how does your example illustrate your philosophy?

In fact, Carneades asserts: 'By fire we may actually obtain from some mixed bodies such substances, as were not pre-existent in them, . . . as it is probable, that compounded bodies differ from one another but in the various textures resulting from the bigness, shape, motion and contrivance of their small parts, it will not be irrational to conceive, that one and the same parcel of the universal matter may, by various alterations and contextures, be brought to deserve the name, sometimes of sulphureous, and sometimes of a terrene, or aqueous body.' Mr. Boyle has made some experiments to illustrate this opinion; but, instead of quoting them, a similar and more elaborate one by Van Helmont will be given. He devised the following proof for his hypothesis that all bodies 'are materially but simple water disguised into various forms, by the plastic or formative virtue of their seeds.'

Van Helmont planted a willow sapling, weighing five pounds, in an earthen vessel containing 200 pounds of dried earth. Using only rain, or distilled water, he let the tree grow for five years. At that time, he found the tree and the leaves collected in the past autumns weighed 169 pounds, 3 ounces; the earth had lost only two ounces; 'so that 164 pounds of the roots, wood, and bark, which constituted the tree, seem to have sprung from the water.' And yet if he had distilled the tree with fire, would he not have found the usual products instead of such a preponderance of water?

What an illustration of a false hypothesis being blasted by an erroneous explanation! How excited Boyle would have been if he had but known that most of the accrued weight of the tree was terrene carbon sequestered from the air by light.

Boyle, after a long exposition, gives as his opinion that fire, or other agent, does not resolve bodies into just four elements, or into three principles; some are composed of three sensible elements; others of four; and others of more. 'It can scarce be denied, but that the major part of bodies, that are divisible into elements, yield more than three. For, besides those, which the chemists are pleased to name hypostatical, most bodies contain two others, phlegm [i.e. water] and earth.'

Not only has fire not been proved to be an agent which will reduce compounds to elements or principles, but they themselves give no explanation of the physical qualities of bodies: 'Not to accumulate examples to this purpose, *because I hope for a fitter opportunity*

to prosecute this subject, let us at present only point at colour . . .
For about colours, neither do they at all agree among themselves,
nor have I met with any one, of which of the three persuasions soever, that does intelligently explicate them. The vulgar chemists
are wont to ascribe colours to mercury; Paracelsus in divers places
attributes them to salt; and Sennertus, having recited their differing opinions, differs from both; and refers colours rather unto
sulphur.' *

Boyle's work on colours will be discussed in the following chapter; however, it may now be mentioned that he instances the pris-
matic colours and asks: How can salt, sulphur, or mercury have any
part in the spectral colours exhibited by a glass prism, which are
evidently dependent on the geometric figure of the instrument?

When Boyle turns from a discussion of chemical elements and
principles to the pretensions and methods of the chemists, he shows
himself as unawed by great reputations, and as great a master of
satire, as Galileo. He has endeavoured, and successfully he thinks,
to prove that substances separated by fire have not the purity and
simplicity requisite for *primae materiae.* The task has been made
more difficult by the intolerable ambiguity of the chemists and the
unreasonable liberty they take with words:

I find that even eminent writers (such as Raymund Lully, Paracelsus,
and others) do so abuse the terms they employ, that as they will now
and then give divers things one name; so they will oftentimes give one
thing many names; . . . they refrain not from this confounding liberty;
but will, as I have observed, call the same substance, sometimes the sulphur, and sometimes the mercury of a body. And now I speak of mercury, I cannot but take notice, that the descriptions they give us of that
principle or ingredient of mixed bodies, are so intricate, that even those,
that have endeavoured to polish and illustrate the notions of the chemists, are fain to confess, that they know not what to make of it either by
ingenuous acknowledgements, or descriptions, that are not [?] intelligible . . . As for the mystical writers scrupling to communicate their
knowledge, they might less to their own disparagement, and to the trouble of their readers, have concealed it by writing no books, than by
writing bad ones . . . And indeed I fear, that the chief reason, why
chemists have written so obscurely of their three principles, may be, that
not having clear and distinct notions of them themselves, they cannot
write otherwise than confusedly of what they but confusedly apprehend:

* *Works,* Vol. 1, p. 556. Italics mine.

not to say, that divers of them, being conscious to the invalidity of their doctrine, might well enough discern, that they could scarce keep themselves from being confuted, but by keeping themselves from being clearly understood.[19]

Again:

There is great difference betwixt the being able to make experiments, and the being able to give a philosophical account of them . . . Although they might freely have called any thing their analysis presents them with, either sulphur, or mercury, or gas, or blas, or what they pleased; yet when they have told me, that sulphur (for instance) is a primogeneal and simple body, inflammable, odorous, etc., they must give me leave to disbelieve them, if they tell me, that a body, that is either compounded, or uninflammable, is such a sulphur; and to think they play with words, when they teach, that gold and some other minerals abound with an incombustible sulphur, which is as improper an expression, as a sunshine night, or a fluid ice.[20]

And lastly, to illustrate the prevailing confusion of ideas and terms in the chemistry of the time, the following passage is worth quoting:

When they anatomize a compound body by the fire, if they get a substance inflammable, and that will not mingle with water, that must pass for salt; whatsoever is fixed and indissoluble in water, that they name earth. And I was going to add, that whatsoever volatile substance they know not what to make of, not to say, whatsoever they please, that they call mercury. But that these qualities may either be produced, otherwise than by such as they call seminal agents, or may belong to bodies of a compounded nature, may be shown, among other instances, in glass made of ashes, where the exceeding strong-tasted alcalizate salt joining with the earth becomes insipid, and with it constitutes a body; which, though also dry, fixed and indissoluble in water, is yet manifestly a mixed body; and made so by the fire itself.[21]

And here we may profitably take leave of the youthful Sceptical Chymist; for Boyle had with an extraordinarily successful effort demolished the dogmatic hypotheses which had held almost undisputed authority for centuries. From that day, belief in the four essential elements of earth, water, air, and fire, or in the three hypostatical principles of a mythical salt, sulphur, and mercury, quietly died. He had still before him the harder task of instituting in their stead the still prevailing hypothesis of an atomistic and mechanistic universe.

XIII

BOYLE AS CREATIVE NATURAL PHILOSOPHER

ROBERT BOYLE, at the age of thirty-four, had established his reputation as the creator of a new experimental chemistry; and, as the 'Sceptic,' he had discredited the four elements of the Schoolmen and the three hypostatical principles of the Chemists, or Spagyrists, as *primae materiae* of the cosmos. He had gained a sympathetic support to the revival of the atomic hypothesis of the Epicureans, but modified by the substitution of a vaguer corpuscle for the atom of Democritus, and shorn of the antireligious doctrine of the action of chance. Boyle's essential idea lay in the notion that the elemental form of bodies was an imperceptible mass or corpuscle, possessing only weight and geometrical attributes, rather than an elementary earth, water, air, and fire, or a salt, sulphur, and mercury, which were either material bodies, recognizable by our sense perceptions, or else were symbolic of such bodies. And, what was even more important in his opinion, he was convinced that the actions of these corpuscles, as well as those of living bodies, were a witness of the power and wisdom of the Christian God.

There remained for Boyle the even harder tasks to construct a new mechanical philosophy based on corpuscular matter, actuated by motion and rest only, and to displace the belief in substantial forms. His philosophy would differ from the attempt of Descartes to modernize science in that it would be an induction from his experiments. We shall review his work from the publication of the first edition of the *Sceptical Chymist* in 1661 to the appearance of its second edition in 1680, when he added, as an *Appendix,* experiments to prove that the four elements and the three principles could be produced artificially by chemical menstruums as well as by fire.

Boyle also included in that *Appendix* his celebrated definition of a chemical element as the furthest he could go in reviving Epicurean atomism. In the person of Carneades, he there defines the chemical element thus:

To prevent mistakes, I must advertise you, that I now mean by elements, as those Chemists that speak plainest do by their principles, certain primitive and simple, or perhaps unmingled bodies; which not being made up of any other bodies, or of one another, are the ingredients of which all those called perfectly mixed bodies are immediately compounded, and into which they are ultimately resolved: now whether there be any one such body to be constantly met with in all, and each, of those that are said to be elemented bodies, is the thing I now question.[1]

On the surface, there is apparently nothing original in Boyle's definition; it seems merely to state that a chemical element is any substance which is not a compound, or mixture, of two or more other substances.* Thales, according to Aristotle, was the originator of this kind of philosophy when he pronounced water to be the universal element—but no one knew what he meant by this water. But we do know that the water of Thales, the four elements of Empedocles, of Aristotle, and of the Schoolmen, the three principles of the Spagyrists, and the water of Van Helmont, whatever meaning they may have had originally, had been lost in a sea of mysticism and perplexed by a multitude of interpretations. In Boyle's time, they were generally held to be symbols of ideal substances, embodying certain supposedly fundamental qualities—water, the fluidity of bodies; sulphur, typical of inflammability, etc.

But Boyle's definition of the word *element,* interpreted in connexion with his theoretical and experimental ideas, gives an absolutely novel and original significance to it. One can regard it as marking the break between mediæval alchemy and modern chemistry; and, even more significant, between idealism and empiricism.

Boyle offered a new criterion by which an element may be judged; and the reader has only to recall how he had discussed the accepted definitions of an element and found them to be inadequate. What the chemists called earth he claimed was any solid precipitate resulting from their operations; it was the *caput mortuum* or dead-head, and since earth was essentially inert and valueless, it was thrown out. He found it was often not an element, but

---

* This view is often taken by historians and critics. For example, Professor T. L. Davis (*Boyle's Conception of Element, Isis,* Vol. xvi, 1931) states that Boyle's definition was the same as that used by philosophers beginning with Thales. He even quotes that very erratic thinker, Sir Kenelm Digby: 'Element, a body not composed of any *former* bodies, and of which all other bodies are composed.' There is certainly a difference, if one interprets the meaning of *former* as used by the mystics. Also Digby was a person who guessed on every subject, shrewdly or wildly.

a compound body which should be analysed to discover its ingredients. The element air, he asserted, was a very complex body, a mixture of various effluvia, or gases, one of which was necessary for life and combustion; fire was suspected by him to be either a stream of special corpuscles or the motion of those composing a body itself. He was even more explicit and disdainful of the pretensions of the three principles. He scornfully called them mere names, and not things which can be understood or on which even their inventors could agree.

In brief, Boyle had reversed the whole of the previous scientific method: instead of assuming a hypothetical element which would direct and interpret experimentation, he said that the elements themselves can be discovered only by experiment; that any body—gold, or sulphur, or phosphorus, or air—is an element until it has been proved by analysis to be a compound; and that it is the function of the chemist to find by analysis those bodies which cannot be decomposed. Merely as an hypothesis, he offered the opinion that such chemical elements, however many they may prove to be, may themselves be found later to be complex aggregations of an universal world-stuff, existing as discrete corpuscles which are individually imperceptible. If these geometrical aggregations of corpuscles can be changed, then the elements are transmutable, and such a possibility is the justification of the alchemist's dream of transmuting base metals into gold.

It was not Boyle's revival of the atomic hypothesis which started the ever-increasing activity in chemistry, for little or no practical use was made of it for many years; and it is doubtful whether such hypotheses are not at best impotent 'aids' to experimental science. It was rather his definition that a chemical element was any substance which could not be further analysed which gave the impetus to chemistry, together with his insistence, by precept and example, that the prime function of the chemist is to subject all manner of substances to synthetic and analytic experimentation, and finally to investigate their properties. While he could lay no claim to the discovery of any of the now known ninety-odd chemical elements, his guess, if you will, that the atmosphere is a compound gas which should be analysed was the first step towards the discovery of oxygen by Priestley. Nor, when his advice was understood and followed, was it any longer feasible for an unknown substance to be pronounced dogmatically, on the authority of an adept, an earth, a sulphur, or a mercury.

The question may also be asked, why Boyle's mechanistic hypothesis won such an immediate and lasting acceptance by metaphysicians, when those of Descartes, of Gassendi, and of Hobbes had but a temporary vogue? The answer must be that the time was ripe; it fell on fallow ground and was found to be stimulating. The particular cause of its success can confidently be ascribed to its mathematical and metaphysical development by Isaac Newton and John Locke, whose genius dominated the thought of the succeeding century.

To Newton was permitted the discovery of the law of universal attraction of matter. On the foundation of that law, he and his successors developed the science of mathematical mechanics which Rankine the Scottish physicist rightly declared to be the most nearly perfect and exact of theoretic sciences, in that it abstracted from matter all its qualities except the quantitatively measurable ones of mass, force, position, and motion. Nor can it be denied that, since the beginning of the nineteenth century, each of the other sciences has attempted to make its discipline, as far as possible, conform with that of mechanics, and its exactness has been judged by its degree of conformity.

Locke, friend and disciple of Newton and Boyle, developed the philosophy of empiricism which, in spite of all attacks, still dominates the whole field of science. Today, our faith in our sense perception and in our reason is the almost exclusive test of truth, while reliance on intuitive, or revealed, knowledge is at its lowest ebb in history.

Before resuming the discussion of Boyle's ideas, a digression is advisable in order to review the natural philosophy of Aristotle. Following the example of Galileo, all the Renaissance scientists directed their attacks against him, on the grounds that submission to his authority had been the chief cause of a sterile science. As a result of modern research, it is now frequently charged that the scholars of the seventeenth century had a false conception of Aristotle's philosophy, and an even more erroneous understanding of its development during the Middle Ages; consequently their attacks were based on a misconception.

According to this criticism, the cardinal error of Bacon (and in fact of Descartes as well) was his contention that Aristotle and the Greeks in general were originators of a purely deductive philosophy. By this he meant, that they started from an assumption of innate certainty of truth, and from this 'inward sentiment of knowledge,' as Bolingbroke termed it, they logically derived an imaginary world which had little, or no, resemblance to one of fact and observation.

A moment's consideration should be convincing that no philosophy of nature could be conceived without a foundation of fact and of observation of phenomena, however fantastic and imaginary its conclusions might be. No writer of romances creates his characters and situations free from his experience and observation of real people, and the legends and myths of heroes and gods undoubtedly were founded on actual events; the mythological monsters of antiquity have distorted or composite animals for their prototypes, and when today imaginative persons wish to describe inhabitants in Mars, they are forced to picture grotesque men. So, too, the philosopher must derive his system from his observation of the facts of nature, however he may erroneously interpret them; and of ancient peoples, the Greeks were notorious for their curiosity.

When Thales declared water to be the essence of matter, can anyone suppose that he chose that substance without prolonged observation of its universality, its necessity for life, its mutability, and its other qualities? And of all the Greeks, Aristotle was the scientist *par excellence*. One has only to study his treatises on biology—alas, few do—to be amazed at the prodigious wealth of his observations, and at the accuracy and importance of the conclusions which he draws from them; to find his peers, one must name the very few giants, such as Galileo, Newton, and Darwin. He can truly be said to have created the sciences of the classification of species, and of comparative anatomy and embryology.

Unfortunately, perhaps, for the progress of science, the Middle Ages neglected his biology, and turned to his treatises on physics for a practical guide to the scientific method. In these, they misunderstood his purpose, which was not to present a survey of the phenomena of the material world, or a manual of experimentation, but rather to portray an imaginative or ideal cosmogony, such as later was attempted by Descartes, by Laplace, and now by Einstein. He would enquire into the nature of such a cosmos, its creation, its causal laws, and its constitution; and then seek a logical and intelligible order in the tangled flux of events.

In order to appreciate the sweep of Aristotle's cosmogony, we must compare it with that of Descartes, or with the Nebular Hypothesis of Laplace, bearing in mind the state of contemporary knowledge. All three begin by postulating a supposedly uniform state of the universe. By some unknown power, in the case of Aristotle a planning Creator, this uniformity ceases; time and orderly change begin with the advent of force and motion. The attempt is then made to trace the subsequent history of events in the broadest outline; but, it would be the height of presumption to suppose that any such cosmogony can be more than an ingenious guess.

Aristotle postulated first a universal matter, as a potential substance and the substratum of natural bodies. Besides this material cause, or the passive power of matter to be changed, he introduced three others: (1) a formal cause, which changed the potentiality of matter into the actuality of the various specific forms of bodies; accepting as he did the Platonic reality of universals, these substantial forms are ideal realities; (2) an efficient cause, as the active power to produce the change which in every case involves the idea of motion; and (3) a final cause, behind and dominating the others, which gives to the cosmic creation its plan and purpose.

Then Aristotle, who believed that ideal universals were learned from concrete experience of individuals, gave a specific example to illustrate his meaning. An architect of a house has, he says, certain materials potentially suitable for his needs. By the formal cause these materials are differentiated from what is not a house; but such a process requires an active power, or efficient cause, which always involves motion; and lastly there is the purpose which the house is to fulfil.

Certainly, such a metaphysical hypothesis would not have crippled the advance of science, nor have warranted the attacks made on it during the Renaissance. We must consider how Aristotle passed from an ideal world to one of sensible bodies with its phenomena and causes; for, of them is the field of science, and in their interpretation is to be found the aid or hindrance to scientific discipline.

As a connecting link between the universal matter potentially able to receive form, and the fundamental stuff of perceptible bodies, Aristotle could choose the atoms of Democritus, as did Epicurus, which had only geometric properties and motion and were governed by the action of chance. But, since such a universe of materialistic chance was abhorrent to him, who everywhere found the plan and purpose of a Creator, he chose the opposing school of philosophy which had begun with Thales and had culminated with Empedocles, who taught that the differences of bodies resulted from varying proportions of four fundamental elements—earth, water, air, and fire. While it is impossible to specify the exact nature of these elements, it seems likely that their authors selected them as generically typical of the three physical states of solid, liquid, and gaseous, and the fourth element as light. Aristotle also endues these passive elements with the active attributes of heat and cold, wet and dry. Thus, the essence of earth is cold and dry; of water, cold and wet; of air, hot and wet; of fire, hot and dry. And since the elements are varieties of the universal matter, they are transmutable; earth to water by change of dry to wet, while the cold is not altered, etc.

Who can rightly assume that these ideas were without the support of careful observation? Is not the earth the solid core of our apparently stationary world, is it not covered by a shell of water, above that by one of air, and over all by the heavens with its pure fire gathered in the stars? And did not Aristotle have evidence to convince him that each of the elements sought its own kind and its own place as planned by the Creator, when he saw earth gravitate to the bottom and air levitate to the top of a vessel of impure water? It is of course true, that as knowledge slowly accumulated and observation was refined, the attempt to reconcile the increasing facts with the old formulæ led to all manner of confusion, as it always did and does today. It took many centuries, and the slow invention of apparatus, before Copernicus could propose, and Galileo could convince, that the earth revolved about the sun. It took another century before Boyle could prove that the air was a body having weight, and Newton could discover the law of universal gravitation. Who knows today why inert matter attracts, or why electricity can both attract and repel? Certainly the profound attempt of Professor Einstein to reconcile that bewildering paradox by a mathematical formula has reduced the universe to a habitation such as dreams are made of. The only real difference one can find between the long stifling of the acquisition of knowledge by a rigid adherence to the hypothesis of Aristotle, and our present state is that knowledge accumulates now far more rapidly than it did then; and, from sad experience and disappointed hopes, we discard our cherished hypotheses more readily. The mere discovery of X-rays in 1895 wrecked, in less than a quarter of a century, the hypothesis of light and electricity built up so laboriously during the nineteenth century. The day before that discovery was made, the physicist complacently believed that his only business was to make his observations correct to the next decimal point; but since then, his hypotheses have been as evanescent as a phantasm.

The causal action of change, or motion, of bodies was, in Empedocles's notion, frankly animistic. To him the same desires of love and hate, of attraction and repulsion, which we see actuating animals and men, also pervade the universe; and as divine beings, or powers, they bring the four material elements into union or disunion. Although Aristotle may have softened and obscured the language of his predecessor of a century earlier, he too is fundamentally animistic. He may specifically grant a soul, or the will to act, only to plants, animals, and men; yet his statement that each element seeks its own kind and its natural place carries with it the idea of desire and of the will to act; in other words, he confused the impulse of inanimate bodies with that of animate bodies. He may have stated that the difference between a live ass and a dead one was something more than physical and chemical changes; but he failed to emphasize that only a live ass can desire or will to move from rest, and that a dead one to move must be impelled by an outside mechanical force. The same confusion exists in the minds of mechanistic biologists who regard a live ass as a machine.

It must be conceded that Aristotle was not as naïvely animistic in his ideas of mechanical causes of action as was Empedocles, and many competent scholars deny it altogether. And it must be admitted that we ourselves are unable to distinguish clearly between animism and naturalism, and also persistently personify Nature in our conversation and writing. But, it seems evident that Aristotle, even in his elaborate and mechanistic explanation of the solar system, endued it with desire and will, and even with moral purpose.

Aristotle first fixed the stars in an outermost shell which revolves daily about the stationary earth as the fixed centre. The furthest periphery is the *Primum Mobile,* whose perpetual rotation is the cause of all other motions. Next, each planet, including the sun and moon, is attached to its shell, whose radius equals its distance from

and, in fact, there probably does not exist an absolute vacuum in the perceptible universe—not because the universe would collapse, but merely because of the volatility of matter, or of substance if that term be preferred.

With the slow fall of the Roman Empire, the classic culture collapsed, and it required centuries to give mere security to life and property, and a new culture. It does not lie in our province to discuss the impressive social and religious fabric which the Middle Ages constructed mainly on the foundation of Christian theology and Aristotelian metaphysics. But the results, so far as our relations with the material world are involved, were unfortunate. Under the guidance of scholastic philosophy, science was not only neglected but was generally discouraged, despised, and even feared. What gradual improvement there was occurred principally in the arts and crafts and in astrology and alchemy—the sciences most likely to be involved in mysticism.

Again unfortunately for science, Aristotle, who in the twelfth century was without a peer as a guide to science, gradually became a dictator, whose *ipse dixit* was the arbiter of the truth. As a result, it became the purpose of the discoverer of new phenomena to explain them in sympathy with his cosmic hypothesis. Such is the invariable history of every causal hypothesis. At the time of its formulation it may be the best possible explanation of the known phenomena; but as time passes and new knowledge accumulates, it increasingly fails to account for the additional experimental facts; and it ultimately becomes a hindrance to knowledge and must be discarded.

Such was the fate of Aristotle's cosmic hypothesis; from a lack of constructive scepticism, it simply throttled new ideas; such also has been the effect of all its successors. Newton's corpuscular hypothesis of the nature and cause of light had to be discarded. So, too, we may cite from other fields Darwin's hypothesis of natural selection; and the psychologists' hypothesis of materialism. It was for this reason that Newton excluded hypothesis from the field of science, and Poincaré warned scientists to regard them as mere verbal analogies to be indulged in as warily as possible.

Whether or not Boyle had a correct understanding of the metaphysics of Scholasticism, he did see clearly that the mediæval scientists had distorted it with their submissive acceptance of animistic and mystic causes, of elementary substances, of substantial forms, and complacent quotations from their master, into a dogmatic discipline which was preventing the free discussion of ideas and hindering the discovery of new and useful phenomena.

To sum up the influence of the Peripatetic philosophy on scientific discipline, no more vivid and just statement could be given than its eulogy put in the mouth of Themistius by Boyle in the *Sceptical Chymist,* and previously quoted.* Although, he says, it is sufficient that this philosophy thus conforms with reason, it also agrees with the testimony of experience. Yet you must be aware of the fact 'that if men were as perfectly rational, as it is to be wished they were, this sensible [i.e. experimental] way of probation would be needless, as it is wont to be imperfect . . . And therefore *the Peripatetics have not been very solicitous to gather experiments to prove their doctrines, but, rather to illustrate them.'*

Because his sceptical examination of the doctrine of the nature of bodies, as taught in the Schools, had been so successful, Boyle was encouraged to make a similar examination into the qualities of bodies, and to compare the doctrine of substantial forms as taught by the Peripatetics with his corpuscularian philosophy.[2]

Boyle states his own hypothesis of qualities in simple and general terms:

I. 'I agree with the generality of philosophers so far as to allow, that there is one catholic or universal matter common to all bodies, by which I mean a substance extended, divisible, and impenetrable.'

II. 'Since we see not how there could be motion and change in matter, if all its (actual or designable) parts were perpetually at rest among themselves, it will follow, that to discriminate the catholic matter into variety of natural bodies, it must have motion in some or all its designable parts.'

III. The qualities of sensible bodies are the result of the size, shape, motion, and rest, etc., of aggregates of corpuscles, each of which is imperceptible to our senses.

In contrast to this hypothesis, the idea of substantial forms as an explanation of qualities is too repugnant to be reconciled with it: 'Namely, that there are in natural bodies store of real qualities and other real accidents, which not only are no moods of matter, but are real entities distinct from it, and, according to the doctrine of

* Supra, Chapter XII, pp. 246-7. Statement now condensed; italics mine.

many modern Schoolmen, may exist separate from all matter what-soever.' For example, they said that grass is green because it has 'greenness' in it. Whereas Boyle held that it is green because of the manner in which its texture sends light to our eyes.

In Boyle's opinion this doctrine of substantial forms is one of the noblest, but also one of the most perplexing enquiries in natural philosophy. His quarrel is with the obscurity and accretions made by the *modern* Peripatetics: 'Because divers of the ancient, especially Greek commentators of Aristotle, seem to have understood their master's doctrine of forms much otherwise, and less incongruously, than his Latin followers, the Schoolmen and others, have since done.* Nor do I expressly mention Aristotle himself among the champions of substantial forms, because though he seems in a place or two expressly enough to reckon forms among substances, yet elsewhere the examples he employs to set forth the forms of natural things by, being taken from the figures of artificial things (as of a statue, etc.) which are confessedly but accidents, and making very little use, if any, of substantial forms to explain the phenomena of nature, he seems to me upon the whole matter either to have been irresolved whether there were any such substances or no, or to speak ambiguously and obscurely enough of them, to make it questionable what his opinions of them were.'

In a noteworthy statement, Boyle attempts to distinguish between an objective and a subjective world, and to explain our cognizance of the former. It is, he thinks, from a confusion of the two worlds that the doctrine of substantial forms originated, and was gradually accepted as the definition of the qualities of bodies.

Suppose, Boyle postulates, there existed only a single object in the world, such as a stone; then 'it were hard to show that there is physically any thing more in it than matter, and the accidents we have already named,' which are the primary qualities proposed by Galileo and Descartes as the essentials of bodies. But, 'there are *de facto* in the world certain sensible and rational beings that we

---

* But not all of them were content with the doctrine; Boyle quotes three outstanding scholars to support his opinion.

'Formarum cognitio est rudis, confusa, nec nisi per περιτασέις; neque verum est, formae substantialis speciem recipi in intellectum, non enim in sensu usquam fuit.' J. C. Scaliger.

'Formae substantiales sunt incognitae nobis, quia insensibles: ideo per qualitates, quae sunt principia immediata transmutationes, experiuntur.' Aquinas.

'In hac humanae mentis caligine aequè forma ignis ac magnetis nobis ignota est.' Sennertus.

call men. They are provided with sense organs,—the eye, the ear, etc.—which are capable of being wrought upon by external bodies by the intervention of spatial motion. These mechanical impressions on the sense organs are interpreted by the mind as color, tone, temperature, etc. which constitute the secondary qualities of bodies.'

Whence, [Boyle argues] men have been induced to frame a long catalogue of such things, as, for their relating to our senses, we call sensible qualities; and because we have been conversant with them before we had the use of reason, and the mind of man is prone to conceive almost every thing (nay, even privations, as blindness, death, etc.) under the notion of a true entity or substance, as itself is; we have been from our infancy apt to imagine that these sensible qualities are real beings in the objects they denominate, and have the faculty or power to work such and such things; as gravity hath a power to stop the motion of a bullet shot upwards, and carry that solid globe of matter towards the centre of the earth; whereas indeed (according to what we have largely shown above) there is in the body, to which these sensible qualities are attributed, nothing of real and physical but the size, shape, and motion or rest, of its component particles, together with that texture of the whole, which results from their being so contrived as they are.

To illustrate his argument, Boyle continues:

When a pin being run into my finger causeth pain, there is no distinct quality in the pain answerable to what I am apt to fancy pain to be, but the pin in itself is only slender, stiff, and sharp, and by those qualities happens to make a solution of continuity in my organ of touching, upon which, by reason of the fabric of the body, and the intimate union of the soul with it, there ariseth that troublesome kind of perception which we call pain.

It is a curious slip to consider pain as a secondary quality of touch dependent on the peculiar fabric of the body, when it is equally produced by intensely concentrated light on the eye, of sound in the ear, and would never then be regarded as a secondary quality of the body.

And Boyle is himself perplexed by the difficulty in discriminating between qualities supposedly inherent in a body and those which are only accidental. His difficulty is this: 'Whereas we explicate colours, odours, and the like sensible qualities by a relation to our senses, it seems evident they have an *absolute being* irrelative to us: for snow would be white, and a glowing coal would be hot, though there were no man or any other animal in the world; . . . as the coal will not only heat or burn a man's hand if he touch it, but would likewise heat wax and thaw ice into water.'

There are two fallacies in Boyle's statement, both of which arise from his ambiguous use of words (as when the biologist uses force as the same word to express a physical change of motion and an active animal instinct, or when the psychologist uses energy of thought and of motion as synonymous). To assign *absolute being* to sensible qualities is to make them entities, or substantial forms. What he means is more clearly explained later: 'Thus snow, though, if there were no lucid body nor organ of sight in the world, it would exhibit no colour at all, yet it hath a greater disposition than a coal or soot, to reflect store of light outwards, when the sun shines upon them all three.'

The second fallacy lies in the ambiguous use of the word *heat,* as that which produces the sensation of warmth and that which affects the physical properties of wax and ice; they are certainly not synonymous, for red pepper is hot to the tongue, but does not thaw ice.

Boyle's distinction between primary and secondary qualities, which is in essence the distinction between the atomic, or corpuscular, hypothesis and the doctrine of forms, which refers only to secondary qualities, is given briefly in his own words: 'If there were no sensitive beings, those bodies that are now the objects of our senses would be but dispositively, if I may so speak, endowed with colours, tastes, and the like; and actually, but only with those more catholic affections of bodies, figure, motion, texture, etc.' It is a curious mental blindness in Boyle, and indeed in all scientific mechanists who restrict knowledge to the data of observation, that he could say in the same sentence that 'colours, tastes, and the like' of bodies can be affirmed only as they affect our senses, and that 'figure, motion, texture, etc.' can be known independently of them. Unless we have an intuitive or a revealed knowledge, it would be just as impossible to postulate anything about the figure, position, or texture of a body except from the same sensations of sight, touch, and hearing.

Boyle's argument for the acceptance of the corpuscular hypothesis in place of substantial forms has been given at a considerable length, because it is, in the main, the same offered by scientists of today.

But it was really unnecessary, for the fallacy regarding the distinction between primary and secondary qualities as essential and accidental lurks in his first assumption, and equally invalidates his conclusion. He first asks us to imagine the world to be represented by a single object, such as a stone, and that there is no living, sentient being which can observe it; then, he states, the object could have only those primary, and essential, qualities which are independent of an observer. But, he concludes, there are *de facto* men with sense perceptions in existence, and therefore the stone is apparently endowed with additional and non-essential qualities such as colour, warmth, etc.

If this postulate be granted, the logical conclusion in regard to the real distinction between qualities naturally follows; but it will be false because the postulate was false and impossible to accept. If knowledge of the external world is derived only from observation, as science requires, how can the existence of a body be assumed without an observer? To add to the confusion, Boyle and the reader do exist and, if so, both the primary qualities of shape, position, etc., and the secondary qualities of colour, etc., are equally evident. Also, if the stone be at a distance, all its qualities vanish together when Boyle and the reader merely close their eyes. This is not a parallel case to the geologist who, from the evidence of rock strata and fossils, describes with some credibility the existence and condition of the earth before the appearance of *homo sapiens*. He is, on the acceptance of the continuity of law and order, by the figure of speech called the historical present, revivifying past events as a biographer may write of Boyle as living and speaking.

There can be no justification, *de facto,* for distinguishing between essential and accidental qualities, since any quality can be affirmed only by its sense perception; it is even less admissible to use the adjectives, primary and secondary, as if a body had at first certain qualities, and then, later, received others. For example, if a body be perceived by sight, both its position and its colour are determined simultaneously by the action on the retina of the same rays of light; and both qualities are absent if either the source of the light, or the eye, be absent.

On the other hand, the physicist, and to a less degree the chemist, has found it to be advantageous to limit his investigations to certain qualities only, those geometric properties which are quantitatively expressible in mathematic equations. Such a discrimination is as feasible as for an athletic director to concern himself only with the physical qualities of men, and for the clergy to emphasize morals. Confusion will occur only when it is forgotten that the conclusions derived are special and approximate.

It will be shown later that Boyle was partially aware of the impossibility of including more than a very limited number of phenomena in his corpuscular hypothesis. Thus, in his treatise on heat, he points out that our sensation of warmth is a deceptive indicator of the intensity of heat in comparison with the change of volume it causes in liquids and gases; and he restricts his experiments mostly to the effects of heat on the composition, change of state and of volume, and pressure of bodies. And, in his treatise on light, he studies the effects of the texture of bodies on the reflection and refraction of light as the cause of colour. It is especially significant that he instances the prism as a fruitful instrument for the study of optics.

It is not surprising that Boyle, when he set himself the task of submitting the hypotheses of science to an experimental test, should choose for his investigation the subject of light. The alchemists had made the succession of colours of metals in their retorts the chief indicator to guide them in their search for transmutation and the philosopher's stone. In order to show the confusion which existed about the nature and cause of colours and of light, and the paucity of experiments from which to derive our ideas, he published his great monograph on Colours in 1664.*

As was customary with him, Boyle wishes to give an easy and simple résumé of current opinions about colours, and experiments of his own devising to encourage others to accumulate adequate data, for the whole subject was in a state of confusion. As to the presumed cause of colours, the Schools differed in details, but they agreed that colour is an inherent quality of bodies which light discloses but does not produce; some leaned towards the Platonic idea, that colour is a kind of flame of minute corpuscles darted by the body against the eye; others followed the ancient Atomists in the belief that colours are not a luminous steam, but a corporeal ef-

---

* *Experiments and Considerations Touching Colours,* London, 1664. *Works,* Vol. 1, pp. 662-778. There is evidence that he had published a preliminary tract on colour the year before, but no copy is known to exist. Cf. Fulton, *Bibliog.,* p. 47. The work was very popular and went into eight editions. Pepys also refers to it.

fluvium and that some external light is necessary to excite and liberate the light corpuscles from the body and carry them to the eye; a popular explanation was that colour was a mixture of light and darkness, or rather of light and shadows; * the chemists assigned the origin of light to one, or the other, of the three principles; the Cartesians attributed colour to the agitation of the retina by the impact of globuli which have both a rotational and linear motion—if the circular speed be the greater, they cause the sensation of red; if the slower, blue; if equal, yellow.†

Boyle inclined to the belief that colour is a modification of light; how, he cannot say, for there was not a sufficient knowledge. He will therefore merely criticize and give new data, in order that at a future time a sound theory may be developed.

The chemists especially, Boyle asserts, 'Argue that a considerable diversity of colours does constantly argue an equal diversity of nature in the bodies wherein it is conspicuous.' He does not wholly agree, and instances the changeable colours on pigeons' necks, of thin films of oil and glass, and of rainbows, where the colour depends on the position of the source and of the eye. This is so evident that these colours are given the distinction of being 'apparent and fantastic'; that is, they are phantoms. 'Yet that oftentimes the alteration of colours does signify considerable alteration in the disposition of parts of bodies, may appear in the extraction of tinctures [dyes], and divers other chemical operations wherein the change of colours is the chief, and sometimes the only thing, by which the artist regulates his proceeding.' For example: the colour of fruit shows its maturity, and when iron is to be tempered, its degree of hardness will be determined by the colour of the heated metal.

Boyle discards the explanation that colour is a quality residing in a body which penetrates throughout it, as the Schools seem to teach; they instance sealing wax as red all through, since when broken all its fragments are red. For, he cites, while light is the usual cause for the sensation of sight and colour, yet a blow on the

* This was the hypothesis of Antonius de Dominis, *De radiis visus,* 1611. He is credited with the explanation of the rainbow. Of colour he says: 'If there be in a body pure light, as in the stars or in fire, and it lose its brilliancy for any cause, it appears as white light. If some darkness be mingled with the light . . . there then occur the intermediate colours.' All colours are varying mixtures of three primary colours: red, green, and blue.

† This hypothesis was modified by Pardies, Hooke, and others. It was the starting point from which Huygens developed the wave theory of light, opposed and temporarily crushed by Newton.

retina will produce the same effect, and so will coughing or illness. And then he cautiously tries to distinguish between light as an objective and as a subjective phenomenon; light may be modified by a body and such effects may be studied; or when so modified, it may strike upon the organ of sight and give the sensation of colour.

It will be shown later that Boyle, in order to make clearer his distinction between the mechanical and sensational effects of colour, emphasized his experiments with a prism. He described a number of observations used later by Newton; but he made no accurate measurements, and thus he missed the capital discovery of the selective refrangibility of the colours, and our ability to use this purely mechanical action of light as the criterion of its nature. It would be surprising if Newton, then a scholar at Cambridge, deeply engaged in grinding lenses and in experiments with prisms, was unacquainted with so popular a work as Boyle's. Barrow, who had been appointed Lucasian Professor at Cambridge the year previous and lectured on optics, was Newton's teacher, fosterer of his genius, and patron, and would undoubtedly be interested in it.

As a result of his discovery that each ray of light experienced a definite and measurable angular deviation by a prism, Newton deliberately limited physics to an investigation of the mechanical properties of natural phenomena, a limitation now exclusively recognized. Rays of light are thus not to be distinguished by whether they appear red or green, but by their position in the spectrum; and the science of optics can be studied by a blind person. Similarly acoustics does not depend on the sense of hearing, for a sound is not classified by its audible pitch, but according to the number of vibrations of a pendular body; so also, the expansion of bodies, and not the sensation of warmth, is the criterion of heat. The reason why odor and taste are omitted is because physicists have found no mechanical effects related to those sensations. The world of the physicist is artificial, but in its limited field it has permitted the development of a very exact theory and of a rich experimentation.

In the second, and experimental, section of his tract, Boyle dealt first with the nature of whiteness and blackness as the simplest forms of colours. He found that water and coloured fluids when beaten into a froth, and solids when they are crushed into a fine powder or have their surfaces roughened, all become white. He also proved, but without measurement, that white surfaces reflect the most light and in all directions. He then defined whiteness as the result of reflection from a body whose surface 'is asperated [roughened] by almost innumerable small surfaces; which being of an almost specular nature [like tiny convex mirrors], are also so placed, that some looking this way, and some that, they yet reflect the rays of light that fall on them, not towards one another, but outwards towards the spectator's eye.'

As for blackness, Boyle compared it to a shadow—a paucity of light reflected from a surface because of its texture. First: the surface may have a particular kind of asperity that causes it to reflect light inwards and absorb it. The surface protuberances (his excellent microscopes show even the smoothest surfaces to be very rough) may be cones, pyramids, cylinders, etc., so placed as to reflect inwards, instead of the spherical protuberances of white bodies which reflect outwards. Secondly: the texture may be porous and 'absorbent to the solary effluvia or corpuscles of some ætherial medium, retaining them and heating the body.' Boyle's experiments proved that black bodies grow hottest when exposed to the sun's rays—a fact which supports either of the causes; but, as he did not find black bodies to be porous, and as he knew of a blind man who stated that they felt roughest to his thumb, he decided that blackness was, in the main, a surface effect.

Boyle's work on colours other than black and white, which comprises Part III, is purely experimental; of the cause of such colours he merely states: 'The cause of diversity of colours in opacous bodies, is, that some reflect the light with more, others with less of shade (either as to quantity, or as to interruption).' In proof, he observed that sheets of paper differently stained reflected different amounts of the sun's rays; but the results were quite inaccurate. However, some interesting discoveries were made. He observed diffraction bands in films. He examined what proportion of pigment would visibly tinge water: his best result was that one part of cochineal faintly tinged 125,000 parts of water by weight. He noted practically the predominate rôle played by salts of all kinds in the art of dyeing; and he first pointed out the useful chemical test that syrup of violets turns red in an acid solution, and green when alkaline.

A few words should be added about Boyle's experiments with prisms. The explanation of the colours of the rainbow, of clouds in the morning and evening, of the prism, etc., was a stumbling block to the Schoolmen, who held that colour was an inherent quality of the body. It was easy to prove that such colours are caused mainly by the refraction of light and vary with the position of the eye and source. If they are true colours, they are evidently not an inherent quality of the body. The Schoolmen could avoid this difficulty only by denying them to be true or genuine colours, and were wont to term them *emphatical*.* But Boyle pertinently remarked that everyone esteems echoes and other sounds from bodies to be true sounds, because they affect a sense organ; why then are not emphatical colours also true?

With a prism, Boyle investigated the emphatic or fantastic colours. By throwing the spectral colours on differently coloured screens, he found that he could compound them with true and stable colours, and also with fantastic and evanescent colours. He also tried to make prisms of coloured glass, and of clarified resin or turpentine, but the results were unsatisfactory. By coating the faces of a prism with red or yellow varnish, he found, as he expected, that the spectrum was affected.

It was contrary to Boyle's express purpose to develop a corpuscular hypothesis of light; but it is evident that he was convinced that the doctrines of substantial forms, and of the chemical principles, were contradicted by the many new facts he had presented. If so, then there remained only the action of the corpuscles of the luminous bodies, or of special ones, to explain the phenomena of colour; and he would leave it to the future to decide the question—one may appreciate his astonishment when less than a decade later, he, as one of a committee appointed by the Royal Society, reported on the letter of Newton which did decide the question of the nature of white light.

That Boyle himself was convinced of the correct answer to the problem seems certain from a remark he made on the false reliance which the alchemists placed on substantial forms:

Divers bodies digested in carefully closed vessels, will in tract of time change their colour . . . And indeed it has been a thing, that has much contributed to deceive many chemists; that there are more bodies than one, which by digestion will be brought to exhibit that variety and succession of colours, which they imagine to be peculiar to what they call

* Emphatical, meaning illusory, or apparent, is now obsolete.

the *true matter of the philosophers* . . . In these operations there appears
not any cause to attribute the new colours emergent to the action of a
new substantial form, nor to any increase or decrement of either the
salt, sulphur, or mercury of the matter that acquires new colours: for
the vessels are closed, and these principles, according to the chemists,
are ingenerable and incorruptible, so that the effect seems to proceed
from hence, that the heat agitating and shuffling the corpuscles of the
body exposed to it, does in process of time so change its texture, as that
the transposed parts do modify the incident light otherwise than they did
when the matter appeared of another colour.

If there was confusion relating to the nature and properties of
light and colour, differences of opinion were much worse with respect to cold; no one, at least, doubted the reality of colour, but it
was debated whether cold was a positive quality or merely a less
degree of heat. Boyle was very sensitive to the weather and, as a
valetudinarian, he kept daily reports of its condition and supplied
himself with a variety of cloaks to meet its every change. It was
natural that he would select the most important of his notes on
temperature for publication.*

Boyle began his treatise on cold with the pertinent remark that,
while cold and heat are of the utmost importance in the economy
of nature, study of them had been neglected and our knowledge
was rudimentary. The reason he rightly attributed to a lack of accurate recording apparatus. We have, of course, in our sensation of
temperature an indication of heat, but it is deceptive in that it depends on the state of our bodies. The same vessel of water will feel
differently to two persons, and may also to the same person when
successively tested. The property of expansion by heat had recently
been used in the form of weather-glasses to advantage, but they
were crude apparatus in comparison with the balance or the yard-
stick.

The first instrument for recording temperature, the air thermoscope, had been invented by Galileo, early in the century. It was
usually called a weather-glass, and it consisted of an unsealed thermometer, containing air, inverted and dipping into a small vessel
of coloured liquid. It was very sensitive to changes of temperature,

* *New Experiments and Observations Touching Cold,* London, 1665. *Works,* Vol. II,
pp. 462-734. To the main body of the text, he added an *Examen of Antiperistasis* and of
Hobbes's doctrine; an account of freezing; and additional notes on the history of cold. The
first edition was largely destroyed by the great fire, and a second edition was issued,
unchanged, in 1683.

but was also affected by variations of the atmospheric pressure and the readings of one instrument could not be compared with those of another. Galileo is also credited with having made the first sealed thermometer about 1612. It was a great improvement, but it also was defective in that, instead of graduating the stem in equal parts between two fixed points, the degrees were designed to represent thousandths of the volume of the bulb, an uncertain quantity.

In Boyle's time, the use of weather-glasses was widespread, but the invention of sealed thermometers was unknown in England. He comments:

These are in some things so much more convenient than the others, that (if I be not mistaken) it has already proved somewhat serviceable to the inquisitive, that I have directed the making of the first of them, that have been blown in England. In the beginning indeed I had difficulty to bring men to believe, that there would be a rarefaction and condensation [i.e. expansion and contraction] of a liquor hermetically sealed up, because of the school-doctrine touching the impossibility of a vacuum, and especially, because I had never seen any experiment of this kind, nor met with any that had: but after some trials, which my conjectures led me to make successfully enough, that in hermetically sealed glasses, both air and water might be alternately rarefied and condensed; I found my work much facilitated by the sight of a small sealed weather-glass, newly brought by an ingenious traveller from Florence, where it seems some of the eminent virtuosi, that ennobled that fair city, had got the start of us in reducing sealed glasses into a convenient shape for thermoscopes. But since that, the invention has in England by a dexterous hand, that uses to make them for me, been improved, and the glasses we now use are more conveniently shaped, and more exact than the pattern, I caused the first to be made by.[3]

Not only was Boyle responsible for this pioneer work, which I have never seen mentioned, but he also recognized the need of fixed points from which to measure. In fact, he ventured to propose a method, awkward enough, of standardizing thermometers as follows: Immerse the bulb of an alcohol thermometer in the essential oil of aniseed, which has the property of losing its fluidity during most of the winter: 'You may, by observing the station [height] of the spirit of wine in the thermoscope, when the oil begins manifestly to curdle about it, be in some measure assisted to make another weather-glass like it.' And, in a footnote, he re-

marked that an ingenious man had proposed to him as a standard
the freezing of distilled water.

But Boyle, although he believed that cold was probably a lessen-
ing of the speed of the corpuscles of bodies which constituted heat,
was confused by his ignorance. He could not distinguish between
the solidification of water by lowering its temperature and the fact
that quicksilver, which no one had been able to solidify by that
method, may be congealed by the fumes of lead, although they
will not so affect any other fluid. He also was puzzled by the unknown reason why 'ginger is hot in the mouth' as well as heated
water; as an example, he cited opium, 'of which three or four grains
have too oft destroyed the heat of the whole mass of blood in a
man's body, though that be a very hot, subtile, spirituous liquor';
yet, when he dissolved enough opium in a glass of water to kill
very many men, a good thermometer showed no cooling at all of
the water. So he hedged by wondering whether, besides those corpuscles or bodies whose motions produce the sensation of cold in
general, 'there may be particular agents, which in reference to this
or that particular body may be called frigorific; though they would
not so much refrigerate another body.' And thus, when puzzled,
he would, like Descartes, slip into the mediæval covert he was supposed to be clearing.

In spite of Boyle's vacillation about the nature of cold, I believe
that his study of thermometers and his suggestion of the need for
fixed points to make them comparable, and his pioneer observations with freezing mixtures, influenced Newton, in 1701, to propose a scale with the freezing of water as zero, and the temperature
of the human body as 12°. Perhaps he also influenced Fahrenheit,
in 1714, to select for zero a freezing mixture of ice and salt, under
the belief that it was the lowest obtainable temperature.

The cause of the rise or fall of a weather-glass was generally attributed, as was that of the barometer, to the *horror vacui*. Boyle
scornfully rejected this as 'a way of explicating, that little becomes
a naturalist, to attribute to the senseless and inanimate body of
water an aim at the good of the universe, strong enough to make it
act, as if it were a free agent, contrary to the tendency of its own
private nature, to prevent a vacuum.' He correctly assigned the
cause to the effect of cold on the density and spring of the air; but
he will not stop to examine, 'whether the spring of the air depends
upon the springy structure of each aerial corpuscle, as the spring of

wool does upon the texture of the particular hairs, it consists of, or upon the agitation of some interfluent subtile matter, that in its passage through the aerial particles, whirries each of them about, or upon both of these causes together, or upon some other differing from either of them.' Just here he made an unfortunate mistake by not stopping to examine the effect of temperature on his famous law of gases; we can excuse his neglect on the grounds of his suspicion of the accuracy of his thermometers.

The main body of Boyle's tract is a chronicle of his many experiments on cold, some few on general effects, but most of them on those which occur at solidification of liquids. To realize the essential difficulty of the problem, we must not forget the prevailing opinion, that there existed in the universe a fixed amount of heat and cold, whether they were entities or qualities. Although there were divergent speculations, most natural philosophers followed Aristotle, who taught that the reservoir of heat resided with the elements of fire and gases, and of cold, with liquids and solids. With this in mind, Boyle's opening statement is revolutionary:

It seems probable enough, that among the bodies, we are conversant with here below, there is scarce any except fire, that is not, at sometime or other, susceptible of actual cold (at least as to sense). And even concerning fire itself, till that difficulty be clearly determined, which we have elsewhere started; namely, whether fire be not, as wind, . . . rather a state of matter, or matter considered whilst it is in such a kind of motion, than a distinct and particular species of natural bodies, there may remain some doubt.

Because of the infrequency of cold weather in England, Boyle took advantage of the fact, known in Italy and in some other countries, that a mixture of salt and snow freezes water more readily than snow alone. But, he discovered that this was not a special property of sea-salt, for he also obtained cooling mixtures with the substitution of nitre, alum, vitriol, sal-ammoniac, or sugar; but sea-salt caused the lowest temperature. He also tried various spirits and oils of salts, etc., with varying success. He found the general law for such mixtures, and formulated it in the sentence, 'no salt, that helps not the snow to dissolve faster than else it would, did enable it to produce ice'; and he had, unconsciously, discovered the fundamental principle of latent heat.

With his mixtures, Boyle was able to congeal many liquids such as some wines, milk, beer, and others; he also listed many which would not solidify, such as mercury, and other wines. Although he could, with his sealed weather-glasses, make only rough estimates of the temperatures of freezing, he was able by an ingenious experiment to disprove the notion that it was the ultimate effect of cold on a given body. A sealed weather-glass was kept in water till it began to solidify and the column then stood at five inches. It was then plunged into the mixture of snow and salt, and the column rapidly fell to the bottom of the stem. On replacing it again in the same glass of water, the column returned to its original height; thus proving that the ice when mixed with salt had been cooled below its temperature of freezing. Since it was a doctrine of the Schools that heat naturally levitated, he enquired whether cold had the opposite tendency by suspending a phial of salt and ice in a glass of water; and he did freeze the layers of water at the bottom before the top, but he thought the result was not satisfactory. He also made a long series of experiments on the preservation of animal and vegetable bodies by cold.

Boyle was able to disprove by actual volumetric measurement the prevalent notion that water and other liquids must contract on solidification, which he stated had of late been called in question by some more speculative than the rest, who cited the fact that ice rose to the surface of water and floated. He cited that modern writers had attempted, without success, to decide the question by freezing water in a sealed weather-glass, or bolt-head as it was often called, and noting the height of the column before and after freezing. It seems, oddly enough, that the experiment had failed because they had permitted the water to change to ice first at the surface, and the bulb invariably burst. By the simple device of turning the water into ice first at the bottom of the bulb, the experiment succeeded, and Boyle correctly recorded that the volume of ice was approximately one-ninth more than that of the corresponding water. By the same means, he found the contraction of oils on solidifying.

Then Boyle remarked on the bursting of the bulbs:

It will not be impertinent or unseasonable to take notice, that not only those School-philosophers, . . . but divers modern virtuosi are wont to ascribe the phenomenon to this, that the cold of the external air, contracting the air and liquid within, the ambient air must break the sides of the glass to fill that space, which being deserted upon the condensation of the included air, the liquor would otherwise leave a vacuum abhorred by nature . . . The above mentioned experiments sufficiently evince, that in many cases, it is not the shrinking, but the expansion of the liquors contained in the stopped vessels, that occasions their bursting; therefore in these cases, we need not, nor cannot fly to I know not what *fuga vacui* for an account of the phenomenon.

Boyle then proceeded to show the enormous force exerted by the solidification of water by many demonstrations, including the now classical experiment of bursting a plugged iron bomb. He asked the question, whence this prodigious force? If cold be but a privation of heat, as the Cartesians contend, that æthereal substance, which 'agitated the little eel-like particles' to make water a fluid, may well when it quitted them leave the little eels in fixed postures as a solid ice; but whence comes the enormous force of these now quiescent particles which act as if they were coiled springs? Although he thought the expansion of the ice may be better explained by the Epicureans, who assume that cold is caused by the ingress of swarms of cold corpuscles, he asked why those corpuscles, which penetrate the water so quietly and easily, should exert such a violent force as to break the glass or metal vessels when they can enter such substances as readily as they can penetrate water? But there was an even greater objection to that explanation, because he had found that oils contract in volume when they solidify.

Boyle next discussed the question of the *primum frigidum,* and concluded that it is either a fallacy, or has not been proved by experimental evidence. While some contend for earth, some for water, others for air, and some moderns for nitre; all seem to agree 'that there is some body or other, that is of its own nature supremely cold, and by participation of which, all other cold bodies obtain that quality.' He then criticized at length the pretensions of each: of the earth he objected that it does not freeze itself; in contact with cold air it is chilled only to a little depth, and in deep mines it is warm; he might admit it may be the *summum frigidum* but not the *primum.* Of water, he noted that rivers and ponds freeze at the top, and hence the air must be the colder. The Stoics made a bid for air, but the Aristotelians classed air as essentially warm and moist, and he asked why the depths of the ocean are cold? Of them all, he finds none which deserves the title of *primum frigidum.* And in general, since such qualities as gravity, motion, colour, and sound have no need of a reservoir, why should heat and cold need one?

As an appendix to his treatise on cold, Boyle added a discussion of the mystic and animistic doctrine of Antiperistasis.* The dialogue is opened by Themistius with the arrogant assertion that authority, reason, and experience all require our acceptance of such a principle. He will, however, advance only the last two arguments, because it is useless to expect obedience to authority in such a rebellious age:

What can there be more agreeable to the wisdom and goodness of Nature, who designing the preservation of things, is wont to be careful of fitting them with requisites for that preservation; than to furnish cold and heat with that self-invigorating power, which each of them may put forth, when it is environed with its contrary? . . . When a body, wherein either of them resides, happens to be surrounded by other bodies, wherein the contrary quality is predominant, the besieged quality (by retiring to the innermost parts of that which it possesses, and thereby re-collecting its forces, and as it were animating itself to a vigorous defence) is intended or increased in its degree, and so becomes able to resist an adversary, that would otherwise easily destroy it.

As illustrations of Antiperistasis, Themistius alleges that in summer, because the lowest and highest strata of the air are almost insufferably hot, the cold, expelled from the earth and water by the sun's rays, retires to the middle stratum of the air, and there defends itself against the heat of the other two. 'And as the cold maintains itself in the middle region, by virtue of the intenseness, which it acquires upon the account of Antiperistasis; so the lightning that flashes out of the clouds, is but a fire produced in that middle region, by the hot exhalations penned up.' But we need not go so far for a proof of the principle which preserves the golden mean throughout the universe. In summer, when the air is hot, the cold retreats to cellars and vaults; and in winter, when even the lakes and rivers are frozen, the same cellars and vaults become the sanctuary of the heat.

Carneades answers sceptically:

* *An Examen of Antiperistasis. Works,* Vol. II, pp. 659-86. Boyle presented the subject as a dialogue between Themistius the Aristotelian, Carneades the sceptic corpuscularian, and Eleutherius the inquisitive gentleman. The dictionary defines this antæan principle as an 'opposition by which the quality opposed acquires strength.'

According to the course of Nature, one contrary ought to destroy, not to corroborate, the other. And next, it is a maxim among the Peripatetics themselves, that natural causes always act as much as they can. And certainly, in our case, wherein we treat not of living creatures, I cannot but think the axiom physically demonstrative. For inanimate agents act not by choice, but by a necessary impulse; and, not being endowed with understanding and will, cannot of themselves be able to moderate or to suspend their actions.

As for the example of the cellar being cold in summer and warm in winter, he questions the truth of the assertion, because it may only seem so to our sensation by contrast with the outside temperature in the two seasons. This example is an excellent illustration of the difficulties which confronted scientists when they lacked such essential apparatus as a thermometer, and of how easily one can be deceived by his sensations and memory.

As Boyle had attacked successfully the doctrine of substantial forms in his treatise on colour, so in this one on cold he brought into the open many errors of fact which had resulted from neglecting to experiment, and shook the dependence on animistic causes. There still remains for us to consider his final great work on effluvia, under which title he included all the phenomena resulting from the mutual actions of bodies separated by space, such as gravity, radiant heat and light, electricity and magnetism; and which we now, in science, class under the general term of radiant energy. In early times, such phenomena were frankly classed as occult, and were considered subject to animistic causes; and even today, in spite of our materialistic philosophy, the best explanation of them we can give involves the supposition of occult bodies or occult forces. We have learned much about the properties of light; but we deceive ourselves, like little children, if we think we have made any clearer the mystery of how we perceive the light generated in the sun, by imagining an occult æther whose nature is contrary to all our experience; we can measure the fall of an apple to the earth by the law of gravitation, but we have to suppose an occult force of attraction which offends all our repugnance to action at a distance. We are fortunate in having discarded many of the grosser forms of superstition; we know that epidemics of disease are caused by living organisms rather than by malignant steams; we have found perceptible causes for numerous phenomena once under the spell of magic formulæ. But we have, in our attempt to explain all mental and spiritual qualities by so-called natural causes, endowed material corpuscles and atoms with powers as occult, and as fantastic, as the mediæval monks ascribed to immaterial demons and angels.

We owe much to Boyle for his endeavour to substitute natural for mystical causes, but we do not owe to him the belief that biology, psychology, and theology are only branches of chemistry and physics. What he thought of that belief, we can read in his own words:

The School philosophers do not only refuse to acquiesce in sensible agents, but, to solve the more mysterious phenomena of nature, nay and most of the familiar ones too, they scruple not to run too far to the other side, and have their recourse to agents that are not only invisible but inconceivable, at least to men that cannot admit any save rational and consistent notions: they ascribe all abstruse effects to certain substantial forms, which, however they call material, because of their dependence on matter, they give such descriptions to, as belong to spiritual beings; as if all the abstruser effects of nature, if they be not performed by visible bodies, must be so by immaterial substances; whereas betwixt visible bodies and spiritual beings there is a middle sort of agents, invisible corpuscles; by which a great part of the difficulter phenomena of nature are produced, and by which may intelligibly be explicated those phenomena, which it were absurd to refer to the former, and precarious to attribute to the latter.*

After Boyle published his *Origin of Forms* in 1666, he was practically silent for five years, gathering his forces to complete his endeavour to modernize science; he then, during the following three years, produced five tracts which really finished the task he had set out to do.[4] In one way or another, each of these works attempts to explain some of the 'difficulter phenomena of nature' in terms of the 'middle sort of agents.' He would see if his experimental results were consistent with the actions of effluvia—by which he meant streams of corpuscles, either composing the bodies themselves or of a special nature—and thereby displace the animistic steams, vapours, virtues, and incantations, which it was the custom to evoke to conceal ignorance, and to dull enquiry.

* *Works*, Vol. III, p. 278. It has interested and amused me to change this passage by substituting the 'modern mechanistic philosophers' for the 'school philosophers,' and by interchanging 'sensible agents and bodies,' with 'spiritual agents and bodies.' It will be found then to express our unbalanced materialistic philosophy of today with singular accuracy.

In the first place, all natural philosophers, Aristotelians, Cartesians, and Atomists, however they might explain phenomena, can agree that effluvia *could* be the effect of small particles. And so Boyle collects almost endless examples of emanations; which he discusses under five headings.[5]

1. 'The strange extensibility of some bodies, whilst their parts yet remain tangible.' As illustrations, he cites the drawing of gold and silver into wires of great length, and hammering them into thin sheets; also, he tells of a gentlewoman who unwound from a silk cocoon much over three hundred yards of silk, weighing less than two and a half grains.

2. 'The multitude of visible corpuscles that may be afforded by a small portion of matter.' He calls attention to the cloud of steam from boiling water, and of smoke from burning wood. As a very striking example, he dissolved one grain of copper in spirits of sal-ammoniac and found that one part in 28,534 by weight distinctly tinged the water blue. He admires also the complexity of a cheese-mite or of the embryo of an egg, which seen 'by the microscope, appears to be an animal furnished with all necessary parts.'

3. 'The smallness of the pores, at which the effluvia of some bodies will get in.' Scaliger reports that the poison of some spiders is so virulent, that it will penetrate the sole of a shoe if they should be stepped on. He is especially impressed with the magnetic effluvium from lode-stones, which penetrates all kinds of bodies.

4. 'The small decrement of bulk, or weight, that a body may suffer by parting with great store of effluvia.' Under this heading, he can instance the odors of bodies, even of metals, with almost no loss of weight. The effluvia from magnets would be the most striking example, but he cautiously points out that the corpuscles emitted from either pole may be replenished by those from the other; or, perhaps, magnetism may be the result of streams of magnetic matter, supplied by the earth, which pass through the lode-stone.

5. 'The great quantity of space that may be filled, as to sense, by a small quantity of matter, when rarefied or dispersed.' It is unnecessary to retail the many examples he cites of keenness of scent of animals, and of the widespread diffusion of the effluvia that cause plagues.

In order to fortify his thesis that effluvia could be regarded as streams of minute corpuscles in rapid motion, and at the same time to strip from them the legends and mystic properties which had accumulated from very ancient times, Boyle could not have made a happier choice than his careful study of the origin and virtues of gems. He comments on an accepted origin of gems, which agrees with Aristotle (*Meteora*, Bk. III.): 'that a dry exhalation, whether fiery or firing, makes, among other fossils, the several kinds of unfusible stones; or to tell us, according to the more received doctrine, that gems are made of earth and water finely incorporated and hardened by cold,' is to accept a generality too indefinite to be of use, and one which is perhaps untrue.

'As to the history of gems, that has been so fabulously delivered, that, especially among the moderns, many learned men, philosophers and physicians, have . . . been induced to deny them any virtues at all.' Boyle is sceptical, but he believes that certain of their medical virtues are well authenticated, and he will offer later a possible explanation consonant with the corpuscular hypothesis. 'For my part,' he writes, 'I never saw any great feats performed by those hard and costly stones (as diamonds, rubies, sapphires) that are wont to be worn in rings; . . . but I will not indiscriminately reject all the medicinal virtues that tradition and the writers about precious stones have ascribed to those noble minerals.'

Of the formation of gems, Boyle gives this accurate and, I believe, original explanation. The transparent ones were, he thinks, once in a fluid state and were then mixed with various kinds of metals or mineral substances, which give to them their colours and virtues. He then discusses his theory under five heads and gives many pertinent illustrations to prove that it is consonant with the doctrine of corpuscles.

(1) The transparency of gems favours his conjecture that they were first in a fluid state, which would allow their corpuscles to arrange themselves to give an easy passage to rays of light. (2) Gems are crystals and therefore their corpuscles are arranged in geometrical patterns which could occur only in a fluid state. This fact is disguised because they are usually seen after they have been cut; but he examined many in the rough and had consulted gem experts. He also precipitated many dissolved chemical salts and obtained crystals. (3) His theory is favoured also by the internal structure of gems, for he found that all kinds, even the diamond, have

cleavage planes and are not of a uniform texture. 'No such thing has been noted by the most curious eye'; and this property is also true of salts precipitated from the fluid state. (4) Of the colours of gems, some at least he found to be accidental, for they were deprived of their colour if they fell and were fractured, or were powdered, or heated in a fire. This would follow if some coloured mineral juice or tingeing exhalations had mingled with the fluid stone. And it is a fact that gems are usually in or near mineral deposits. Also the same kind of gem occurs in different colours and may be parti-coloured, as if its colour were caused by an external agent. (5) He found that gems are heavier than other stones, as if they contained a mineral.*

Of the medicinal virtues of gems, Boyle cites many cases which he believed authentic, such as the power of the blood-stone to stop bleeding at the nose—a myth almost universally accepted and probably to be traced to its red spots, an example of the doctrine of signatures. He also instances a case, reported to him by an eye-witness, of a *lapis lyncurius* which, when rubbed, moistened, and exposed to the sun, produced an edible mushroom. If we consider the almost universal belief in the medicinal and magic powers of gems, supported as it was by what was accepted as reliable observation, no more devastating attack could have been made on animistic causes than his derivation of those powers from corpuscular effluvia: 'I conceive, that some, at least, of the real virtues of divers gems may be derived from this, that whilst they were in a fluid form, or, at least, not yet hardened, the petrescent substance was mingled with some mineral solution or tincture, or with some other impregnated liquor; and that these were after concoagulated, or united and hardened into one gem.' Thus, any virtue a gem may have is caused by the slow liberation of its occluded material effluvia, which may, as salts, be of a medicinal nature and penetrate the skin.

Boyle had progressed in his corpuscular studies to a point where he could attempt an *experimentum crucis* which would settle the question. He had in his years of apprenticeship greatly shaken the Aristotelians and the Spagyrists by proving that air had elasticity and weight; now, in the height of his powers and reputation, he

* The reader may, to refresh his memory, consult the chapter on alchemy in order to appreciate the originality of Boyle's work on gems, which really was the basis of the science of crystallography.

would attack their innermost stronghold and prove experimentally that fire also was body having weight: 'I thought it worth the enquiry, whether a thing so vastly diffused as light is, were something corporeal, or not? and whether, in case it be, it may be subjected to some other of our senses, besides our sight, whereby we may examine, whether it hath any affinity with other corporeal beings that we are acquainted with here below.' [6]

For his purpose, Boyle determined to subject metals to the action of intense light on the hypothesis that, if it were corpuscular, a sufficient number of its minute particles might be added to the metal to increase its weight. He hoped to use the pure flame of sun-light, but, although he had good lenses, the English winter baffled him and he was too impatient to wait for sunny days; so he substituted fire. Copper, tin, lead, and other metals were successively subjected to a hot fire until they were well calcined, or, as we now say, oxidized. In every case the metal was found to have gained considerable weight.

After several improvements in his practice, he finally succeeded in calcining his metal in a sealed glass vessel. Two ounces of tin filings were heated by burning sulphur, which was supposed to give a pure flame; the glass retort was provided with a long, thin stem, which was left open to permit some of the heated air to escape and so prevent breaking when it was hermetically sealed. After heating it for three and a half hours, he found a considerable amount of a darkish calx and an increase of weight of four and a half grains as he remembered it. He also noted that air rushed into the retort when the seal was broken. From this and similar experiments, he concluded that flame was a body having weight, and that some, at least, of its corpuscles were sufficiently minute to penetrate the pores of glass.

This tract on the perviousness of glass was severely criticized by Père Chérubin d'Orléans, who argued that Boyle should have weighed the retort and all its contents, before and after the calcination. If he had then found an increase in weight, his conclusion that the increase of weight was caused by the entrance of foreign matter would have been justified. Though Chérubin's explanation of porosity was faulty, his criticism of Boyle's work was acute and correct.[7] Boyle was aware of this criticism and, in a letter to an unknown correspondent,[8] he rather haughtily replied that he was 'more willing to pass by, than imitate such a dogmatical way of writing'; nor did he think Chérubin's supposition would disable his argument. He added however: 'I must let you know for a certain reason, that needs not now be told, I remember I did weigh a sealed retort, with matter in it, and found it increased in weight, but thought not fit to lay much stress on that circumstance.' It was most unfortunate for his reputation that this faulty observation should have misled him.

Boyle had made a great discovery in proving that by calcination or oxidation metals gain weight, whereas the opinion was held, 'that much is driven away by the violence of the fire, and the remaining parts, by being deprived of their more radical and fixed moisture, are turned into dry and brittle particles . . . Whence I conclude, that the calx of a metal even made as they speak, *per se,* that is, by fire without additament, may be, at least in some cases not the *caput mortuum,* or *terra damnata,* but a magistery of it.'

But how much greater an achievement would have been Boyle's if he had heeded Chérubin's criticism. He would certainly have found that the weights of his sealed vessel, before and after calcination, were equal, and would have been driven to the conclusion that the increase in weight of the metal was caused by an equal loss of the air; nor could he have missed the truth that calcination was a union of the metal with corpuscles of air and not of fire. Or, he could have heated the metal in a vacuum; or, he could have attached a pressure gauge to the retort. If he had had the patience to try any of these ways, he would have solved the age-long alchemistic mystery of the death of a metal by fire and its resurrection by fire when a few grains of wheat were added. It was this mystery of the cycle of chemistry which gave to the ancient alchemists their symbol of the serpent with its tail in its mouth; and as a symbol of death and resurrection of the body, it fostered that weird, and almost blasphemous, coalescence of the philosopher's stone and the Christ.

Enough has been given in this discussion of Boyle's creative work to show with what arguments he opposed the doctrine of substantial forms and other tenets of the mediæval philosophy of nature. Interspersed through this work he gave, here and there, brief and rather tentative statements on what he meant by his corpuscularian 'hypothesis,' and he used this term deliberately, as was the usual

custom in the seventeenth century to express an assumption or speculation, and not a matter of proof. Now at last, he could answer in
his *History of Particular Qualities*[9] the grand objection to his doctrine of qualities: 'viz, that it is incredible that so great a variety
of qualities as we actually find to be in bodies should spring from
principles so few in number as two, and so simple as matter and
local motion; whereof the latter is but one of the six kinds of motion reckoned up by Aristotle and his followers, who call it *lation;*
and the former, being all of one uniform nature, is according to us
diversified only by the effects of local motion.'

And to answer this objection, he drew up a logical scheme of
nature from which to make discoveries and inventions.

1. Local motion in various parts of the universal matter tends
   in different ways. It will follow that matter must be divided into distinct parts.
2. These parts, each being finite, must be of some bigness or
   size.
3. Each part must have a determinate shape.
4. Some parts of the matter will be arrested in their motion by
   their mutual implication [connexions or actions] and will
   be in a state of rest in the popular sense of the word.

These 'are the most primary and simple affections of matter.' Because there are some others which flow naturally from them and
are very general and pregnant, although not universal, he adds
seven 'that are the most fertile principles of the qualities of bodies
and other phænomena of nature.'

5. Each corpuscle, as well as a perceptible fragment of matter,
   has a particular posture or position: as erect, inclined, or
   horizontal.
6. Corpuscles have a certain order or consecution to us, who observe them; or one is before or behind another.
7. Corpuscles are, in great numbers, associated together to form
   a mass or body, and give to it a texture.
8. Because of irregularities of figure of the corpuscles, almost all
   solid and all gross fluid bodies have pores in them.
9. Since most bodies, besides their bigger and more stable corpuscles, have smaller ones, whose motions are greatly increased by heat and other agents, and are thus easily sep-

arated from a body to cause those subtile emanations, called effluvia.

10. (a) Durable aggregations of simple corpuscles constitute primary concretions, or elements [i.e. gold, phosphorus, tin, etc.]

(b) These elements may be mingled together to form compound bodies.

(c) Compound bodies may be mingled to make decompounded bodies, and so afford a way whereby nature varies matter, which we call mixture or composition.

11. Every body—whether it be a corpuscle, element, or compound of any order of mixt—exists not isolated, but in a universe of bodies, near or remote, great or small, catholic or particular agents; 'and all of them are governed as well by the universal fabric of things, as by the laws of motion established by the author of nature in the world.'

12. Thus, 'we have enumerated eleven very general affections of matter, which with itself make up twelve principles of variations in bodies.'

Boyle nowhere claims to have a proof for the corpuscular hypothesis; and, in calling it such, he specified it as incapable of certainty because the existence of body is postulated on observation. But he is so captivated by its simplicity, plausibility, and applicability to the facts of experiment that he would discard for it the dogmas of substantial forms, real qualities, the four elements, the three principles, which had stifled the acquisition of knowledge. He will cite only as an analogy:

On behalf of the corpuscularians, apply to the origin of qualities a comparison of the old atomists employed by Lucretius, and others, to illustrate the production of an infinite number of bodies, from such simple fragments of matter as they thought their atoms to be. For since of the twenty-four letters of the alphabet associated several ways, as to the number and placing of the letters, all the words of the several languages in the world may be made; so, say these naturalists, by variously connecting such and such numbers of atoms, of such shapes, sizes, and motions, into masses or concretions, an innumerable multitude of different bodies may be formed . . . The best way I know of doing this is by algebra or symbolic arithmetic, by which it appears, that of so few things so many associations may be made.

EPILOGUE

BOYLE, by his achievements in chemistry, won for himself a legitimate place in that dynasty of intellectual giants which began with Copernicus, and included also Kepler, Galileo, Descartes, and Newton; each accepted and developed the fundamental ideas of his predecessor and ushered in the Scientific Renaissance. In the course of a century and a half, from the publication of Copernicus' *De revolutionibus* in 1543 to Newton's *Principia* in 1687, this royal line and their followers had replaced the animistic natural philosophy of the Middle Ages with that mechanistic empiricism which has become the canon of science.

By an odd trick of fortune, Boyle's own work on effluvia and on the increase of weight of metals by calcination had much to do with the failure of his doctrine of the elements to gain general acceptance for more than a century. Strangely enough, chemical theory reverted to alchemy with the weird invention of phlogiston. Under the leadership of Stahl and his school, which included such eminent chemists as Cavendish, Black, Scheele, and Priestley, combustion meant the liberation of an inflammable principle called phlogiston instead of sulphur.* And conversely, since a metal could be recovered from its calx, or oxide, by heating it in the presence of coal, this regeneration was accomplished by absorption of phlogiston. Boyle's supposed proof of the corpuscular nature of fire and flame was a bulwark of strength for the phlogistonists; but his demonstration that all metals gain weight by calcination was an equal stumbling block to their hypothesis.†

It is generally accepted that the doctrine of phlogiston was derived from the Aristotelian dictum of the absolute levity of the element, fire; and his modern followers were driven to strange devices when trying to reconcile increase of weight with loss of matter. The doc-

---

* For a discussion of the later developments of this subject, see the 'Historical Studies on the Phlogiston Theory,' by Partington and McKie, *Annals of Science,* October 1937.

† Boyle was not the first to observe this increase of weight; Drs. Partington and McKie instance Biringuccio (1480-1538) and Jean Bodin (1596) as having noted this fact in the calcination of lead. There is no record that Boyle was acquainted with the work of his predecessors; and it is certain that the opposite opinion prevailed.

trine of phlogiston became more and more incapable of coping with the new wealth of observations which was being accumulated, and it received its quietus with Lavoisier's scornful statement:

All these reflections confirm what I have advanced, what I have endeavoured to prove, what I shall repeat again, that chemists have made of phlogiston a vague principle which is not rigorously defined, and which, consequently adapts itself to any desired explanation. Sometimes this principle is a principle of weight, and sometimes it is not; sometimes it is free fire, sometimes it is fire combined with the earthy element; sometimes it passes through the pores of vessels, sometimes they are impenetrable to it; it explains both causticity and non-causticity, transparency and opacity, colours and the lack of colours. It is a veritable Proteus which changes form at every instant.[1]

Then Lavoisier continues, in words almost identical with those used by Boyle a century earlier, to urge a saner scientific method: 'It is time to bring chemistry back to a more rigorous way of reasoning, to strip from the facts, with which this science is constantly enriched, what reasoning and prepossessions have added to them; to distinguish what is fact and observation from that which is systematized and hypothetical.'

Phlogiston was the last gasp of the dying alchemy, and it never again revived. Lavoisier had established the balance as the criterion of chemistry and with it he was able to follow the chemical ingredients as they passed through various chemical changes. Boyle's corpuscular hypothesis required, to be workable, Dalton's conception of the atom and molecule as invariable units of mass, and Avogadro's law that, under the same conditions of temperature and pressure, equal volumes of gases contain equal numbers of molecules. Another absolute necessity to cope with the mass of discoveries accumulating in the eighteenth and nineteenth centuries was to replace the uncouth jargon of the alchemists with a nomenclature for the elements and their compounds which would rival the accuracy and conciseness which the mathematicians had devised for their subject; and we owe such an invention to Berzelius, who improved and extended the suggestions of Lavoisier and Dalton.

If the last century was notable for the enormous growth of our knowledge of the chemical elements, of their compounds, and of their uses, the cause of their association and of their disassociation was neglected and the chemist remained attached to his animistic affinities. It is possible that the application of modern thermo- and electrodynamics may give us a quantitative and mathematical solution to the problem of chemical varieties of bodies. If so, then the science of physics, which had been limited to the investigation of the variations of energy of body, defined only by its inertia; and the science of chemistry, which had been concerned with the variations of body without regard to those of energy; may be united as branches of the complete science of mechanics, which will embrace the phenomena and laws of the material universe. If such can be accomplished, the ambition of Boyle and the natural philosophers of the seventeenth century will have been realized.

APPENDIX

THE SPIRIT OF ANGLICANISM *

By Paul Elmer More

IT is convenient to date the beginning of the period under discussion with the publication of the first four books of Hooker's *Ecclesiastical Polity* in 1594, when the Anglican Communion was first made aware of itself as an independent branch of the Church Universal, neither Roman nor Calvinist, but at once Catholic and Protestant, with a positive doctrine and discipline of its own and a definite mission in the wide economy of Grace. The year 1691 has been chosen to close the period, as dating the schismatic activity of the Non-Jurors, and as marking a notable break in English ecclesiastical history.

Within this period of nearly a hundred years a considerable diversity of opinion may be discovered among admittedly Anglican writers on points of doctrine and discipline. England, it is important to remember, did not produce at that time, and indeed has never produced, a single theologian to whom appeal can be made for a final sentence in disputed questions, as the Germans could appeal to Luther and the Presbyterians to Calvin, nor had she any such ultimate court of authority as the Counter-Reformation possessed in the Council of Trent. Of this condition the apologists of the age were well aware; they could even turn it into a boast, as when Chillingworth declared proudly that we 'call no man master on the earth.'

Diversity of opinion and diffusion of authority are patent on the surface of the Caroline literature. But withal an attentive student of the whole movement will be more impressed by the unity within the variety and by the steady flow of the current beneath all surface eddies towards a definite goal. What we have to look for in the

---

* The *Essay*, as given, is complete, except for the omission of some illustrative passages which do not concern Boyle's theology. Since these omissions do not seriously break the continuity of thought, they have not been indicated.

ecclesiastical literature in England is not so much finality as direction; and if this implies a degree of inconsistency among those groping for the way, such pliancy of mind in approaching the mysteries of revelation may prove safer than premature fixation. The finished system of Calvin fell into ruins as soon as a single flaw was detected in its chain of logic, and a single discrepancy between fact and theory may bring the 'fundamentalism' of Rome, in so far as it clings to the belief in the complete inerrancy of the Bible, to the same doom.

If challenged to state the motive that started the Church of England on her peculiar course, the historian is likely to reply that it was political rather than religious. The first impulse towards independence was given by the Papal refusal to admit the annulment of Henry the Eighth's marriage to Catherine of Aragon, and this conflict, however much it may have concerned that monarch's taste in wives, was presented to the people as though the monarchy and national autonomy were at stake. Henry was a Catholic still. He applied the 'Whip with the Six Strings' [the Six Articles] with an inquisitorial zest that must have been infinitely distressing to the cautious Cranmer. And then no sooner was the jurisdiction of the Bishop of Rome discredited than there arose a new party, influenced from Geneva, which denied the authority of all bishops whatsoever. And again the issue, as presented to the people, became confused with politics. It was henceforth the cry of the Court and the Church that episcopacy and monarchy were indissolubly bound together: No Bishop, no King! Between these opposite intrusions from the Continent the Church of England was thus directed, primarily by reasons of State, to the *via media* which has been her watchword from that day to this. It is in the light of this thrust of civil influences from abroad that we should interpret the special form which the Erastianism of the age took in England, and should consider the disabilities imposed upon Romanist and Nonconformist alike, which were not removed until well into the nineteenth century.

Such quite clearly is the external origin of the *via media* which was to become the very charter of the Church. It may have begun as a protest against the political claims of Rome on the one side and the Genevan theories of state on the other. It may have looked at the outset like a shift to avoid difficulties, a *modus vivendi,* at the best a 'middle way' as commended by Donne because 'more convenient and advantageous than that of any other Kingdom.' But behind it all the while lay a profounder impulse, pointing in a positive direction, and aiming to introduce into religion, and to base upon the 'light of reason,' that love of balance, restraint, moderation, measure, which from sources beyond our reckoning appears to be innate in the English temper.

So understood, this principle of balance and measure is at once English and Greek. And the point is, that though in matters of human expediency it may seem to result in a compromise, in the sphere of religion, where ultimate principles are involved, it depends upon a positive choice of direction which is intrinsically different from compromise. And this difference can be illustrated by the heretical and the orthodox attitude towards the primary doctrine of Christianity. Here the Fathers were confronted by the plain fact that the Founder of their faith was presented to them by a tradition going back to those who had lived with him, as at once, in some unique manner, both divine and human, both God and man. Reason was thunderstruck by such a paradox; the wisdom of the schools could make nothing of it. Logic could deal with him as God only or as man only, and indeed as one or the other he did so appear to the docetic or humanitarian philosophy of Gnostics and Adoptionists. But theology was bound to discover a path between these two exclusions; and the great heresy, the first to threaten the very existence of Christianity as a religion, was an attempt to explain the *via media* as a compromise. To the Arians Christ was neither quite God nor quite man, but a something intermediary which resembled the natures of both without being purely either. Against this plausible and seemingly reasonable escape between the horns of faith's dilemma (which in fact possessed the virtues neither of reason nor of paradox), the Church, by the Definition of Chalcedon, simply thrust its way through the middle by making the personality of the Incarnate so large as to carry with it *both* natures. Evidently in this case at least the principle of measure does not produce a diminished or half truth, but acts as a law of restraint preventing either one of two aspects of a paradoxical truth from excluding the other. Nor is the middle way here a mean of compromise, but a mean of comprehension.

The course of the Anglicans was peculiar in this, that deliberately and courageously they clung to the principle of mediation in regions of doctrine and discipline, where, as they contended, the Romanist and the radical Protestant did in fact stray aside into vicious extremes of exclusion. If we follow this contention on measure and restraint through its ramifications, we shall find that it revolves about the nature of authority in Tradition and Scripture as bearing upon two main points: (1) the practical distinction between fundamentals and accessories of religion, and (2) the axiomatic rejection of infallibility.

The distinction between fundamentals and accessories, or, in the more usual language of the day, between things necessary for salvation and things convenient in practice, was clearly drawn by Hooker and recurs constantly through the ensuing literature. The fundamentals are few and revealed, the accessories are indeterminate and more or less dependent on human invention.

For the Anglicans of the seventeenth century those few things necessary for salvation were summed up conveniently in the Creeds, particularly in the so-called Apostles' Creed. And for the truth of this Creed they appealed, as did other Christians, to the double authority of Tradition and Scripture. They held the common belief that the twelve articles of the Creed went back to the actual Apostles, each of whom made his individual contribution to the formula, and so handed on the deposit of the faith to the keeping of successive generations. But behind the Creed, guaranteeing its truth and in general confirming the authority of tradition where right, and correcting it where astray, was the sacred canon of written books. For this reason, Chillingworth, while allowing due weight to tradition in its place, could speak of the Bible as the religion, and, in case of dispute, the sole religion, of Protestants.

Certainly no Anglican divine of the seventeenth century, if questioned, would have admitted that faith in the Incarnation, as the one thing necessary, could be divested of such accessories as the Virgin Birth and the literal Ascension into heaven, which are included in the Creed and based on the record of Scripture. But the continued emphasis on what is fundamental was leading the Church in the direction of an utter simplicity—a simplicity which embraced the fundamentals in a single article of faith: 'Jesus Christ is the Son of God.'

And it is certain that in thus isolating the few things, or the one thing, in the Bible necessary for salvation, they saw themselves

placed between the two fires of Romanist and Puritan. In their controversy with the former it was the question of tradition. To the
Anglicans the value of tradition was measured by its tenacity of the
original *depositum fidei*. It was not that they rejected the principle
of development utterly, but that in matters fundamental they limited its competence to an interpretation of dogma held strictly at
every step to the test of Scripture. The quarrel with Rome was because of her practice of extending the fundamentals of faith by increments on the warrant of her own inspired authority, and so of
creating, as it were, instead of obeying tradition. South was voicing
the common view of all Protestants when he made the specific
charge: 'The Church of Rome has [in this respect] sufficiently declared the little value she has for the old Christian Truth, by the
new, upstart articles she has added to it.'

In their repudiation of the Roman efforts to cover her dogmatic
innovations under the authority of tradition, and in their insistence
on the Bible as the sole final criterion of orthodoxy, the Anglicans
stood with the Protestants; but on the other side they departed from
the Reformers of the Continent, and from the Puritans at home, in
their rejection of what they regarded as an illegitimate extension of
Scriptural authority. Again it was a question of fundamentals and
accessories. Certain inferences from the central dogma of the Incarnation they allowed as self-evident, even in a way as essential
to the faith that saves; but they hesitated over, and with the passing
of time drew back more resolutely from, the doctrines of absolute
predestination, effectual calling, justification by faith alone, imputed
righteousness, and the whole scaffolding of rationalized theology
which Luther and Calvin had constructed about the central truth
out of an unbalanced exposition of isolated texts. Not that way lay
the simplicity of faith. Here they stood with Rome in so far as they
would admit the immense value of tradition in much that was vital
to religious observance, though it might not be necessary to salvation.

The true thread of continuity, the Anglicans held, was broken
either by superimposing new and disputable dogmas upon the divine revelation after the manner of Rome, or by disallowing due
weight in the practical sphere of religion to the wisdom of accumulated human experience after the manner of Geneva.

Closely connected with the distinction between fundamentals and accessories was the axiomatic denial of infallibility. One of the surprises awaiting a student of the ecclesiastical literature of the seventeenth century is the frequency with which this word 'infallibility' occurs in unexpected places. It was the veritable bugbear of the English mind of that age as it has become again since the Vatican Council of 1870, and upon the attitude to all that is conveyed by those fatal syllables hangs the ultimate philosophic difference, or let us say incompatibility of temper, between Roman and Anglican Catholicism and, in a fashion less sharply defined, between radical and Anglican Protestantism. 'Two things there are,' says Hooker, 'which trouble greatly these later times: one that the Church of Rome cannot, another that Geneva will not, err.' And in a sweeping assertion Hales sums up the Anglican position thus: 'Infallibility either in judgement, or interpretation, or whatsoever, is annext neither to the See of any Bishop, nor to the Councils, nor to the Church, nor to any *created power* whatsoever.' Now such a statement, which might be supplemented by quotations from other and more authoritative, at least more Catholic writers, if taken superficially would seem to leave religion a prey to the universal flux of uncertainty; but not if full weight be given to the phrase 'created power.' Evidently this does not exclude from infallibility those necessary truths which proceed directly from a divine and uncreated source.

Taking together then the two axioms in regard to fundamentals and infallibility, we can see that the Anglicanism of the seventeenth century comes to something like this: The means divinely ordained for the salvation of mankind is plainly set forth in the Bible in the story of the birth and life and death and resurrection of Jesus Christ, the Son of God. This truth, as Chillingworth maintained, is of such 'admirable simplicity'—though its simplicity and plainness rather enhance than diminish its significance—as to need no interpreter. But there are recorded in the same book other facts and doctrines, a vast body enveloping, so to speak, the central truth, which, however great their importance, are not necessary to salvation, and do not open their meaning so immediately. For the interpreting of these secondary truths, and for the drawing of inferences therefrom, upon which rests the whole structure of disputable theology, there is no oracular organ of infallibility appointed among men or in any human institution.

Looking backwards, then, upon the theology of the Caroline divines, we can see that their manifest intention was to steer a middle course between the excesses of Romanist and Radical Protestant. Clearly also such a middle course was not in the nature of compromise or of hesitation to commit themselves to conviction, but was governed by a positive determination to preserve the just balance between fundamentals and accessories which was threatened by an authority vested in the infallibility whether of Tradition or of Scripture.

NOTES

CHAPTER I

1. *True Remembrances.*
2. Ibid.
3. Ibid.
4. Townshend, *Life and Letters of the Great Earl of Cork*, p. vi.
5. *Lismore Papers*, 1st Series, Vol. 1.

CHAPTER II

1. *Works*, Vol. 1, p. xiii.
2. Information given by the Lord Treasurer. *Lismore Papers*. Entry for 13 January 1628/9.
3. *Lismore Papers*, 1 April 1629.
4. *Works*, Vol. 1, p. xiv.
5. Ibid.
6. *Lismore Papers.*
7. *Works*, Vol. 1, p. 16.
8. Townshend, op. cit. p. 214.
9. *Lismore Papers.*
10. Birkenhead: Sunday *Times*, 1937.
11. Townshend, op. cit. p. 271.
12. Ibid. p. 289.

CHAPTER III

1. *Works*, Vol. 1, p. xviii.
2. Ibid. Vol. 1, p. xvii.
3. Evelyn, *Diary*, Bohn Edition, Vol. 1, p. 249.
4. *Works*, Vol. 1, p. xix.
5. Ibid. Vol. 1, p. xxii.
6. Ibid.
7. Townshend, op. cit. p. 402.

CHAPTER IV

1. *Works*, Vol. 1, p. xxvii.
2. Townshend, op. cit. p. 234.
3. *Works*, Vol. 1, p. xxvii.
4. Ibid.
5. Ibid. Vol. 1, pp. xxvii-xxx.
6. *Sunday at Home*, 1863.
7. *Works*, Vol. 1, pp. xxx-xxxiv.
8. Ibid. Vol. 1, pp. xxxiv-xxxv.
9. Weld's *History of the Royal Society*, Vol. 1, p. 30.
10. *Works*, Vol. 1, p. xxxvi.

11. Ibid. Vol. vi, p. 49.
12. Cf. *supra*. pp. 59 and 61.
13. *Works,* Vol. i, p. xxxix.
14. Ibid. Vol. ii, p. 247. The essay is reviewed in Chapter VIII.
15. Ibid. Vol. i, p. xlviii.
16. *Lismore Papers.*
17. *Works,* Vol. i, p. xliii.
18. Ibid. Vol. i, p. cxxxvii.
19. Ibid. Vol. vi, p. 534.
20. Evelyn, *Diary,* Bohn Edition, Vol. iii, p. 349.
21. *Works,* Vol. i, p. clix.
22. Ibid. Vol. i, p. xli.
23. Ibid. Vol. i, p. cxxxvi.
24. Masson, *Life of Robert Boyle,* p. 171.
25. *Works,* Vol. vi, p. 54.
26. Ibid. Vol. vi, p. 137.

CHAPTER V

1. *Works,* Vol. i, p. lii.
2. Ibid. Vol. vi, p. 523.
3. Cf. Wood, *Life and Times,* and *Athen. Oxon.;* Aubrey, *Lives;* Mallet, *Hist. Oxon.;* Mullinger, *Hist. Camb.*
4. *Athenae Oxonienses,* Vol. iv, p. 989.
5. See More, *Life of Newton, passim.*
6. *The Diary of Robert Hooke,* Robinson and Adams, London, 1935.
7. *On the Spring and Weight of the Air. Works,* Vol. i, p. 3.
8. *Works,* Vol. i, pp. 6 and 7. The quotation is taken from the second edition of 1662.
9. Ibid. Vol. i, p. 2.
10. Linus, *Tractatus de corporum inseparabilitate.* London, 1661.
11. Hobbes, *Dialogus physicus, sive De Natura Aeris.* London, 1661.
12. *Works,* Vol. i, p. 134.
13. Ibid. Vol. i, pp. 189-242.
14. Ibid. Vol. i, p. 188.
15. Ibid. Vol. vi, p. 142.
16. Ibid. Vol. vi, p. 288; and Evelyn's *Diary and Correspondence,* Bohn Edition, Vol. iii, p. 116.

CHAPTER VI

1. Mallet, *History of Oxford University,* Vol. ii, p. 404.
2. *Works,* Vol. vi, p. 61.
3. For the founding and early history of the Royal Society, consult the accounts by Bishop Sprat, Birch, Weld, and the *Record of the R. S.,* 3rd ed., London, 1912.
4. Thomas Sprat, *The History of the Royal Society,* London, 1667, pp. 112 and 113.
5. *Plus Ultra,* pp. 92, 93.
6. *Works,* Vol. i, p. xcv.
7. *Diary,* 30 November 1680.
8. See Fulton's *Bibliography* for titles, etc.
9. Cf. Chapter v, pp. 101 and 102.
10. *Works,* Vol. vi, p. 56.
11. Ibid. Vol. i, p. lxvii.

12. Ibid. Vol. I, p. xviii.
13. Ibid. Vol. I, p. ccv *et seq.*
14. Ibid. Vol. I, pp. clviii-clxxi.
15. Ibid. Vol. I, p. lxxiii, and Vol. VI, p. 192.
16. Wood, *Fasti Oxon.*
17. *Works,* Vol. I, p. cxxxix. For correspondence with Pococke, see Vol. VI, pp. 323-5. Published at Oxford in 1677, in quarto.
18. Ibid. Vol. VI, pp. 557-78.
19. Ibid. Vol. VI, p. 614.
20. Ibid. Vol. I, p. cviii.
21. Ibid. Vol. VI, pp. 591-9 and 601-10.
22. *Autobiography,* p. 16.
23. *Works,* Vol. I, p. lxxvi.
24. Ibid. Vol. I, pp. lxxvi-lxxxv.
25. Ibid. Vol. VI, p. 187.
26. Ibid. Vol. VI, p. 222.
27. Ibid. Vol. VI, p. 229.
28. Ibid. Vol. VI, p. 531.

CHAPTER VII

1. *Works,* Vol. I, cxxxiv.
2. Ibid. Vol. VI, p. 459.
3. Morrice, *Earl of Orrery's State Papers;* Masson, *Life of Robert Boyle,* pp. 275-9.
4. *Works,* Vol. I, p. xcix.
5. *Diary,* Bohn Ed., Vol III, p. 351.
6. *Works,* Vol. I, p. xcix.
7. Ibid. Vol. I, pp. clvii-clxxi.
8. Evelyn's *Diary and Correspondence,* Bohn Edition, Vol. III, pp. 346-52.

CHAPTER VIII

1. *Works,* Vol. VI, p. 4.
2. Ibid. Vol. V, pp. 255-311. Cf. also Fulton's *Bibliography,* p. 107.
3. Boswell, Vol. I, p. 312, Birkbeck Hill Edition.
4. Letter from J. Evelyn to Boyle, 29 September 1659. *Diary,* Vol. III, p. 121, Bohn Ed.
5. *Works,* Vol. II, pp. 323-460. Listed as VIII in Fulton's *Bibliography.* 1st Edition, 1665; 2nd Edition, 1669. It was published four times in the nineteenth century.
6. Ibid. Vol. II, p. 361.
7. Nichols' *Ed. of Swift's Works,* 1812, Vol. I, p. 113.
8. *Works,* Vol. II, p. 451.

CHAPTER IX

1. *Works,* Vol. I, p. xxiii.
2. Ibid. Vol. I, p. xxiv.
3. Ibid. Vol. I, p. cxl.
4. *The Excellency of Theology; Works,* Vol. IV, p. 17.
5. *Works,* Vol. V, p. 130.
6. Ibid. Vol. V, pp. 508, 509.
7. *Diary,* 16 March 1668/9.
8. *Works,* Vol. VI, p. 510.

9. Ibid. Vol. II, pp. 1-246.
10. Willey, *Seventeenth Century Background,* p. 265.
11. Locke, *Essay,* IV, 18, sect. 4.
12. Locke, *Reasonableness of Christianity. Works,* Vol. VI, p. 5.
13. *Works,* Vol. IV, p. 455.
14. Ibid. Vol. IV, p. 15.
15. *Cosmical Suspicions: Works,* Vol. III, p. 322.
16. *Works,* Vol. IV, pp. 1-78.
17. Ibid. Vol. V, p. 515.
18. Ibid. Vol. IV, p. 32.
19. Ibid. Vol. IV, p. 26.
20. Ibid. Vol. IV, p. 36.
21. Ibid. Vol. IV, pp. 43, 44.
22. More, *Life of Newton,* p. 91.
23. *Works,* Vol. IV, p. 63.

CHAPTER X

1. *Science and the Modern World,* Chapter III.
2. *The Metaphysical Foundations of Physics,* p. 236.
3. Willey: *The Seventeenth Century Background,* p. 41.
4. *Les origines de l'alchimie,* 1885; *Introduction à l'étude de la chimie des Anciens et du Moyen Age,* 1889; *La chimie au Moyen Age,* 3 vols., 1893.
5. *Les origines,* Pref., p. xiv.
6. *The Secret Tradition in Alchemy,* 1926; *Lamps of Western Mysticism; The Hermetic and Alchemical Writings of Paracelsus,* 2 vols., 1894.
7. *The Secret Tradition of Alchemy,* p. xvi.
8. Waite, *The Secret Tradition,* p. 118.
9. *Les origines,* p. 208.
10. The collection was published in Paris in two volumes, 1672, 1678. For the quotation, cf. Figuier: *L'alchimie,* p. 561.
11. *L'alchimie,* p. 17.
12. Figuier, *L'alchimie,* p. 68.
13. *Les origines de l'alchimie,* p. 207.
14. *The Secret Tradition in Alchemy,* p. 118.
15. Ibid. p. 342.
16. Ibid. p. 343.

CHAPTER XI

1. *Phil. Trans.,* Vol. XI, No. 122, pp. 515-33. Republished, *Works,* Vol. IV, pp. 219-30.
2. Macclesfield, *Correspondence,* Vol. II, pp. 395. Also *Works,* Vol. I, p. 286.
3. Masson, *Life of Boyle,* p. 289.
4. First published, *Works,* Vol. I, pp. cxii-cxvii. Reprinted, Macclesfield, op. cit. Vol. II, pp. 407-19.
5. *Works,* Vol. IV, pp. 371-9.
6. Ibid. Vol. IV, p. 374.
7. Ibid. Vol. IV, p. 375.
8. Ibid. Vol. III, p. 94.
9. Ibid. Vol. III, pp. 1-137.
10. Ibid. Vol. III, p. 102.
11. Ibid. Vol. III, p. 59.
12. Ibid. Vol. III, p. 60

13. Ibid. Vol. III, p. 60.
14. Ibid. Vol. I, p. cxxxii.
15. *Life of Locke,* Vol. I, pp. 410-13.
16. *Works,* Vol. I, p. cxxv.

CHAPTER XII

1. Cf. Chapter VIII, p. 140.
2. 'The experimental philosophy of Robert Boyle,' by Professor P. P. Wiener. *The Philosophical Review,* Vol. XII, November 1932.
3. *Experiments on the Spring and Weight of the Air,* 1660. *Works,* Vol. I, pp. 1-117.
4. *Works,* Vol. I, p. 74.
5. *Tractatus duo.* By J. Mayow, Oxford, 1668. And *Tractatus quinque,* 1674.
6. *Works,* Vol. I, p. 105.
7. Ibid. Vol. I, p. 105.
8. Ibid. Vol. I, p. 100.
9. Ibid. Vol. I, p. 108.
10. *Suspicions about some Hidden Qualities of the Air,* London, 1674. *Works,* Vol. IV, p. 85.
11. *Works,* Vol. IV, p. 90.
12. *Essays of Effluviums,* etc., 1673. *Works,* Vol. III, p. 709.
13. *Certain Physiological Essays: Works,* Vol. I, pp. 298-457.
14. *Works,* Vol. I, p. 570.
15. Ibid. Vol. I, p. 586.
16. Ibid. Vol. I, p. 569.
17. Ibid. Vol. I, p. 469.
18. Ibid. Vol. I, p. 478.
19. Ibid. Vol. I, p. 520.
20. Ibid. Vol. I, pp. 522, 523.
21. Ibid. Vol. I, p. 528.

CHAPTER XIII

1. *Works,* Vol. I, p. 562. *Sceptical Chymist, Appendix.*
2. *The Origin of Forms and Qualities,* Oxford, 1666. *Works,* Vol. III, pp. 1-137.
3. *Works,* Vol. II, p. 494.
4. *Tracts about the Cosmical Qualities of Things,* Oxford, 1671. *Works,* Vol. III, pp. 290-354.
   Tracts on Rarefaction of Air, London, 1671. *Works,* Vol. III, pp. 495-510.
   Origin and Virtues of Gems, London, 1672. *Works,* Vol. III, pp. 516-61.
   Tracts Touching the Relation Betwixt Flame and Air, London, 1672. *Works,* Vol. III, pp. 562-95.
   Essays of Effluviums, London, 1673. *Works,* Vol. III, pp. 659-730.
5. *Works,* Vol. III, p. 661 *et seq.*
6. Ibid. Vol. III, p. 706.
7. An account of this criticism is given in an essay: 'Chérubin d'Orléans: A Critic of Boyle.' By Douglas McKie, *Science Progress,* July 1936.
8. *Works,* Vol. III, p. 41.
9. Ibid. Vol. III, pp. 292-305.

EPILOGUE

1. *Réflexions sur le phlogistique: Œuvres,* t. II, p. 640.

Index

THE POLITICS OF ACID RAIN

To my wife Connie
for her patience and understanding

The Politics of Acid Rain

Policy in Canada, Great Britain and the United States

MARSHALL E. WILCHER
Assistant Professor, Department of Political Science
Pennsylvania State University

Avebury

Aldershot · Brookfield USA · Hong Kong · Singapore · Sydney

Published by

Avebury

Gower Publishing Company Limited,
Gower House, Croft Road, Aldershot,
Hants, GU11 3HR, England

Gower Publishing Company
Old Post Road, Brookfield, Vermont   05036
USA

ISBN   0-566-07002-2

Contents

Foreword

This work would not have been possible without the cooperation of numerous public officials, scholars, and professionals on both sides of the Atlantic. The portion on Great Britain was facilitated by a sabbatical leave and residence at the Department of Politics, University of Exeter. The research was also partially funded by a research grant from the Commonwealth Education System of the Pennsylvania State University.

1 Introduction

Purpose and scope of study

Since the late 1960's industrialized countries have
recognized the need to develop public policies to
alleviate damage done by human activities to our
natural environment. A major part of that damage
has been the result of air pollution. One of the
most troublesome aspects of the effort to clean up
the air has been the phenomenon known as acid rain.
Acid rain results when sulfur and nitrogen oxides
and their transformation products return from the
atmosphere to the Earth's surface. The major source
of acid rain is the emission of these pollutants
from coal powered electricity generating plants. As
scientific evidence has accumulated on the effects
of acid rain on certain bodies of water, marine life
and forests, pressure has mounted on governments to
reduce sulfur and nitrogen oxide emissions from
stationary coal powered plants.

As the issue has gained prominence and its effects
are better understood acid rain has been placed on
the public policy agenda of many governments. It
has been the subject of numerous scientific studies,
private and public research, industrial and regional

1

disputes, international negotiations and international discord. Because the emissions can be transported through the atmosphere across national boundaries long distances from the source, acid rain has become a strident international problem. The stature of acid rain as a public policy issue and the impetus for its adoption to the agenda varies widely among countries. In some countries its significance results from the damage caused by emissions from other countries, in others its significance results from being the source of emissions transported to other countries and in some its significance results from regional domestic policy influences within the country.

Because of differences in governmental institutions and structure, the extent of governmental intervention in the industrial economy, the degree of reliance on coal for power generation, and the extent of acid rain damage, national responses to the acid rain problem have varied.

The purpose of this study is to examine and compare acid rain policies and the politics of acid rain in Canada, Great Britain and the United States. In a sense, the study is one of comparative public policy. However, because of the narrow focus on the acid rain issue within the broad category of environmental policy, such a comparison is limited. Despite this limitation, the comparative aspect will be addressed. Before describing the outline of the study, some comment on the effects of acid rain is appropriate.

Acid rain damage

As one interested in policy rather than science, the writer does not pretend to understand all of the scientific data on acid rain. However, a review of some of the scientific findings and controversial issues surrounding the debate is useful. The underlying reason for the interest of governments and international organisations in acid rain is the damage it inflicts on human health and the natural environment. The combustion of fossil fuels (mainly coal) produces both sulfur and nitrogen oxides. Acid rain results when these pollutants are transported through the atmosphere and return to the surface.   The sulfur oxide (SO$_2$) component, representing over two thirds of the acidity in deposits, produces most of the acidity in sensitive water bodies.   The nitrogen oxide (NO$_x$) portion, representing slightly under one third of the acidity, is gaining increased attention for control because of other forms of acid rain damage.

 The threat of acid rain was not particularly recognized or appreciated in the early years of the environmental crisis.   Dating as far back as the British response to the tragic smog accident which took around 4,000 lives, government initiatives were quite naturally aimed at the effects of pollution on human health.   Sanitation, smoke control and the threat of carbon monoxide were crucial issues.   One response to those threats in most industrialized countries was the construction of tall stacks to transport emissions away from the source, creating the main venue for acid rain.   For all of the debate over acid rain damage, the effects and damage to human health have not been the dominant concern. Only in recent years have some scientists pressed the argument that acid rain contributes to ill health.   A 1984 US government study concludes that acid rain does not directly affect human health but indirect effects, such as increases in aluminum or lead in water supplies deserve to be monitored. Effects to human health are often mentioned in the acid rain literature but generally have not been used as the major reason for emission controls in national and international policy debates.   In a study of six US government research reports, a team of independent scientists provided a summary of acid rain damage to the environment.

 Acid deposition can acidify streams, lakes and soils.   Acidification can change biological populations and communities as well as reduce the number of species in them.   Long term acid deposition, particularly of sulfuric acid, has acidified surface waters in the northeastern United States and southeastern Canada to the extent that certain species of fish and insects have been reduced or occasionally eliminated.   A host of other biological effects has also been noted.   Acidification and associated biological effects have been found where sensitive surface waters receive acid deposition.   Acid deposition

3

can acidify soils, especially those which are moderately acidic initially. Acidification decreases the availability of nutrients and thus alters biological communities in soil. Acid deposited on leaves can leach nutrients which, if not replaced, will affect the trees. Some forests in eastern North America have been increasingly damaged during the past few decades. Acidity alone or in conjunction with other pollutants such as ozone can contribute to this damage. In addition to affecting biological communities in sensitive surface waters and soils, acid deposition and its precursors can decrease atmospheric visibility and corrode materials. (Ad Hoc Committee on Acid Rain, Is There Scientific Consensus on Acid Rain?, 1985)

A word about the ozone component. Ozone is formed at ground level with man made pollutants from motor vehicle exhausts, industry and a variety of small sources. Whereas ozone in the upper atmosphere shields the earth from damaging ultra violet radiation from the sun, it is generally agreed that ground level ozone can contribute to fog, respiratory damage to humans and damage to trees and crops. There is increasing belief that ozone is a major contributor to forest damage. This explains the general tendency for many scientists and professionals to recognize the lesser role of acid rain in forest damage. Even in the Federal Republic of Germany, where forest damage is most pronounced, it is generally considered that ozone from NO_x motor vehicle exhausts is a major contributor to tree damage.

Despite the massive amount of research and data accumulated on acid rain major debates remain among scientists. One of the main questions is that regarding linearity. That is, is there a linear relationship between emissions and deposits? Another point in dispute is the source/receptor relationship. That is, attributing deposits at a specific receptor site to a specific emission source. The relative importance of local and distant emission sources to the total acid deposition at a specific site is also a source of disagreement among scientists.

4

What does seem to be well established is that acid rain is a threat to certain aquatic systems while the relative contribution to forest damage is not known.

Outline of the study

Chapter 2 is a brief survey of some of the distinctive differences in the structural arrangements of the governments of the three countries which may aid in explaining policy outcomes. In Chapters 3, 4, and 5, the evolution of acid rain as a public policy issue in each country is traced. The major legislation on air pollution and acid rain is documented. The role of internal and external influences in the policy debate is addressed and the current state of affairs in each country is discussed. In Chapter 6 several comparative perspectives are examined. The importance and role of interest groups in each policy context is examined. Another comparative dimension relates to the constraints placed on policy flowing from the institutional and structural arrangements of the political systems. The importance of domestic regionalism in each country is also discussed. Finally, the importance of external actors, such as other countries, international organisations and non governmental organisations (NGOs) is addressed. These comparative perspectives provide the basis for some concluding remarks.

2 Power and structural arrangements

Power and structural arrangements

The politics of acid rain in the three countries
have taken different paths and had different
outcomes at least partially because of differences
in the structural and power arrangements of their
political systems.   Great Britain is a unitary
system with power concentrated in the hands of the
national government.   Local authorities are often
authorized to carry out national policy. The United
States is a federal system in which some significant
powers are shared by the national and state
governments with the national government being
clearly dominant.   Canada is also a federal system,
and while the federal government is dominant in some
areas, provinces either share or hold broader powers
than the states in the United States.

Both Canada and Great Britain utilize the
parliamentary form in which there is a fusion of
executive and legislative power. This fusion means
that a prime minister and cabinet, given a working
majority and the party discipline characteristic of
both systems, can agree on a policy as a government,
convert it into legislation in the parliament, and
then administer it as the government's program. The

provinces in Canada also use the parliamentary form. The United States, utilizing the presidential form, separates the power from the executive and the legislative powers. This separation, as opposed to the fusion in the other systems, often means that the president and the majority of congress represent different political parties, policy preferences or ideological persuasions. Another distinguishing factor is the lesser ideological orientation of US political parties and the lack of party discipline. There are also some differences in the use of administrative regulation in the three systems. Legislation in Britain and Canada tends to be less detailed and prescriptive than in the US. Both in Britain and Canada there is more use of delegated legislation in which a skeletal framework is established and details are left to administrative departments, regulatory agencies or local authorities for issuance of directives for implementation. While clearly the U.S. Congress leaves some latitude to many regulatory agencies, much legislation is quite detailed and prescriptive leaving less latitude and flexibility in implementation.

The difference in approach between Britain and the US has been documented by David Vogel (Vogel, 1986). His work illustrates the American penchant for establishing limits, standards and deadlines in legislation rather than through regulation. The US Clean Air Act provides an example of this practice and the proposals for acid rain control are added examples. In the case of Britain, however, Vogel points out the absence of deadlines or standards and the reliance on the best possible means for implementation. He also notes 'extremely limited use of either emissions or environmental quality standards.' (Vogel, p. 77). This tradition has been broken in recent years because of certain European Community (EC) environmental measures. Nigel Haigh, who has studied the ECs impact on Britain's environment policy extensively, notes that the EC introduced the concept of mandatory air standards to Britain and suggests that Britain's 'old established air pollution policies would be changed.' (Haigh, 1985, p. 8.).

In the case of Canada, its practices are often described as somewhere in between the US and

8

Britain. Some attention is given to targets, ceilings, etc., but the practice of cooperation and consultation between federal and provincial authorities, the use of informal and voluntary agreements, and the establishment of more flexible deadlines is prevalent. At federal level, the practice of broad legislation prevails. At provincial level more restrictive prescriptions are utilized.

A third major distinguishing factor of the political systems is the degree of governmental ownership or involvement in certain industries. In Britain and Canada, in the tradition of democratic socialism, some important industries are owned or managed by government boards, authorities or quasi government corporations. In the US, while a few quasi government corporations exist, the vast majority of economic sectors and industries are regulated as opposed to being owned by the government.

The systems also differ markedly in the number of major governmental units. Whereas in Britain the national government is the single major unit, in Canada there are ten provincial governments. In the United States there are fifty state governments. In Britain, the national government is the focus of power, where as in Canada the federal government must contend with ten provincial governments. In the US the national government must contend with fifty state governments.

A final point regarding the political systems is the role and stature of interest (pressure) groups in the political process. The significant feature is that many such groups in Britain and Canada are formally consulted on policy initiatives and often advisory councils are appointed to be involved in these consultations. In the US the view of interest groups are made known through lobbying and Congressional hearings, but the groups are not formally inside the system. This tends to support the cooperative dimension in Britain and Canada as opposed to the conflictual dimension of the US system.

The implications and repercussions of these facets of the three political systems on environmental and

acid rain policy outcomes in particular are
discussed in Chapter 6.

3 The politics of acid rain – Canada

Background

The constitutional foundations of the federal system of Canada are the British North America Act of 1867, the Constitution Act of 1982, and in the realm of individual liberties, the Canada Charter of Rights and Freedom of 1982. As it has evolved, environmental protection has become an area of concurrent responsibility and jurisdiction. Protection of the environment is not specifically mentioned in the constitutional documents. Because threats to the environment have wide ranging effects on the state of the economy, human health, inter provincial relations and federal lands and fisheries, a federal role in environmental protection is inevitable. One clause in the British North America Act is often cited as a basis for federal government involvement in any policy sector not specifically assigned to the provinces empowers the federal government to 'make Laws for the Peace, Order and Good Government of Canada.' (British North America Act of 1867). Environmental protection has come to be accepted as one of jurisdictional overlap. (Gibson, 1983, p. 126). Having made that statement, the protection of the environment has been predominantly a provincial responsibility.

This shared responsibility has led to a tradition and practice of extensive consultation between among federal and provincial ministers, departments and public service officials. The practice has contributed to the capacity of various levels of government to reach goals, targets and accords within the framework of broad legislative arrangements without further restrictive measures.

The evolution of environmental problems as a public policy issue in Canada can be traced to the conservation movement, and is at least partially attributable to the force and presence of the movement in the US around the turn of the 20th Century. As in the US, the movement was a reaction to the unchecked exploitation of natural resources. The most powerful thrust of the early conservation movement was the wise use of resources for economic growth and development for human activities. As early as 1906, the Canadian Forestry Association provided a focal point for conservation efforts, and in 1909, Canadian delegates attended the North American Conservation Congress. That conference's recommendations led to the establishment of the Commission on Conservation, chaired by Clifford Sifton. Sifton, along with American progressive conservationists, considered development and conservation as complementary activities. The Commission, with both federal and provincial representatives, became an important research agency and was involved in such activities as forestry, lands, fish and wildlife, water, minerals, fuels and public health. However, as the Commission expanded its activities, it caused friction among the federal bureaucracy and ministries and was disbanded in 1921. The Commission had provided a valuable forum for conservation issues. During the next three decades, the conservation movement was vastly overshadowed by the trying times. The 1920's were years of significant economic growth in Canada, much of which was based on production and some exploitation of forest resources. In the 1930's, the economic crisis led to more direct government intervention in resource management. During the 1940's, the paramount demands of the World War II effort required more exploitation of natural resources. The immediate postwar period saw further economic expansion, based largely on Canada's energy and mineral resources. In the 1960's, a 'new conservation' movement was born in Canada. The distinguishing characteristic of the new conservation from the past conservation movement was its social orientation rather than the purely economic focus which dominated the earlier movement. The turning point was the 'Resources for Tomorrow Conference of 1961'. The conference focused on the strategic importance of natural resources in Canada, the necessity to conserve nonrenewable resources, foreign control of Canadian resources, and some concern was expressed about pollution and the environment. Gradually in the 1960's environmental issues became part of the political and public policy agenda. A conference on pollution and environment was sponsored by provincial resource ministers in 1966. A federal Department of the Environment was established in 1969 (known as Environment Canada). Since that time, environmental issues have been an important public policy issue in Canada. (Burton, 1972).

The signal piece of legislation dealing with air pollution is the Clean Air Act of 1971. The bill establishes three ranges of air quality objectives -- tolerable, acceptable and desirable. The tolerable range relates to immediate dangers to human health. The acceptable range relates to human health, vegetation, soil and water. The desirable range established long range goals for pollution control levels. Based on these ranges, provincial governments issued orders and regulations governing emissions within their jurisdictions. It was not until the mid-70's that the acid rain component of air pollution drew increased government and public attention. The attention originally was fueled by threats to marine life in lakes and streams in Northeastern Ontario and Quebec and focused largely on the large INCO smelter at Sudbury, Ontario. As scientific studies accumulated data on acid rain damage and the long range transport of air pollutants, public awareness and government interest in acid rain took form. In the late 1970's much of the interest was directed to the US contribution to Canada's acid rain deposits. That interest was intensified when a bilateral US-Canadian team of scientists found that 50% of Canada's deposits originated in the US and was carried through the atmosphere from Midwestern US coal power electricity plants to Ontario and Quebec. The US role in the politics of acid rain in Canada is discussed at length later in this chapter. The added attention given to acid rain required no new legislation as regulations flowing from existing laws, primarily provincial, could be issued at ministerial and departmental level. At this point, Canada did not have stringent SO_2 controls and the impetus for action gained throughout the 1970's.

In 1982, Canada adopted long range goals for significant sulfate deposition reductions, establishing deposition levels which would result in a 40-60% reduction. A major purpose of this initiative was to explore and determine means and the resources required by the various provinces to reach these levels. Provinces were given wide latitude in planning measures to reach their share of the reductions. Some emission reductions were achieved by 1984, particularly in Ontario. Some observers attribute those reductions to have occurred because of socioeconomic causes rather than governmental environmental measures. In a more significant and concrete development in February 1985, the 7 eastern provinces (Manitoba, Ontario, Quebec, New Brunswick, Prince Edward Island, Nova Scotia and Newfoundland) entered a tacit agreement with the federal government to meet the long range goal by 1994. The western provinces of British Columbia, Alberta and Saskatchewan were not included in the pact. The acid rain problem is not as pronounced in those provinces, and although pockets of awareness exist, acid rain as a public policy issue is not significant. The 1985 accord has been ratified by provincial authorities and measures have been taken to move toward the target goals. Some of the provinces, such as Prince Edward Island and Newfoundland, have very low amounts of emissions and aim to meet the goals without new regulations. In some other provinces, namely Nova Scotia and New Brunswick, regulations to meet the goals have not been fully propagated. The provinces of Manitoba, Ontario and Quebec, the provinces which produce around 75% of Canada's total SO_2 emissions, have issued regulations to meet the reduction levels. I will give special attention to Ontario and Quebec, the preponderant producers.

Ontario is Canada's most populous province and is the base for much of her industrial plant. The current basic legislation is the Environmental Protection Act of 1980. After the 1985 agreement, Ontario initiated a 'Countdown Acid Rain' program. The program entailed issuance of non appealable regulations establishing annual SO_2 ceilings for the four major emitters in the province. The program aims at reducing province wide emissions from the 1980 level of 2,194 kilotonnes to 885 kilotonnes by 1994. The regulations call for semi annual progress reports from the four emitters. The relations do not specify how the reductions will be achieved but do require reports on technological developement, abatement methods and the financial implications. The four major emitters are INCO, Inc. and Falconbridge, Ltd. (nickel/copper smelters in Sudbury), Algoma Steel Co. (Wawa, Ontario) and Ontario HYDRO. HYDRO owns all fossil fuel electricity generating plants in the province. The four firms produce 80% of Ontario's total SO_2 emissions. After the first two years of the program, the January 1988 reports revealed that the total emissions from the four sources dropped from 1,147 KT to 1,095 KT, well below the allowable limit of 1,389 KT. More stringent legal limits are to be implemented by 1990 (Countdown Acid Rain, 1988).

Quebec has pledged to cut emissions by 45% from 1980 levels by 1990, a tighter schedule than Ontario's date of 1994. Roughly one half of Quebec's emissions are produced by the NORANDA Mines, Limited, smelter, which is Canada's second largest emitter. The provincial government has issued a regulation which requires NORANDA to reduce emissions by 35% in 1989 and by 50% by 1990. Plans call for the reductions to be achieved by capturing the SO_2 in smelter gases to produce sulfuric acid. The costs are expected to be in the $125 million range. (Stopping Acid Rain, 1988)

The most recent major federal environment measure is the Canadian Environmental Protection Act of 1988. The Act is the culmination of several years of public, private and government consultation and consolidation and combines several pieces of legislation which have been enacted since 1970. The bill does entail a more stringent compliance and enforcement role for the federal government.

Acid rain politics - domestic influences

The most striking point about the internal politics of acid rain in Canada is the lack of opposition to emission reduction programs. The high degree of consensus on the need to reduce emissions is uncommon to the other systems studied. Upon close examination, however, the consensus for controls is not so surprising. In the following paragraphs, the role of the major actors in the debate is discussed.

The Prime Minister and the Cabinet

Canadian leaders have consistently supported acid rain control programs. Prime Ministers Trudeau and Mulroney may have little else in common, but both have been consistent in their awareness of acid rain damage and keeping the issue on the public policy agenda. (The short tenures of Prime Ministers Clark and Turner could also be included). Prime Minister Trudeau was in office during the early years of the recognition of the problem (1968-79) (1980-84). It is impossible to examine the domestic acid rain policy development in Canada in the 1970's without considering the role of the United States. The role of the United States as an external influence is considered later in this chapter, but because of the magnitude and nature of its relationship to the policy, it must be mentioned in the discussion of the internal debate. In 1976, about the time Canadian public awareness was on the rise, the Trudeau and Carter Administrations agreed to a joint study of acid rain and its movement along the border. The study, conducted by a bilateral team of scientists, reported in 1978 that 50% of Canada's acid rain originated in the United States. This finding received wide attention in Canada and spurred the government to begin a campaign to publicize the dangers of acid rain domestically and pursue further negotiations with the United States. Prime Minister Trudeau continued to actively pressure for an emissions control policy on all fronts and some long range goals were developed. Despite Prime Minister Trudeau's statements and protestations, pockets of criticism existed on the lack of constructive action. Prime Minister Mulroney, assuming office in September 1984, continued these policies and under his administration some domestic emission reductions have occurred, important federal goals have been established and the Canadian Environmental Protection Act has been enacted. He has pressed the US for action. He has been successful in getting the US to agree to a 5 year, $5 billion dollar clean coal technology demonstration program. At the executive level, acid rain policy goals have been consistent. The policy debate has been over whether the government is doing enough domestically to cut emissions and in pressuring the US for a reduction program. Opposition Members of Parliament and environmental groups have been critical of Prime Minister Mulroney as being too acquiescent and perhaps subservient to US policy because of his personal relationship with President Reagan.

Cabinet department level - Environment Canada

Environment Canada, the cabinet level department responsible for administering pollution policy, has aggressively followed the lead of prime ministers in implementing policy. The present minister, Tom MacMillan, has been very visible in giving the issue a high profile with the public, provincial authorities and the US. Mr. MacMillan has recently led a $500,000 publicity campaign on acid rain damage aimed at the US public. Environment Canada and its ministers have been persistent advocates of emission reduction programs.

House of Commons

The role of the House of Commons, the dominant house of the Canadian Parliament, must be considered in the context of the parliamentary form of government. Given that recent prime ministers have supported reduction programs, their dominance of the House of Commons and the Cabinet implies that the House of Commons plays an important, but somewhat submissive role in policy-making. For the opposition parties there is the opportunity to criticise the government. On the issue of acid rain, however, the

17

opposition has had a frequent ally in the majority party. This criticism is generally not aimed at government action to reduce emissions, but to chastise the government for not doing enough, particularly in relations with the US. Spokesmen for the opposition parties have been particularly critical of Prime Minister Mulroney's agreement in 1987 to the 5 year, $5 billion research program, primarily because the agreement establishes no specific emission reduction targets.

In a formal sense the House of Commons has studied the acid rain question through the committee system. In July 1980, a Subcommittee on Acid Rain of The Standing Committee on Fisheries and Forestry was formed to conduct a detailed investigation for government action. Such committees do not have a purely legislative role but may hear evidence and make recommendations for government action. They are also a good barometer of public opinion on an issue, as their composition reflects the full range of party and regional views. In approximately a years time, the Committee received evidence at four public hearings in Canada, travelled to London, Stockholm and Washington for briefings and visited Canada's largest polluting facilities. The Committee issued its report, Still Waters, in 1981. The report contained thirty eight recommendations on a wide variety of dimensions of the issue. Some of the more important recommendations are paraphrased below.

The Sub Committee recommended that:

   a. conversion of oil fired electricity plants to coal be carried out utilizing the best available emission control technology for oxides of sulphur and nitrogen.

   b. all new coal-fired electricity plants planned or under construction in Canada be compelled to utilize the best available technology to control emission control technology for oxides of sulfur and nitrogen. Here the subcommittee put special emphasis on the Province of Ontario and Ontario Hydro, the operator of the major facilities in that Province.

   c. specific INCO, Falconbridge, and Noranda Mines facilities meet emission levels established by the subcommittee in 5 years. The efforts were to be accompanied by economic incentives.

d. NO_x emission control standards, at least as stringent as those used in the U.S., be established and that legislative authority to regulate motor vehicle emissions be transferred to the Department of Environment.

e. Research program be established, continued, or developed on the effects of acid rain on forests, crops and soils, drinking water and fish contamination.

f. Environment Canada, in consultation with provincial authorities review all aspects of monitoring acidic precipitation in Canada.

g. Liming, suggested by some as a viable alternative to emission reductions, should not be regarded as a solution to the acidification of lakes.

h. Efforts should be accelerated to make Canadian and US precipitation chemistry monitoring systems compatible in terms of providing data for comparability.

i. The Clean Air Act be amended to strengthen its provisions permitting the Federal government to establish National Emission Guidelines and National Emission Standards. (These recommendations were apparently aimed at strengthening the federal governments powers and role in air pollution policy).

j. Environmental protection legislation in general should include a broader treatment of noncompliance penalties, legal remedies, legal staff for environmental protection agencies and the harmonization of federal and provincial enforcement of legislation.

k. Governments should consider innovative regulatory concepts.

l. Canada and the US should reach an agreement by the end of 1982, on the necessary legislation and mechanisms to substantially reduce acid rain.

m. Canadian governments, interest groups and individual Canadian citizens utilize all political, legal, administrative and media channels to bring about the reduction of US SO_2 emissions. This initiation should be accompanied by a major public awareness program and information program aimed at generating public concern in the US. The effort should also attempt to have influential US media representatives invited to Canada to be convinced of the threat posed to Canada by acid rain.

n. Canadian efforts to publicize the acid rain problem should be made in international parliamentary association, particularly with US legislators.

The Subcommittee had clearly addressed the important aspects of the problem and had recommended an extensive agenda to the government for action. Less than two years later, however, members of the Subcommittee noted "little or no progress towards achieving significant emissions of NO_x and SO_2 in Canada and negotiations for a US-Canadian reductions agreement were at an impasse. Former Subcommittee members requested the formation of a new panel to investigate all aspects of acid rain and in March 1983 received official sanction to undertake the new study. This group placed more emphasis on NO_x emissions reduction and focused on progress made by Governments on the recommendations for SO_2 reductions in their earlier report, Still Waters.

After fifteen months of study in which the group held a number of public hearings, visits to Washington, and other field visits the report issued then second report, Time Lost - A Demand for Action on Acid Rain, in 1985.

The report's major recommendation deals primarily with the NO_x problem, focusing a new motor vehicle emission standard, reduction of level in gasoline and changes in motor vehicle regulatory authority. Another important recommendation would provide incentives for NO_x and SO_2 reductions in the form of accelerated capital tax provisions.

In reviewing progress on its recommendations made in its initial 1981 report, the Subcommittee noted several major deficiencies in government action. In particular, the panel stressed that non-ferrous

20

smelters, motor vehicles and coal-fired power plants, domestic SO_2 and NO_x emissions remained much too high. The report specifically noted the failure of Ontario Hydro, a major emissions source, to utilize the best available technology (in this case, scrubbers), as recommended in the Still Waters report. They were also critical of the failure to adopt more stringent motor vehicle emissions standards as formerly recommended by the Subcommittee. The Subcommittee lauded the 1985 federal provincial agreement but stressed the importance of following through on its implementation.

The report was especially sensitive to the same comparative aspects of US and Canadian air pollution policy. In particular they pointed out the wide disparity in the use of scrubbers in coal-fired plants, with Canada with none installed at the time as opposed to approximately one hundred in the US. They also noted the much less stringent Canadian auto emission standards than those of the US. In the House of Commons study groups view, despite the fact Canada's unilateral emissions reduction would still leave Canada with the 50% contribution from the United States, Canada should still undertake a significant reductions program. The group had received some testimony suggesting that Canada's 50% of the acid rain does not fall in the most sensitive areas and implying that the US contribution is causing most of the damage. The subcommittee rejected that view, citing Environment Canada's contention that much of Canada's damage is caused by domestic emissions, and continued to stand by its 1981 recommendations. They urged all federal and provincial governments involved to begin the clean up of acid rain in Canada. A prime motivation for the House of Common's group was to remove the American argument in countering Canadian demands for action. American opponents to a reduction program, somewhat to the Subcommittee's embarrassment, had often used the shortcoming of Canada's domestic program to deflect Canadian calls for action.

The extent to which the House of Commons deliberation and recommendations influenced the adoption of the landmark 1985 federal/provincial agreement is difficult to assess. What is known is that many of the 1981 recommendations are being implemented that since the vigorous reinforcement and call for action in the second report Canada is undertaking significant strides in emissions reductions. A special committee on acid rain still exists and the committee was consulted by the US and Canadian special envoys appointed by the governments to study the issue.

Interest groups

In the 1980's, opposition of Canada's interest (pressure) groups to reduction of SO_2 emissions has been virtually non existent. Such organisations as the Canadian Labour Congress, the Canadian Manufacturer's Association and the Canadian Electrical Association support government policy. Canada's largest emitter, INCO, has also supported control programs. Despite this visible and vocal support, some major emitters, such as Ontario HYDRO, have been criticised for being inconsistent in developing plans and strategy for control programs. Since 1985, however, with the 'Countdown Acid Rain Program', HYDRO has made legal limits on schedule. Concern has been expressed as to whether 1990 and onward limits can be met but a present HYDRO has a retrofit schedule planned to facilitate those reductions. In the case of INCO, because of high production costs, foreign competition and diminished demand, the firm has been receptive to government overtures for aid in developing clean coal technology to assist in the reduction of emissions. One group that has been opposed to NO_x reductions through the establishment of more stringent auto emissions standards is the Canadian auto industry. Because acid rain contains some NO_x and the auto is the major source of NO_x emissions, the House of Commons committee heard testimony from representatives of the industry. The witness disputed the need for reduction of motor vehicle emissions on the grounds that they contribute little to acid rain and that the cost of catalytic converters did not yield benefits proportionate to the costs. On the issue of reductions of industrial emissions, their opposition wanes.

Environmental groups

Environmental groups have been an important actor in

the acid rain debate in Canada. They had been vocal critics of Canadian governments for the slow pace of their emission reduction programs and especially critical of Prime Minister Mulroney's efforts vis-a-vis the United States. The most notable of these groups are the Canadian Coalition on Acid Rain and Pollution Probe. The Coalition on Acid Rain has formed an alliance with a similar group in the United States which has played an active role in lobbying for action in Washington. Environmental groups have been a potent ally of Canada's effort to raise public awareness in Canada and in publicising the US contribution to Canada's acid rain problem. Environmental groups have participated in the House of Commons deliberations on acid rain. During the public hearings and other consultations such groups as the Coalition on Acid Rain, the Izaah Walton League of America, The Quebec Association Against Acid Rain, the Montreal Urban Commission, Greenpeace, The Saskachewan Natural History Society, The Movement Against Acid Rain and The Wilderness Society of Newfoundland and Labrador.

Public opinion

Public awareness of acid rain in Canada and the threat it poses to the natural environment has grown steadily. A leading scholar of US-Canadian relations cites polls which indicate 85% of Canadians are aware of the issue (Carroll, 1983). This awareness is particularly prevalent in Ontario and Quebec, the most populous region of Canada. This high level of awareness is attributable to some degree to governmental public information campaigns. These efforts were adopted as a government initiative in 1978 and have been continued with varying degrees of emphasis and priority. In recent years, these campaigns have had a dual thrust, aimed at dramatizing the threat of acid rain to Canadians and seeking to influence US citizens to pressure their government for action. The major newspapers in Eastern Canada follow developments in acid rain policy closely. Acid rain is newsworthy and important to Canadians.

This extraordinary level of consensus among Canadians is also attributable to at least two other

23

factors. The major Canadian sources of pollution are located in two large geographical provinces, Ontario and Quebec. Because most of Canada's populace live in these provinces, those associated with the source of acid rain are often on the receiving end of pollution originating in the province being transported to other parts of the province where many own property or spend vacations. Also contributing to the consensus are the economic costs of damage to Canadian tourism, fisheries, the maple sugar industry and forests. It has been estimated that forest products in Eastern Canada alone account for about $15 billion annually. Sport fishing produces about $1 billion to the economy. It has been estimated that acid rain damage may amount to over 5% of Canada's GNP. It should be noted that most of the acid rain transported from US sources are deposited on Ontario and Quebec creating at least the perception that the US contributes heavily to this economic damage.

For over a decade acid rain has been an important issue on the public policy agenda. A striking degree of consensus for action on the problem has developed. Despite this high level of support for action significant progress on emission reduction has only recently been achieved. This movement may be partially attributable to the House of Commons Subcommittee's insistence for unilateral action. On the one hand the severity of the problem demanded Canadian emission reduction. On the other hand, the action removed Canadian inaction as an argument for the American opponents. Another perceptible trend appears to be movement toward more federal power in environmental policy. In any case, the high level of consensus has facilitated governments at all levels to pursue an active reduction policy.

Acid rain politics - external influences

The long range transport of air pollution (LRTAP) across national boundaries was first given serious consideration at the United Nations Conference on the Environment at Stockholm in 1972. At that meeting Sweden brought the subject to the attention of the participants. An important development was the work of the Organization for Economic Cooperation and Development (OECD), which conducted a study in the early 1970's which concluded that LRTAP did in fact occur. Since that time LRTAP has received increasing attention in North America and Europe in national, bilateral and multinational policy making entities.

The United States and acid rain policy in Canada

The politics of acid rain Canada have been inextricably linked to the United States. In 1977, the US Carter Administration, at the request of Prime Minister Trudeau, agreed to participate in a joint scientific study of the problem along the border. The work, carried out by the Bilateral Research Consultation Group, found that 50% of acid rain deposits in Canada originated in the US and that about 15% of the US deposits originated in Canada. This finding sparked Canadian efforts to reach an agreement with the US on an emissions reduction program. Negotiations began in 1979 and in 1980 the countries agreed to a document expressing their intent to develop a bilateral agreement aimed at effective domestic control programs and also 'to take interim actions available under current authority to combat transboundary air pollution.' (Memorandum of Intent, 1980). The agreement also established technical and scientific working groups to assist in the preparation for further negotiations. President Reagan, visiting Ottawa in 1981, expressed his intention to honor the agreement. Since that time, acid rain has become a troublesome issue and source of considerable discord between the two countries. There was some disagreement among the joint working groups on important scientific conclusions. During the next few years Canadian officials and environmental groups were persistently critical of US inaction, but the Reagan Administration consistently maintained that not enough scientific evidence existed to justify a costly control program. With Prime Minister Mulroney's election in 1984 and the emergence of a close ideological and personal relationship with President Reagan, some Canadians were optimistic about the possibility of a US emission reductions program. In 1985, the leaders agreed to appoint special envoys to study the acid rain issue. Canada was represented by William Davis, former Premier of Ontario and the US by Drew

Lewis, former Secretary of Transportation. Their report, issued in January 1986, recognized that acid rain is a serious problem in both the US and Canada and constitutes a serious transboundary problem. The report recommended:

a. The U.S. government should implement a five-year, five billion-dollar control technology commercial demonstration program. The federal government should provide half the funding - 2.5 billion dollars - for projects which industry recommends, and for which industry is prepared to contribute the other half of the funding.

b. The results of the Canadian technology development program should be shared with the United States.

c. Both the United States and Canada should review their existing air pollution programs and legislation to identify opportunities, consistent with existing law, for addressing environmental concerns related to trans-boundary air pollution. The results of these reviews should be made available to the chief environmental officials of both countries for their consideration in the management of their respective programs.

d. Agencies contemplating changes to laws or regulations that may alter the flow of transboundary pollutants should give timely notice of their intent to agencies of the other country through diplomatic channels.

e. Acid rain should remain high on the agenda of meetings between the President and Prime Minister. They should be prepared to intercede personally from time to time to resolve difficulties and ensure progress. The U.S. cabinet official heading the technology development panel and a Canadian cabinet official would jointly advise the President and Prime Minister.

f. Our two governments should establish a bilateral advisory and consultative group on transboundary air pollution. Such a group, comprising both diplomatic and environmental management officials, should provide the forum for discussion and first-level consultations on issues

26

related to transboundary pollution. It should also provide advice to the directors of each country's environmental programs and to the Secretary of State and Secretary of State for External Affairs.

g. Standard, accurate methods to measure dry deposition should be developed and monitoring networks deployed. The networks should be of sufficient size and adequate statistical design, and implemented with adequate quality assurance and quality control procedures, in order to enable researchers to measure total acid deposition for sensitive areas across North America.

h. The environmental damage of surface water acidification should be understood in terms of biological changes. This would help to quantify the relationship between changes in surface water chemistry and changes in aquatic biota more clearly. Special attention should be focused on both rates and types of biological change.

i. Research should be accelerated to investigate the potential link between forest and tree decline and acid rain as a causal or contributing factor.

President Reagan accepted the recommendations and in the ensuing years some projects have been funded. Prime Minister Mulroney lauded the agreement as a step in the right direction, but opposition critics in the House of Commons and environmental groups view it as a further US delaying tactic. (Report of the Special Envoys on Acid Rain, 1986). Canada, through its public relations campaign, diplomatic channels and complaints by the prime minister, has continued to pressure the US for concrete action. At an April 1988 Canadian-US summit meeting, President Reagan promised to consider the Prime Minister's proposal for a bilateral agreement on acid rain. Negotiations towards an agreement were initiated. The main obstacle to an accord has been the US refusal to establish a specific reductions target.

The role of the US in the Canadian debate has another interesting dimension. During the early years in which Canada's criticism of the US evolved (roughly 1976-84), American policy makers and interested argued that Canada's domestic reductions programs left much to be desired and that Canada should reduce her own emission levels before blaming the US. The House of Commons subcommittee report mentioned this point. This argument was apparently noted by Prime Minister Mulroney and the 1985 federal and provincial agreement to cut emissions by 50% was a positive indication of Canadian intent and action. At least in a marginal way the Canadian policy initiative was affected by the US criticism of Canada's domestic policy. To a considerable extent, the Canadian program has disarmed American critics of this argument.

Canadian frustration, particularly among environmentalists and environmental professionals, was further exacerbated and intensified by an 1987 interim report of the U.S. Acid Precipitation Assessment Program task force. The assessment was started in 1980 and in September 1987, a mid-term assessment report was issued. Canadian governmental agencies found the report to be lacking in several respects, not the least of which was the report's failure to include Canadian information. There was particular disagreement with the executive summary of the report. Specifically, Canada found the summary conclusion that acidification has done little significant damage to lakes". Another point of disagreement was the conclusion "that the effects of acid rain have leveled off." Two other conclusions by Canada were "that emissions from U.S. have not grown and will soon decline", and "that the problem of acid rain is no worse than was anticipated 10 years ago." (The NAPAP Report, 1988, Environment Canada).

International organisations and acid rain policy in Canada

Another external influence on Canadian policy is related to the important role Canada has played in supporting environmental protection in international organisations. This role has been especially important in the United Nations Economic Commission for Europe (ECE). The ECE is a regional organisation originally established to exchange economic data and statistics. As it has evolved, the ECE has been the setting for some significant environmental accords. The ECE's membership includes the countries of Europe plus the US and Canada. Because it is the major European organisation with members on both sides of the Iron Curtain, it provides an organisational setting for discussion and negotiation of common environmental problems. LRTAP is virtually inevitable in Europe in which many countries occupy such a small geographic space. Canada and the Scandinavian countries were among the early leaders in environmental matters and were at the forefront of the negotiation and agreement of the Convention on Long Range Transboundary Air Pollution in 1979. The pact was signed by 32 European countries, the European Community and the United States and Canada. It asks the signators to work to gradually reduce and prevent air pollution and LRTAP. In 1985, Canada also helped to lead agreement to a Protocol to the Convention which commits signators to a 30% reduction of SO_2 emissions by 1993. The Protocol has been signed by Canada and over 20 ECE members. More recently, Canada has been active in ECE negotiations for an agreement freezing NO_x emissions at 1987 levels. Canada's involvement in these negotiations, while contributing to the improvement of the global environment, provides another avenue in which Canada can exert pressure on the US. The US has not agreed to the 30% reduction but has hinted that it may agree to the NO_x freeze.

Canada's acid rain policy has been affected by a number of domestic and external forces. Among the three countries studied, Canada is unique in that opposition to acid rain control programs is minimal and politically impotent. The emissions reduction program is well underway. In the provinces producing the bulk of her emissions the legislative and regulatory mechanisms are in place. The program's objectives may become more difficult to reach as measures become more costly in the latter years of the reduction schedule. Canada will continue to press for a specific US commitment and will maintain its active role as a leading force for meaningful environmental agreements in the international arena.

4 The politics of acid rain – Great Britain

Background

Protection of the environment has a long history as a policy issue in Britain. The concept of the environment has always been broadly defined. A reflection of the scope of this definition is illustrated by the responsibilities of the Department of the Environment, the cabinet level organisation for environmental protection. Land use planning, development of new towns, policies for inner cities, housing and urban transport policy, conservation of the countryside, preservation of historic buildings, protection of trees, land reclamation and the control of pollution are all listed among the responsibilities of the Department of the Environment in Britain. Amongst these many and varied functions, the control or air pollution is vulnerable to diminished importance.

The legislative history of air pollution dates from 1863 when the first Alkali Act was passed. That law was followed by the Works Regulation Act in 1909, which amended and replaced the 1863 measure. These laws established an Alkali Inspectorate, now the Industrial Air Pollution Inspectorate, which has the

31

responsibility of controlling emissions from registered chemical and industrial processes. After the death of over 4,000 people in the London smog tragedy in 1952, the Clean Air Act of 1954 was passed. The bill's major provisions are:

a. the prohibition of dark smoke from all chimneys in all areas.

b. allowed local authorities to introduce smoke control areas.

c. established a requirement that smokeless fuel must be used in smoke control areas.

A later bill, the Clean Air Act of 1968, gives the Secretary of State power to establish emission standards for grit and dirt. Another pollution control measure was the Control of Pollution Act of 1974, which provides the framework for expansion of control into the areas of the sulfur content of distillate fuels and the lead content of petrol.

Britain's air pollution control legislation has been affected by the environment programme of the European Community (EC). After her entry into the EC in 1973, Community measures on sulfur content of gas oil and diesel fuel and limiting lead in petrol and vehicle emissions were integrated into the British programme. A discussion of the EC as an external influence on British policy is included later in this chapter. In a 1980 directive the Community agreed to a measure dealing directly with SO_2, the major component of acid rain. The directive established ground level air quality standards for smoke and SO_2. This introduced the notion of mandatory air quality standards to Britain and marked a significant change in air pollution policy (Haigh, 1985, p. 7). These measures have not resulted in new clean air legislation. In 1982, the Government expressed the view that no new legislation was necessary to comply with the EC directive. One of the principle reasons for this position was the existence of a national monitoring network in Britain. The actions required were to be accomplished under existing legislation and administrative powers of the Department of the Environment in coordinate with local authorities. Also in 1982, the Government announced it was conducting a review of air pollution legislation. This review was still underway in the Winter of 1987. It should be noted that the EC legislation established ground level standards for SO_2 and did not address emissions into the atmosphere which are the primary contributors to acid rain. One of the results of these ground level source standards was the adoption of tall stacks technology to remove pollutants away from the source. LRTAP results from this process.

During the years 1982-84, the acid rain debate took form in Britain. Britain was an early leader in air pollution control, but as other nations and international organizations adopted new control initiatives in the 1970's, Britain was perceived to lag behind in reacting to certain forms of pollution. Acid rain is among these pollutants. Although on issues such as land use, conservation of the countryside and protection of wildlife public interest is generally high, government and industry did not have to respond to a public outcry for a reduction of industrial emissions in the early 1980's. However, the year 1984 marked a period of increased activity related to acid rain. These activities included actions by a variety of Government individuals, institutions and organisations. A number of public and professional groups also became involved in the issue. The interplay of these forces in the debate over acid rain is included in the following discussion.

Acid rain politics - domestic influences

The Conservative Party has been the majority party in the House of Commons since 1979 and thus, with Prime Minister Thatcher at the helm, has been in control of the government during the period in which acid rain has received added attention in Britain. During the Conservative tenure, the government has focused primarily on economic growth in Britain, which had generally lagged behind the Federal Republic of Germany, France and others in the post World War II period. Because of the structure of the political system and the leadership style of Prime Minister Thatcher, it is certain that any significant decision on acid rain control would have her approval.

The Parliament as an institution has played only a minor role in the evolution of acid rain policy. As the British system is structured, no new legislation or statutory authority is required to reduce emissions. Such a decision could be reached through administrative regulation in the energy or electricity fields by government appointed boards or appropriate ministries. However, one arm of the Parliament, the House of Commons Select Committee on the Environment, has played an important role in acid rain politics. Select Committees have no legislative role but do have the power to call government witnesses, scrutinize government policy and make recommendations to the government. The Committee's role is discussed later in this chapter.

The Department of the Environment (DOE) is the major government ministry involved in air pollution. The DOE, in keeping with the broad definition of the environment in Britain, is responsible for a wide range of government services. An example of the scope of its functions is its responsibility for housing policy. Air pollution control and abatement is only one of its many responsibilities. The DOE monitors and prepares environmental legislation. Throughout the acid rain debate, the DOE has stressed Britain's past record of reducing emissions, the general point of incomplete scientific knowledge and the need to develop new control technologies. In 1982, on the recommendation of the Royal Commission on Environmental Pollution, the government decided to undertake a review of air pollution control legislation. It was about this time that pressure was mounting in the European Community for stronger controls and the Scandinavians began to pressure Britain on the acid rain issue. The review of legislation has been ongoing since but several significant developments have occurred.

In 1984, a government research agency completed a DOE sponsored study of acid rain. The report found that some parts of Great Britain had levels of air pollution causing serious damage. However, the report concluded that more research was needed before any action was taken.

A major event in the debate was a 1984 report issued by the House of Commons Select Committee on the Environment. (House of Commons Environment Committee, Fourth Report, Session 1983-84, Acid Rain, July 1984). The report was the result of a long and tedious study in which the committee collected written and oral evidence from a wide range of public officials, representatives of the scientific community, and environmentalists. The committee visited areas of Scandinavia and the Federal Republic of Germany to view damage. The report drew attention to damage to buildings and materials, fresh water ecology and damage to forests. The committee found that the situation was serious enough to require immediate action. The most significant and far reaching of these recommendations were:

a. The government should commit itself to the ECE Protocal calling for 30% emission reductions by 1990.

b. The government should agree to the proposed EC Directive calling for a drastic reduction of NO_x and SO_2 emissions by the late 1990's.

Some of the Select Committees other recommendations were:

a. Research programmes should be established or stepped up on acid rain's effect on stone, concrete, materials, and the effects on low-level emissions on buildings.

b. The British Forestry Commission, using both British and German experts, should conduct a forest survey. The Forest Commission was asked to undertake detailed NO_x and ozone monitoring. Research should also begin on acid rain damage to trees.

c. The government should commission research on the effects of acid rain on human health and visibility degradation.

d. The Committee also made a number of recommendations relating to NO_x emissions.

Beginning in 1984 some awareness of the effects of air pollutants on Britain itself was emerging. The DOE study which noted serious pollution and high levels of acidification in Northern England and Scotland helped increase this awareness and spur more research. The government's Forestry Commission found a new type of forest damage, but attributed the damage to climatic conditions rather than air pollution. In early March 1985, a representative of the Central Electricity Generating Board (CEGB) stated 'it has proved remarkably difficult to detect any significant effect of gaseous emissions from modern power stations on crops and trees in the UK.' (Follow Up to Environment Committee's Report on Acid Rain, Session 1985-86, HMSO, 1985). In contrast to these findings by Friends of the Earth (FOE) environmentalist group conducted a study that found that acid rain caused serious damage to Britain's forests. The government considered the FOE research to be scientifically flawed.

During a 1985 follow up review to assess progress on the recommendations of its 1984 report, the Select Committee heard from representatives of the Departments of the Environment and Energy and received oral communications from other Government officials, Norwegian and Swedish officials and the Federal Republic of Germany. The Committee reiterated its impatience over the lack of concrete action on the major recommendations. During the review a Department of Energy representative informed the Committee that 1984 emission levels were 25% below the 1980 levels and the tetrofit of two plans could achieve the additional 5% reduction to 30%. He added that this plan would cost approximately £ 300 million and result in at least a 1% annual increase in electricity rates. An alternative, which explained the lack of positive steps toward flue gas desulfurisation (FGD), was a reduction over a longer term achieved through a combination of increased nuclear generating capacity and cleaner and more efficient coal combustion. Alluding to the cost of achieving the 60% reduction target of an European Community proposal, the Government estimated a cost of £ 1.5 billion and a 10% increase in electricity rates. A Department of Environment minister told the Committee that conclusive findings about forest damage in Britain were still lacking. Government inaction was to lead to a second follow up study by the House of Commons Select Committee. (Follow Up to Environment Committee's Report).

A major and important actor in the British policy debate has been the Central Electricity Generating Board (CEGB). The CEGB is the quasi governmental agency which operates most of Britain's nationalized electrical power generating plants. The CEGB is managed by a government appointed board and a chairman appointed by the appropriate minister. The Board consults regularly with the government. The CEGB has been labeled by critics and environmentalists as 'Europe's largest polluter.' Its twelve largest coal fired plants are responsible for two thirds of Britain's SO_2 emissions. As awareness over the effects of acid rain grew, the CEGB found itself on the defensive and the major voice countering criticism of Britain. The Board has conducted extensive research and contributes substantial monetary resources to sponsored research activities. In the early 1980's, the Board rejected calls for expensive and immediate installation of flue gas desulfurisation (FGD) units until more was known in several areas of scientific research. In 1984, a Board official maintained that a cut in emissions does not result in a corresponding cut in acid rain. In 1985, a member of the Board considered it unwise to draw quick conclusions and folly to throw money at the problem in the absence of further scientific knowledge. He estimated that the cost of complying with the EC draft proposal, entailing FGD installation at each of the 12 major generating plants, would cost over £ 1.4 billion. The CEGB, like other British agencies, questioned the validity of the research related to forest damage.

In a significant development in 1986, the government seemed to adopt a shift in policy. In its research program the CEGB (along with British Coal) had contributed to a research program managed by Britain's Royal Academy of Science and the Norwegian Academy of Science and Letters. The program was to review past research and initiate some new research programs. The review provided enough evidence of acid rain's contribution to surface water acidification and fishery damage in Scandinavia to prompt the CEGB to take an unexpected stance and announce a dramatic (considering past behavior)

37

policy shift. The Board recommended the retrofitting of three of Britain's twelve largest coal-fired plants with FGD. The government accepted and the plans were announced by Prime Minister Thatcher on a visit to Norway. The plan also called for a newly constructed fossil fuel power stations to use sulfur free technology. The CEGB stressed the program was not based on forest damage, but on early findings of the joint British and Norwegian research on fresh water and fisheries in Norway and Sweden. (Acid Rain, The Political Challenge, Institute for European Environmental Policy, London, 1986, pp. 15-21). In October 1987, plans for a £ 600 million retrofit project for two plans were formally announced. Because of the CEGB's responsibility under its Parliamentary statutory authority relating to the beauty of the countryside, the Board could recommend this action to the government and its approval would not require Parliamentary approval. In 1988, the government was to be exposed to further pressure from the House of Commons Select Committee in another review of air pollution policy. Pressure also was coming from the EC. These events are discussed later in the chapter.

Other domestic policy influences

A variety of other actors have been involved in acid rain politics in Britain. Several quasi governmental and official governmental organisations have played a marginal role. Such organisations as the Royal Commission on Environmental Pollution, British Coal (the CEGB's largest supplier), the Natural Environmental Research Council, and a number of government research agencies have contributed to the debate. The Royal Commission on Environmental Pollution has conducted a number of studies over the years, but has not been particularly critical of government policy.

The major domestic opposition to acid rain policy in Britain has been from the House of Commons Select Committee, the Labour Party and a number of relatively small environmental groups. A more recent source of opposition has been the statements from the Duke of Edinburgh and the Prince of Wales criticising government pollution policy. The activities of the House of Commons committee have already been discussed. The Labour Party has been critical of the government's policy in parliamentary debates, public statements by Shadow Cabinet spokesmen, in sessions of the House of Commons Select Committee's deliberations and in its manifestos (platforms) at annual conference. For example, the 1986 statement contains a provision for restructuring the government's organisation for environmental protection and strengthening the inspection and monitoring of air pollution. The Labour Party calls for a 30% reduction of SO_2 and NO_x emissions by 1993, and while it does not mention the joining of the ECE 30% club, the Party is committed to a 30% reduction by 1993 (as opposed to the government's position in 1986 of attaining a 30% reduction by the late 1990's. (NEC Statement to Annual Conference, 1986, Labour Party, London). The Labour Party has representation on the Select Committee which has recommended prompt action. The Party has also participated in many of the private and professional meetings on the issue. (Acid Rain, The Political Challenge, pp. 56-57).

In a broad and general sense, a private environmental movement has a long history in Britain. In such areas as nature conservancy and preservation of wildlife, some influential voluntary organisations have existed for many years. Those groups have usually had formal and amicable relations with the government with highly placed and titled persons serving as leaders, patrons. and directors. One study of environmental groups in politics found that the older, established groups had close contact and access to the government while the newer groups, such as Friends of the Earth and Greenpeace, tended to 'challenge existing policies and procedures.' (Lowe and Goyden, 1983). Perhaps the oldest environmental group related to air pollution was the Smoke Abatement Society, which dates from the turn of the century. A successor organisation, the National Society for Clean Air, was active in campaigning for the Clean Air Acts of 1956 and 1968. The Society has produced publications and sponsored discussions and meetings on acid rain.

The most vocal and persistent environmental group active in the acid rain debate in Britain has been the Friends of the Earth (FOE). It has been regarded as the most successful of the new environmental organizations. FOE is an international network of activists with a Secretariat in the Netherlands. The organisation is active in numerous policy issues in most industrialised countries. The FOE's acid rain campaign in Britain has pressed for immediate accession to the 30% club, installation of anti-pollution devices on the CEGB's twelve largest power stations and British accession to the EC's draft directive on SO_2 and NO_x reductions. The FOE has staged demonstrations, participated in the annual International Acid Rain Weeks, printed public information materials and sponsored scientific research. FOE has also contributed to the Select Committee's inquiries. The organisation keeps a constant watch on domestic policy, Britain's role in the activities of international organisations and legislative, administrative and scientific activities in other countries. The FOE has enjoyed a degree of respectability in policy circles but some of its scientific activities have been questioned as to the validity of their findings. FOE also participates in the activities of the Swedish-Norwegian NGO Secretariat on Acid Rain. The overall impact of the FOE in criticising and pressuring British policy initiatives is difficult to assess, but the impact surely has been disproportionate in comparison to the size and resources of the organisation.

Another well known environmental group, Greenpeace, has carried out some high profile publicity events to dramatise the issue, but has not achieved the degree of respectability enjoyed by the FOE.

The acceleration of acid rain as a domestic and external issue in Britain has spurred interest in the intellectual, professional and government circles. This trend resulted in a spate of seminars, conferences and workshops drawing a wide range of participants. Among others, the Minister of the Environment, Chairman of the CEGB and the Chairman of the House of Commons Select Committee on the Environment have participated in such meetings. This participation is a sign of the government's interest in communicating its position and also reflects its defensive posture. Other frequent participants in such events include representatives of Norway and Sweden, the FRG and the Commission of the European Community. Two of the most notable of these meetings were those sponsored by the European Environment Bureau (EEB) and the Institute for European

Environmental Policy (IEEP). The EEB is one of a number of interest group federations accredited to represent interests at the European Community in Brussels. The EEB attempts to influence Community environmental policy and lists among its members several pressure groups from Great Britain. The IEEP is a non profit organisation devoted to analysis of national and Community policy. These meetings, held outside the confines of official relations, offer settings in which nations can communicate policy positions. They also provide a means through which various interests can present their positions in the presence of policy makers.

Finally, the Spring of 1988 saw the emergence of another influential source criticising government inaction. Two members of the Royal Family, the Duke of Edinburgh and the Prince of Wales, make critical statements regarding government pollution policy. (The Times of London, February 24th and May, 19th, 1988).

The impact of these events and other domestic policy influences and further developments in 1988 is discussed after a survey of the external influences on Britain's acid rain policy.

Acid rain politics - external influences

Because Britain exports a large proportion of locally produced SO_2 emissions, she has been labelled as Europe's worst polluter. Most of these emissions fall on Sweden and Norway. Those nations have led the campaign for general emissions reductions and consistently emphasise Britain's major contribution. For some time a program initiated under the auspices of the United Nations Economic Commission for Europe (UN ECE). The European Monitoring and Evaluation Program (EMEP), has gathered data on SO_2 emissions for all European countries. The EMEP emissions data for 1983 is shown in Table 4.1. These findings have generally been used as the basis for applying pressures on Britain to take some action to reduce emissions. EMEP has estimated that as much as 17% of SO_2 deposition in Norway originates in Britain. In 1987, the British Government, pointed to more recent data, contended that the levels had fallen to 7% in Norway and 5% in Sweden. Another vocal advocate of

41

Table 4.1

Sulfur Dioxide Emissions - Selected Countries
Data for 1983 in most cases

Country	Million Tons Per Annum
Austria	294
Canada	4,520
Czechoslovakia	3,250
France	2,250
Federal Republic of Germany	2,750
German Democratic Republic	4,000
Hungary	1,650
Italy	3,150
Norway	100
Poland	4,100
Spain	2,633
Sweden	330
Great Britain	3,690
USA	20,800
USSR	11,800
Yugoslavia	1,176

Source: OECD Environmental Data Compendium, 1985 and
ECE EMEP, 1983.

significant emissions reductions has been the Federal Republic of Germany (FRG). The FRG has focused on EC measures which obviously affect British policy. Britain is a small contributor to the FRG's total acid deposition, but as long as she exports more than one half of her emissions, external pressures for significant reductions will continue. In any case, Britain's role as a villain in the acid rain debate seems entrenched.

Because much of the acid rain debate in Britain has been influenced by actions of international organisations and other countries, a review of the external forces involved is essential to establish the context in which Britain's policy has evolved. The forces have both a multilateral and bilateral dimension. After Sweden tabled a report on the acidity of lakes in Sweden at the Stockholm Conference in 1972, air pollutants emitted in one country and transported to other countries were to attract more and more attention as an international issue. In recent years, the activities of the EC and the UN ECE have affected Britain. In addition, bilateral relations between Britain and Sweden, Norway and the FRG have been affected by the acid rain issue.

Multilateral influences

European Community (EC). The EC, of which Britain became a member in 1973, is recognized as the international organisation with the most advanced powers of Member States. The EC adopted an environmental programme in 1973. Up to 1987, the Community had agreed to several air pollution measures. The most important of these are in the form of a Council Directive. A Directive is binding on the Member States but leaves the form and process of implementation to the Member States. The measures relating to air pollution are:

a. Council Directive 70/220/EEC on air pollution by gases from engines of motor vehicles.

b. Council Directive 75/716/EEC on the approximation of the laws of the Member States relating to the sulfur content of certain liquid fuels.

c. Council Directive 80/779/EEC on air quality limit valves and guide valves for sulfur dioxide and suspended particulates.

d. Council Directive 82/884/EEC on a limit value for lead in the air.

e. Council Directive 84/360/EEC on the combatting of air pollution from industrial plants.

f. Council Directive 85/203/EEC on air quality standards for nitrogen oxides.

g. Council Directive 85/210/EEC on the approximation of the laws of Member States concerning the level content of petral.

Because of its binding powers, the Community has the potential of having a powerful influence on national environmental policies. The EC has already substantially affected British policy (Haigh, 1984). While the measures agreed to by 1987 were not particularly far reaching or stringent, Nigel Haigh has noted that the EC's policy on air pollution introduced the concept of mandatory air standards to Britain (Haigh, 1984). A more stringent and far reaching air pollution was proposed in the EC in 1983.

After scientific evidence confirmed increasing damage to German forests, the FRG pushed for more stringent controls of SO_2 and NO_x . This represented a significant reversal of the FRG's posture in the EC, as she had formerly joined Britain in being generally obstructionist on environmental issues. In 1983, the FRG proposed a draft EC directive dealing with large combustion plants (stationary sources) and power stations. The proposal called for new standards for all new plants constructed, and for emissions reductions for all existing large plants of 60% for SO_2, 40% for NO_x and 40% for dust. These reductions were to be based on data for 1980 and were to be achieved by 1995. In 1988, a compromise version of the proposal was adopted by the EC.

The European Parliament (EP), another of the major institutions of the EC, has also contributed to the acid rain debate. The EP is comprised of popularly

elected representatives of the Member States, with
the four largest (France, FRG, Great Britain, and
Italy) having a larger and equal number of
representatives. Except for a role in the budget
process, the EP has little formal power. In
carrying out its activities, the EP uses a committee
system. The Environment and Health Committee has
been concerned about acid rain since 1983. Pollution
from large combustion plants and exhaust gases from
motor vehicles have received particular attention.
Regarding SO_2 emissions, in 1984 the Parliament
delivered an opinion endorsing the 1983 draft EC
directive calling for reductions. In 1985, the EP
adopted a second resolution condemning certain EC
members for their irresponsible attitude on acid rain
and called on them to join in the ECE 30% club.
(European Parliament EN/111/N/1, 1987). The EP
provides yet another forum and setting in which
representatives of other nations can criticize
Britain's pollution policies, and has been a
persistent supporter of stronger Community
environmental measures.

The Commission of the European Communities is
another EC actor which has contributed to external
pressure on Britain. The Commission is the
"international" arm of the Community, comprised of
highly placed citizens of the Member States who are
sworn to take a Community perspective rather than
those of their individual "national" positions. The
Commission develops policy initiatives to be placed
on the agenda which may be unpopular to some Member
States. Although not a decision making body the
Commission has considerable clout in the Community.
The Commission is organized along functional lines,
one of which is the environment.

The Commission has been a consistent supporter of
significant SO_2 reductions and a consistent critic of
Britain's failure to accede to international accords.
The Commission's support for reduction was manifested
by its support of the German draft directive, and in
communications with the House of Commons Select
Committee in its original report and in its follow up
report. In a letter to the Select Committee in 1985,
the Commission expressed its support of the
Committee's original recommendations and its
disappointment with the British government's

response.   (Follow up to the Environment Committee
Report on Acid Rain, 1985).

The Commission also co-sponsored a major conference
on acid rain in London in 1986 and during the
meeting, Mr. Stanley Davis, the environment
commissioner, urged Great Britain to demonstrate a
commitment to a reduction program and Community
agreement.(Acid Rain, The Political Challenge, 1986).

United Nations Economic Commission for Europe (ECE)
The purpose of the ECE is to gather and exchange
economic data and statistics.   However, the
Commission has emerged as an important actor in
international environmental policy. The breadth and
geographical scope of its membership, encompassing
all the nations of Europe plus Canada and the United
States, provides a basis for the kinds of
consultation, consensus or conflict beyond the
capacity of other organizations.   The regional
economic commissions have no binding power.   Even
when a majority accede to an agreement, members do
not have to comply.   Notwithstanding its
organisational deficiencies and obvious ideological
fragmentation the ECE has provided the context for
the most wide ranging, comprehensive and
controversial international accords on environmental
matters.   Europe is a relatively small geographic
area encompassing 34 countries.   Transboundary
pollution in such a setting is inevitably a serious
problem. The solution to the problem is complicated
by the number of countries, ideological differences,
differing economic systems and disparities in wealth.
It is not surprising that the earliest large scale
interest in and concern over the long range transport
of air pollution (LRTAP) occurred in European based
international organisations.   The focus on LRTAP by
the ECE and earlier in the Organisation for Economic
Cooperation and Development (OECD) has borne fruit.
Technical exchanges, consultations and international
working groups have resulted and some international
agreements have been achieved.

The OECD, the Western organisation for economic
cooperation, established an Environment Committee in
1972. As part of its programme, a working group was
formed to study the question of LRTAP.   That study,

46

completed in 1977, confirmed the long range movement of air pollution beyond national borders. (OECD, Programme on LRTAP, Measurements and Findings, 1977). These findings spurred concern and the pace of international action quickened. Largely though the initiative of Norway and Sweden, the ECE placed the issue on its agenda. After some stubborn negotiating a majority of the ECE members reached an agreement. The pact was signed by 32 European countries, the Commission of European Communities, Canada and the United States. During the negotiations, strong resistance was expressed by Great Britain and the FRG. By 1983, a sufficient number of countries had ratified the Convention to bring it into force. The provisions do not bind the signators to take specific measures. Article 1 of the Convention reads:

> The Contracting Parties, taking due account of the facts and problems involved, are determined to protect man and his environment against air pollution and shall endeavor to limit and, as far as possible, gradually reduce and prevent air pollution including long-range transboundary air pollution. (Convention on Long Range Transboundary Air Pollution, ECE, 1979).

The pact also commits signators to develop policies and strategies to combat air pollution, research and development, information exchange and stresses the need for implementation and further implementation of the monitoring and evaluation network. As noted previously, the ECE had established a monitoring and evaluation network (EMEP) with stations in twenty two countries. The Convention also established a permanent working group on LRTAP. In 1985 a Protocal was added to the 1979 Convention aimed at reducing SO_2 emissions by at least 30% as soon as possible, but no later than 1993. The reductions were to be based on 1980 emission levels as determined by EMEP. The Protocal asks the Contracting Parties to study the necessity for further reductions beyond the 30% level. At that time, twenty one nations signed the Protocol. Notable exceptions were the United States, Great Britain and Poland. The agreement represents a significant intrusion on national air pollution policies and has been the source of substantial international discord. The signators of the pact have become known as the 30% club, a symbolic tool used by signator countries to identify non signers as villains in the acid rain debate. Those who have not signed point to their past record of SO_2 emission reductions and the need for more scientific evidence on damage as justification. From the outset, the nucleus of pressure for joining the 30% club has been a group of countries led by Canada and the Scandinavians. In 1988, the ECE was the center of negotiations for an accord on freezing NO_x emissions at current levels.

National governments as external influences

Several national governments have mounted an attack on Britain as an exporter of SO_2 emissions. The most important of these are Sweden, Norway and the Federal Republic of Germany.

Sweden. Sweden complained about external sources of acids and the acidity of their lakes as early as the 1972 UN Conference on the Environment at Stockholm. At that time little was known about the sources of the acids or movements of emissions. Sweden maintained that only about one-quarter of acid rain falling in Sweden originated there. Sweden has consistently reduced her emissions over the last two decades and in 1985 committed to a 65% decrease over 1970 levels. The Swedes estimate that they will be contributing only 8% of their total sulfur emissions by 1995. In addition to the concern over marine damage, the Swedes are worrying about forest damage. This worry is for both aesthetic and economic reasons, as one estimate suggests that approximately 300,000 Swedes depend on forest products for their livelihood.

The populace is acutely aware of and sensitive to environmental issues. Acid rain is a high profile policy issue. There is widespread societal support for the government's reductions policy. The government carries out an extensive public informational and education program and initiated a well financed campaign to stop acid rain in 1982. Governmental support for reductions, both at home and abroad, has been solid and represents a major foreign policy goal.

Sweden's efforts in international organisations have been aimed at achieving reductions by all nations, but have been most acute in the British case because of Britain's emission exports to Sweden. Sweden has pressed her case in multilateral organisations and in bilateral relations. After the ECE Convention in 1979, Sweden sponsored a follow up conference stressing the scientific and technical aspects of dealing with reductions and in 1985 proposed the 30% reduction leading the Protocol.

Swedish pressure on Britain intensified in the early and mid 1980's. In bilateral relations acid rain is the most serious foreign policy issue between the two nations. The Swedish Embassy in London has an ample public information programme and educational materials on acid rain are available to all upon request. The Government's environmental protection agency, the National Environmental Protection Board, helps finance the private Swedish NGO Secretariat on Acid Rain. The Secretariat has ties with a large network of environmental groups in many parts of the world. A major part of their work is an English language tabloid, Acid News, with correspondents from around the globe who monitor government policies, scientific studies and other related policy developments. Sweden will continue to pressure for significant SO_2 reduction.

Norway. Norway has been at the forefront of campaigning for British reductions and at times has been the most vocal and visible critic. Early on, Norway was at Sweden's side in calling attention to the acidification problem and she is a signator to the ECE pacts. From 1984 onwards, Norway has directed most of their information activities on acid rain towards Britain as the largest single source of sulfur deposits in Norway.

As in Sweden, the threat of acid rain and its effects are well known among the citizenry and there is a high level of environmental awareness. The opposition to British policy was openly expressed in 1985 when the Norwegian Minister of Environment arranged a press conference to voice serious objections to a film produced by the CEGB which maintained that scientific evidence did not justify the excessive costs of cleaning sulfur emissions. The event received little public attention in the

British media but received much attention in Scandinavia.

It was on a visit to Norway in September 1986 that Prime Minister Thatcher announced Britain's intention to reduce emissions. Norway has maintained its information campaign and readily provides materials in London upon request. Some schools in Britain use these materials.

The Norwegian Embassy in London has been a major actor and as recently as October 1987, the Prime Minister complained about acid rain to the Foreign Office in London. (The Independent, London, Oct. 27, 1987).

The Federal Republic of Germany (FRG). The FRG has only recently become a major advocate of stronger pollution control policies. In the 1960's and 70's emphasis on control measures, as in other industrialized countries, focused primarily on damage to human health. Under the SPD/FDP coalition government in 1971, the FRG adopted its first environmental programme. A major piece of legislation is the Federal Emissions Control Act of 1974. During the 1970's concern over the environmental effects of fossil fuels brought about some enthusiasm for the pollution free qualities of nuclear energy, but a vocal and sometimes violent movement against nuclear energy cast doubt on the political feasibility of a large scale shift to nuclear energy.

The emergence of the FRG as a force for more stringent domestic and international controls of SO_2 and NO_x came in 1982. The catalyst for this emergence was the revelation of widespread damage to German forests. Forests cover much of the FRG and hold a special place in German history, culture and life. In addition, forest damage entails significant economic costs. In 1982, a government sponsored study revealed that 8% of forest trees had been damaged from pollution. Annual studies by the Ministry of Food, Agriculture and Forestry have found steady increases in forest damage. By 1983, the number of damaged trees had reached 34%, by 1984 to 50%. During the last two years, however, the rate of damage increase had slowed dramatically and the 1986 Forest Damage Survey finds that the amount of damaged

trees was at 52%.   (1986 Forest Damage Survey, Bonn,
1986).   Table 4.2 illustrates the FRG forest damage
research.   Building on the 1982 findings, several
developements have brought about the FRG's forceful
presence in the international environmental policy
arena.   One of these was to make 'environmentalism'
more politically acceptable and in fact, fashionable.
On the political scene, the rise of the Green Party
and its gains in the Bundestag in 1983 did not escape
the notice of the traditional political parties.
While the Greens were a diverse array of groups,
certainly environmental protection was one of the
policy sectors in which they were acceptable to a
wider following.   The Greens pushed the major parties
(CDU/CSU and SPD) towards stronger environmental
planks in their policy statements and goals.   The
former image of exponents of environmentalism as
being 'far out' faded with the evidence of
progressive damage to Germany's forests.   Thus, there
was a dramatic shift in environmental protection
policy supporting stronger measures at home and
pushing for similar measures in the international
realm.   In 1983, the large combustion plants
ordinance was enacted in the FRG and stricter NO_x
measures were adopted in 1984.   By 1986, the FRG had
a comprehensive and detailed air pollution control
programme.   Despite this record and resolve, the
FRG's record of emission reduction has not been
particularly noteworthy.   The 1986 Forest Damage
Survey does estimate that domestic emissions will be
reduced by 65% by 1993.

In the international field, the forest survey's
findings precipitated a reversal of the FRG's former
obstructionist role in the European Community and led
to the FRG's sponsorship of the 1983 draft directive
calling for significant reductions for all EC
countries.   The FRG has not particularly pointed to
Britain in efforts for more stringent Community
measures, but surely their proposal placed added
pressure on Britain to act.   Clearly, the most
effective forum for this is in the EC because of its
more restrictive and binding powers.   In June 1988, a
compromise version of the original German proposal
was adopted by the EC.

Table 4.2

Forest Damage – Federal Republic of Germany

Damage Stage	1983*	1984	1985	1986
	Percentage of forested area			
1 Slightly Damaged	24.7	32.9	32.7	34.8
2 Moderately Damaged	8.7	15.8	17.0	17.3
3 & 4 Severely Damaged and Dead	1.0	1.5	2.2	1.6
Total with Some Damage	34.4	50.2	51.9	53.7

* The 1983 survey is only comparable to a limited extent with later surveys

(Source: 1986 Forest Damage Survey, FRG)

Concluding remarks - Great Britain

During 1987, British policy seemed to harden, resting on the limited retrofit decision of three major plants. The British Foreign Office position at that time is summarized in the following paragraph.

While scientific agreement existed on the contribution of SO_2 and NO_x emissions to the acidification of freshwater lakes and streams in Southern Scandinavia and Britain, there was no solid evidence that emissions from Britain contribute significantly to damage to Continental forests. Britain has stressed that the relative contribution to forest damage of ozone pollution (a product of NO_x) from vehicle exhausts is not known. (It is generally accepted that ozone contributes to forest damage, and increasing emphasis is being placed on the effects of NO_x on trees). Although Britain is a major emitter of SO_2 it is far from being the worst polluter in Europe, as confirmed by 1983 statistics of the EMEP. In fact, since 1970, there has been a reduction of over 40% in Britain. The government remained committed to a 30% reduction from 1980 levels by the end of the 1990's and the retrofit of two coal fired plants is directed toward that goal. All new coal fired plants will be fitted with control technology. The government considered that the ECE 30% club, while a symbol of international concern, sets an arbitrary standard and ignores Britain's past record. Commenting on the EC's draft directive aimed at overall reductions of up to 60% by 1995, the government suggested that programme could not be justified, but that a longer time frame may be acceptable.

The stated reason for the decision to begin retrofit of some plants was acid rain damage to Scandinavia. Clearly Britain was placed on the defensive in the halls of international organisations, in bilateral relations and before the House of Commons Select Committee. In both multilateral and bilateral contexts she has been severely chastised and criticised. The Select Committee added to this pressure by urging immediate action.

During the first half of 1988, it became clear that the limited retrofit program did little to satisfy critics, and indeed, new sources of criticism appeared. Besides the continued outcry by environmental groups, members of the Royal Family called for action on curbing pollution and acid rain. (The Times, London, Feb. 24 and May 19, 1988). The House of Commons Select Committee was completing a second review of air pollution policy and government action on the recommendations of the 1984 report. The situation reached a climax with a flurry of events which preceded a major government policy initiative. In early June there was press speculation that the Select Committee would again call for immediate action and again recommend that Britain join the 30% Club. A spokesman for the Social Democratic Party (SDP) accused the government of attempting to delay publication of the Select Committee's report until after a forthcoming meeting of the EC environmental ministers to consider the draft directive on sulfur emission reductions. The Select Committee's report, released June 15th, called for immediate action to counter acid rain and other forms of air pollution. The report commended the government's earlier retrofit decision and recommended that the government retrofit three more plants by 1993. The Committee did appear, however, to lower its calls for the drastic 60% reduction by the mid-1990's. On June 17th Lord Cathiness, the British Minister of the Environment, agreed to a compromise EC Directive, committing Britain to a 20% cut of SO_2 emissions by 1993, 40% by 1998 and 60% by the year 2003. While the commitment goes well beyond the former British policy of a 30% reduction by the late 1990's, the target date for the 60% reduction was extended from 1995 to 2003 in the compromise Directive. The agreed Directive also calls for NO_x reductions of 15% and 30% by stages. (The Times, London, June 8, 14, 15, 18, 1988). It was through Britain's efforts along with a few other EC members, that reduction levels and target dates not be uniform and take into account national records and differences. In that sense, the agreement can be considered a victory for Britain.

During the evolution of British policy leading to the agreement to the EC Directive, the most recalcitrant government agency has been the CEGB. The CEGB chairman and board members have been adamant

about the correctness of British policy. The CEGB
became the symbol of British inaction among advocates
of change and has been criticised by such diverse
voices as the Select Committee and the Friends of
the Earth. Once the CEGB was convinced of acid rain
damage to Scandinavia, its influence was significant
and decisive.

The most important domestic influence on government
policy has been the Select Committee. The Committee
provided a means by which the government was forced
to account for its environmental policies,
particularly since 1984. The 1984 report on acid
rain, the government's response, the follow up review
of 1986, and the comprehensive air pollution policy
review completed in 1988, have served to keep the
issue on the agenda in the appropriate circles. The
Committee's persistence, while perhaps not decisive,
forced the government to defend its policy before a
critical Parliamentary body. Further, in visiting
damaged areas in Scandinavia and the FRG and in
seeking input from officials from those areas, the
Committee became another conduit through which
pressure was applied on the government.

Despite the efforts of the Friends of the Earth,
other environmentalists and a small group of
professionals and private groups have played a
relatively minor role in influencing policy. Perhaps
the FOE's greatest impact has come from their
participation and contribution to the proceedings of
the Select Committee and in conducting research
activities. Segments of the academic community and
professional community have made a contribution
through their interchange and dialogue outside the
government structure. These occasions provided a
setting in which official views could be heard and
defended. The addition of the Royal Family to the
critics of Britain's pollution policies is also
significant.

In assessing external influences on Britain's
policy, Sweden and Norway were instrumental in the
retrofit decision. In bilateral relations,
international organisations, professional meetings
and in environmentalist circles, they have pressed
their message. The British decision to retrofit was
accompanied by a recognition of environmental damage

in Norway and Sweden indicating that the Scandinavian pressure was a key factor in the government's action.

The Federal Republic of Germany's contribution to the debate, and her persistent efforts in the EC, have placed Britain on the defensive in Community negotiations. It would appear that German pressures were not instrumental in the original limited retrofit decision. However, the commitment made in June 1988 agreeing to the compromise EC Directive is clearly related to external pressures. It is worth noting that the compromise reflects Community deference to Britain's demands.

In considering the influence of the ECE forum on British policy, Britain has had the United States as an ally in resisting accession to the 30% club. The ECE has provided a forum in which Britain can be criticised but the ECE's influence on British policy in this instance has been minimal.

It seems reasonable to conclude that Britain's policy shift was influenced by both national and international influences. This pressure has existed in some form for over a decade. Until the House of Commons Select Committee's extensive involvement in the debate, the domestic pressure for action was minimal. After the Committee became virtually an ally of Britain's critics, domestic pressure increased and the government had to reconsider their policy and moved towards a policy shift.

50 worst emitting facilities. The bill would also establish a superfund to pay offset costs, to be financed by a one mill (one-tenth of a cent) federal tax per kilowatt/hour of electricity used. By retrofitting the worst polluters with scrubbers, the use of high sulfur coal, more adapted to the existing facilities, could continue, and avoid the serious economic and social impact of fuel switching. The burden of the expense of the control program would be spread across the population. The bill was defeated by a vote of 10-9 at the Sub-committee level and never considered by the full House Energy and Commerce Committee or by the entire House.

The most recent proposals have attempted to avoid some of these obstacles but have been no more successful. In a Senate measure approved in committee in November 1987, all states would be required to achieve a proportion of the total reductions equal to their contribution to total emissions, reaching a total of twelve million tons by 1993. Federal costs would be limited to EPA regulatory costs and a clean coal technology research program designed to meet the commitment to Canada. The bill, S-1894 was reported out of committee. The Senate Committee on Environment and Public Works vote reporting S-1894 out reflects the regional conflict inherent in acid rain legislation. The vote was 14-2. Of those 14 affirmative votes, four were from soft-coal producing states, five were from northeastern states on the receiving end of SO_2 emissions and the other four represented states less affected by acid rain. One of the two voting against reporting out the bill represented Virginia, a state with large soft coal operations and deposits. (Senate Report 100-231, 100th Congress, p. 126).

Recent House of Representatives approaches, which did not receive committee approval, would aim at a ten million ton reduction of SO_2 emissions and four million tons of NO_x emissions by 1997. The bill also provides for financial subsidies to electric utilities to cover a portion of rate increases attributed to meeting reduction requirements and to protect electric utility residential customers from excessive increases due to imposition of SO_2 controls. (HR 2666 and 3054, 1988). In early Autumn, 1988, there was some prospect that a Senate compromise version of a reductions bill be considered by Congress. The compromise, which had some Senate leadership support, would aim for a 10 million ton reduction by the year 2000. The costs of the retrofit would be financed by a federal fee of one-tenth of a cent per kilowatt hour of electrical generation, to be paid by fossil fuel burning facilities. Support for this program which reduces the target for reductions and stretches out the timeframe appears to be based on the notion that a more far reaching bill would be enacted after the US presidential election in November.

Congress has been in a stalemate on the acid rain issue. For one thing, efforts to enact acid rain legislation have been complicated by the pressing need to amend the Clean Air Act or extend the Act's health based standards which expired in 1987. The issue is laden with regional, economic and political ramifications. Several reflections of the stalemate are worth repeating. The Northeastern US region, on which most of the acid rain falls, sees itself as the victim of the emissions originating in the Midwest. The lower midwest, the region producing most of the emissions, fears the economic costs of a control program in the form of higher electricity costs, loss of mining jobs and residual costs. States which are neither a major source nor a major receptor maintain they should not be asked to share the costs of retrofit or other reduction methods. Members of Congress usually reflect these orientations. Powerful interest groups, with both regional and industry bases, have been heavily involved in the debate. The financial support of these groups for legislators representing the states in which they operate and for legislators holding key legislative posts, is an important ingredient in the legislative arena. The positions of several of these interest groups are summarized in the following paragraphs.

Interest group politics

Of the various interest groups involved in the debate, most have expressed a vital interest and use every opportunity to state their case. The major means of expressing their views is through direct legislative lobbying, Congressional hearings, publicity campaigns, research, and participation in public meetings.

The Business Roundtable, an organisation of the chief executive officers of large corporations, has estimated that the principle Senate bill would cost the economy approximately $30 billion dollars and around one half million jobs. The group contends Congressional measures should be directed specifically to areas that do not meet clean air standards rather than the proposed blanket approach.

The electric power generating industry, which operates the facilities producing the SO_2 emissions, has been a persistent opponent to control programs. The industry lobbying association is the Edison Electric Institute. Through the Institute and spokesmen for individual companies, the industry has expressed its views. The industry has opposed both the retrofitting of all coal fired plans or massive switching to low sulfur coal on the grounds of high costs, attendant electricity rate increases and loss of jobs. Over the years it has contended that the costs of the various programs have been underestimated by government agencies and environmentalists and that gaps exist in the body of scientific knowledge on acid rain.

Because of the oxides of nitrogen NO_x in acid rain, the motor vehicle industry has an interest in the form and substance of proposed legislation relating to the Clean Air Act. The 30% NO_x component of acid rain has placed the industry on the defensive. Some spokesmen have been critical of the utilities industry for opposing emission control programs, perhaps on the basis that less NO_x from stationary sources reduces pressure for more stringent controls on mobile sources. The transportation industry is still by far the largest source of NO_x emissions. However, with the most recent legislative proposals considering both SO_2 and NO_x reductions in the form of Clean Air Act amendment, the industry stands firmly against more costly automobile emission control standards.

One of the more interesting aspects of the acid rain debate in the US is the position of the coal industry. The issue has caused intra industry disagreements between the high and low sulfur companies and regions. Both usually express concern over the validity of the science and the high costs of implementation of a comprehensive control program. The high sulfur coal industry is concentrated in the Appalachian region extending from Ohio and Pennsylvania through West Virginia and the Ohio Valley. There are also significant high sulfur deposits in the Midwestern states of Illinois and Indiana. This is also the region, primarily in the Ohio Valley, in which many of the worst polluting plants are located. Of particular concern to the soft high sulfur operators is the fear that fuel switching will be stipulated or encouraged by a proposed program. Fuel switching would reduce emissions by requiring coal fired plants to use low sulfur coal. The low sulfur industry is often identified with the Western United States and indeed, a huge amount of low sulfur coal is mined in Colorado, Montana, New Mexico, North Dakota, Utah and Wyoming. However, there are low sulfur deposits in Alabama, Kentucky, Tennessee, Virginia and West Virginia. Fuel switching would obviously enhance the low sulfur industry and those representing that industry take a position that the fuel switching option would entail the least costs. Thus, an intra industry dispute among coal producers adds to the complexity of the acid rain debate.

The United Mine Workers (UMW) union represents 70% of all coal miners in the US. The union has a major stake in any emission control program. Some members would be affected by either a mandatory retrofit program or a fuel switching requirement. The issue with the UMW is jobs and they view any proposal in terms of job losses. Under a fuel switching option the UMW has estimated a loss of from 40-60,000 jobs and under a retrofit approach, the union fears that utility companies would close some old plants rather than undertake the expense of installation costs. The UMW has been opposed to all proposed acid rain legislation.

Most of the above interests have stressed the 25% emission reductions achieved under the Clean Air Act and point to such trends as advances in clean coal technology. Retirement of old coal fired facilities, new automobile fleets, etc., as factors contributing to even further reductions in the future.

Facing this array of powerful group of opposing interests to a mandated reductions program is a

network of environmentalist and conservation groups.
Among the more noteworthy groups supporting acid raid
legislation is the Natural Resources Defense Council,
the Environmental Defense Fund, the Sierra Club, the
Clean Air Coalition and the National Wildlife
Federation.   Because of acid rain damage to
materials, drinking water quality, marine life,
forests, soils and human health, it is argued that
the benefits of control programs outweigh the costs.
From the environmentalist perspective, costs, in
terms of dollars and jobs, have consistently been
overstated by interest groups as a scare tactic to
block legislation. The environmental groups have a
high visibility in Washington and are given full
access to have their message heard but have been
overshadowed by regional and industry interests.
Some of the groups have formed alliances with
counterparts in Canada to push for a US control
program and urged Prime Minister Mulroney to reject
the special envoy report and its recommendations.

The divisiveness created by the issue has also been
manifested by conflict between governors of various
states and regions. Northeastern states have sued
midwestern states, groups of states have sued the EPA
and the New England states have appealed to the
President for action and have met with Canadian
legislators and premiers to discuss acid rain.

Finally, the role of public opinion must be
addressed. Recent polls have shown that over two-
thirds of Americans are aware of acid rain and many
consider it a serious problem. However, this has not
been reflected in pressure for government action.
Acid rain is given more importance in the
Northeastern US., the area most affected by acid rain
damage. In the Summer of 1988, environmental issues
were beginning to receive more public attention.
Concern over the ozone layer, the Greenhouse effect,
and ocean and beach pollution were raising public
awareness and becoming important presidential
election issues.

In any case, it is clear that policy initiatives
are subject to a maze of influences on the domestic
level in the US.

Acid rain politics - external influences

Canada and acid rain policy in the United States

For reasons already enumerated, Canada has been a major actor in lobbying for acid rain legislation in the US and is the principle external influence on US policy.

Canada and the US have a long history of cooperation in transboundary problems. In the environmental realm this cooperation dates back to the Border Waters Treaty of 1909. Since that time, hundreds of disputes dealing with rivers, small lakes or the Great Lakes have been resolved. The major agreement resulting from that cooperation is the Great Lakes Water Quality Agreement which was signed in 1972 and updated in 1978. Much progress has been made in improving the water quality of the Great Lakes and although much remains to be done, an impressive record of international cooperation is beyond dispute. The organisational instrument for these settlements and negotiations is the International Joint Commission which at request of the governments, can work to solve specific problems and disputes. Although a record of unparalled border and environmental cooperation has been amassed, transboundary air pollution is not covered by these arrangements. In recent years, relations between the two countries have been more troubled as a number of issues involving trade, energy investment policy, and fishing rights have emerged. Acid rain evolved as a major irritant to US-Canadian relations in this context. The major developments relating to Canada's campaign for an American emissions reduction program are included in Chapter 3. Our focus here is to address Canada's role in the internal policy debate in the United States. The Canadian Embassy in Washington has a well staffed Environment Section. The office monitors closely US legislative proceedings and EPA activities. Canada has openly participated in the policy debate. Since the late 70's considerable effort has been made to influence American public opinion and government policy. At ambassadorial level, diplomatic contacts with the Department of State, in the form of meetings and diplomatic notes provide the normal ready

communications channels. Canadian ambassadors have
also filed letters with Congressional committees
considering legislation. Embassy relations with the
environmental lobby are also maintained. In order to
reach professional, academic and other institutional
publics, the Embassy arranges for presentations by
Canadian representatives at scientific and
professional gatherings. The embassy is also
receptive to providing public information upon
request. In 1987, Canada embarked on a significant
campaign to influence domestic public opinion in the
US. This campaign includes billboards, radio spots
and has been reported to cost over $600,000 dollars.
As the frustration level in Canada rises, the active
involvement in the internal debate in the US has
intensified, and has provided US proponents of a
control program with a powerful ally.

*International organisations and acid rain policy in
the United States*

The US has also been subject to criticism and
pressure in IGOs. The US is a signator to the ECE
Convention on LRTAP but has not agreed to commit to
the 30% reduction espoused by many ECE members. In
addition, the US has refused to agree to a proposed
freeze of NO_x emissions currently under negotiation
by the ECE, citing that the 1980 base level date does
not take into account the significant reductions in
US emissions beginning in 1970. In late Summer 1988,
the Reagan Administration hinted that it might agree
to the NO_x freeze. Environmentalists regarded this
as a needed step but recognize that such an action
would not require any immediate action as emissions
are projected to decrease well into the 1990's.

Concluding comments - United States

In the autumn of 1988, the prospects for passage of
acid rain legislation are mixed but improved.
Besides the regional and economic interests inherent
in the situation and the lack of support from some
key Congressional and Administration leaders, other
factors work against passage. The coincidence of the
expiration of the non-attainment standards of the
Clean Air Act has competed with the urgency of acid
rain legislation, and because some legislative

proposals have included both in a single piece of legislation the potent forces working against more stringent automobile emissions controls can be added to the array of forces against SO_2 reductions. Another complicating factor is timing. The pressures of the 1988 presidential elections, party conventions, election of 435 members of the House of Representatives and one third of the Senate, drastically compresses the time available on the Congressional calendar.

Several short term futures are possible. One option is that the current non attainment standards could be extended and no other action on the Clean Air Act would be necessary. Another possibility is that supporters of acid rain legislation would attempt to have it attached to another piece of legislation as an amendment. A new ingredient was introduced into the already complex situation when the Governors of two deeply involved states proposed a compromise solution. The plan, proposed by the Governors of Ohio and New York, calls for a ten million ton reduction but extended the deadline to the year 2000. The bill had broader cost sharing provisions, but contained a controversial provision to use a surcharge on imported oil to help fund the programme. A significant point about the compromise bill was that it was sponsored by the leader of a major source state, Ohio, and the leader of a major receptor state, New York. It is instructive to note that the target figure for reductions, ten million tons, and the deadline date of the year 2000, are similar to those supported by Senator Byrd in his compromise proposal. Still another outcome would be the abandonment of acid rain for this session of Congress, with proponents for control hoping for a better presidential climate for passage after the 1988 election. Both major candidates, to a varying degree, have called for improvement of the environment. The rising awareness of public opinion on environmental issues could also contribute to pressures for a control programme. This state of affairs may work to have past opponents (Senator Byrd?) to controls to consider legislation before the election on the assumption that a compromise version now would result in a more modest reduction target and lower costs that a new initiative under a new president. On the other hand, proponents for far reaching measures may want to wait until after the

election for the same reason.   Every indication
points to this outcome,

6 Comparative perspectives

Introduction

In summer 1989, the acid rain policies of all three
countries have evolved to an important stage.   In
Great Britain, a significant policy decision has been
made and Britain's commitment to the compromise EC
directive entails specific emission cuts and a target
date.   The requirements of the EC directive fall
short of those sought by Britain's critics and in
that sense, Britain prevailed in the EC perspectives.
In a significant development Prime Minister Thatcher
emerged as a leading proponent of international
consultation on the depletion of the ozone layer and
the greenhouse effect.

  In Canada, the federal-provincial agreement is
being implemented with major emitters meeting early
goals.   Provincial regulatory mechanisms are in place
and targets have been established.   The achievement
of emission cuts envisaged later in the time frame
may be more difficult.   Canada's environmental
relations with the United States have been improved
with the Bush Administration's commitment to propose
reductions legislation and a pact with Canada.

75

In the United States, in the aftermath of President Bush's election and a more sympathetic Senate leadership, the President was expected to introduce sweeping revisions of the Clean Air Act to include provisions for reduction in SO_2 emissions, urban smog and toxic pollutants.

Comparative perspectives

Having traced the evolution of acid rain policy in the three political systems our next task is to examine the policies from a comparative perspective in several areas. These comparative considerations include the impact of structural and institutional arrangements of the systems on acid rain policy, the role of interest and pressure groups, the impact of domestic regionalism, and the effect of external influences on the policy.

The task is made more difficult by the broad reach of environmental policy. Environmental policy cuts across several policy sector lines. To further complicate matters, the conception of the environment differs in each of the three countires, which could affect the relative priorities, time and resources assigned to air pollution control. The environment is broadly defined in Britain, ranging from such diverse policy sectors as housing and transport to control of pollution. In Canada, the Minister of Environment is responsible for weather forecasting, conservation, wildlife, parks, fisheries and historic sites. In the United States, there is a narrower conception of the environment and the Environmental Protection Agency's functions are limited to control and abatement of pollution in the areas of air, water, solid wastes, radiation and toxic substances. What is clear in all three cases is that environmental policy cuts across and touches upon several other policy sector lines, adding to the complexity of policy formulation and implementation. Adding to this already complex situation is the inevitable movement of air pollution across governmental jurisdictions within national borders and across national borders.

Political systems - structural and institutional arrangements

The task for comparing public policies in different political systems is confronted with the question of the relative importance of the structure of the political systems and their differences and the particular policy area or sector being studied. As Freeman states it, 'Will countries with dissimilar political systems produce significantly different responses to similar political issues or will the imperatives of particular types of public policy compel more or less similar responses, whatever the shape of the political structure involved?' (Freeman, 1984). Clearly our study has shown that the structure and the apparatus has played a major role in acid rain policy in the three settings.

In Canada, the fusion of executive and legislative power at federal and provincial levels, the jurisdictional overlap, the tradition of extensive administrative regulation, and the government control of key industries has eased policy decisions. In Great Britain, the fusion of executive and legislative power, the absence of lower governmental units, government control of key industries and the broad delegation of power and responsibility has facilitated government action. In the United States, the separation of powers, lack of political party discipline, private ownership of key industries, the practice of prescriptive legislation, the adversarial posture of interest groups and the large number of governmental units have all contributed to a policy stalemate. Any decision to reduce SO_2 emissions is inevitably affected by such structural attributes.

In Great Britain, a decision to reduce SO_2 emissions required no new legislation or Parliamentary action. Such an action required only a decision by the government to direct the CEGB, the government appointed board which operates the major power generating plants, to develop plans for the retrofit. The legislative authority for the CEGB's action reflects the broad, general legislation which facilitates action in the British system. The Chairman of the CEGB, in announcing the decision to retrofit some plants, quoted from the Parliamentary

77

statute, "In considering any proposals relating to the functions of the Generating Board, the Board shall take into account any effect which the proposals would have on the natural beauty of the countryside or on any.... flora, fauna, features, buildings or object. (Acid Rain, The Political Challenge, 1986). A policy decision made at the highest level can be implemented by a government agency through administrative regulation.

In Canada, such a decision is more complicated. Although at federal level, the parliamentary system can ensure adoption of a policy, because of the jurisdictional overlap and shared jurisdiction in environmental affairs, the policy process involves extensive consultation and cooperation with provinces. Voluntary agreements establishing broad goals are made between the two governments. At both levels there is generally no need for new legislation. At provincial level governments can establish more prescriptive targets through the issuance of administrative regulations.

The US system is replete with obstacles and a decision to reduce emissions is very complex. Even if the President and a majority of both houses of Congress are of the same political party, high levels of consensus on an issue is rare. The separation of powers complicates decision making. The mix of regional interests represented in Congress and the array of economic interests opposing a bill have blocked all efforts for the reduction of emissions. Another factor is the past record of the individual states in implementing environmental measures and the Environmental Protection Agency's record in enforcing the laws. This record works toward Congressional legislative proposals that are more prescriptive, requiring specific numbers and a specific deadline. The conflictual and confrontational atmosphere inherent in the system has been well demonstrated in the acid rain issue.

In Britain and Canada, once executive authorities made a decision to reduce emissions, the structure eased the process. In the US, even with executive support for emission reductions, it is at least questionable whether Congress would have responded.

The differences in the role, use and power of committees in the legislative process provide another significant comparative dimension for this study. In Canada, the House of Commons Standing Committee on Fisheries and Forestry, which has been involved in the acid rain issue, is a "specialist" standing committee. Such committees have the power to consider legislation, review estimates and investigate particular problems or future policy alternatives. The role of "considering legislation" provides the opportunity for detailed scrutiny of each bill. In this process, after the Second Reading in the House of Commons of a Government sponsored bill, "amendments of principle or major policy differences introduced by the opposition have little hope of adoption in committee." (Jackson, Jackson and Baxter-Moore, 1986). The committees do not write legislation, but do fine-tune it in reacting to Prime Minister and cabinet initiatives. On the issue of acid rain, the Standing Committee on Fisheries and Forestry, through the use of the subcommittee on Acid Rain, have exerted influence in its role of "investigating particular problems. The subcommittee was emphatic in stressing the need for unilateral Canadian action.

In Britain, Parliamentary Standing Committee action also occurs after the second reading. The House of Commons has approved the bill in principle and committee action is meant to "give the bill the detailed consideration for which the Commons did not have time and to make these changes that the second reading debate indicated that the Commons desired." (Dragnich and Rasmussen, 1986). Realistically, the committee cannot substantially change the bill. As in the case of Canadian Government bills with Cabinet sanction dominate the committee process. Since 1979, the Parliament has had select committees empowered to examine the administration and policy of the main government departments. As our discussion of Great Britain's acid rain politics has revealed, the House of Commons Select Committee has played an important role in pressing for action in reducing emissions in Britain.

In the United States, the standing committees serve as "little legislatives", and the Committee action comes before consideration by the entire legislative body. Committees hold hearings, gather information and committee action reporting the bill out of committee precedes floor action. Thus, if there is substantial opposition to the proposed bill in committee, the bill is essentially dead. On the other hand, committee approval of a bill generally means approval albeit in a sometimes modified form by the entire house. In the US case, in the House of Representatives, by late 1988, no acid rain legislation proposal was reported through the House Energy and Commerce Committee. In the Senate bills have been reported out, by The Environment and Public Works Committee, but Senate leadership opposing further acid rain control refused to place the bill on the legislative calendar. The US committee system can clearly be crucial in a bill's survival. In spite of the relative power of legislative committees in the three systems, being the most decisive in the US, committee actions have played a significant role in each case.

Role of interest (pressure) groups

In Britain and Canada, interest groups have played only a marginal role in acid rain politics. In both cases major sources of SO_2 are government affiliated, easing disputes over government reduction decisions and eliminating one of the major actors in the acid rain debate. In Britain nationalization of other key industries also contributes to this state of affairs. Because of the consultative and advisory aspects of interest group activities in the two countries, the adversarial posture between government and business is largely removed. The dominant business group in Britain, the Confederation of British Industries, has an intimate relationship with the Conservative government and in any government would be consulted. Canada's largest polluter, INCO, has expressed support for emission reductions and has been given economic incentives to do so. Interest group opposition in Canada has been in the form that the government is not doing enough, rather than doing nothing. The groups have been generally supportive of the general direction of policy, particularly since the 1984 major policy development.

In Britain, where environmentalist groups have
carried out publicity campaigns and demonstrations
and been given access to the House of Commons Select
Committee's deliberations, the influence on
government policy has been minimal. Their influence
has been vastly overshadowed by external pressures.

In the US, interest groups have had a major role in
the impasse over acid rain policy. A powerful group
of economic interests have opposed a control
programme. For one thing, the major source of SO_2
emissions, the electric utility industry, is a key
opponent. The coal industry, motor vehicle industry,
and trade unions have been major opponents. The
groups contribute heavily to Congressional elections
through political action committees. The
environmentalist lobby, through a network of
important and well financed groups, has played a role
and formed pockets of Congressional support, but are
not nearly as strong as the network of opposing
groups.

Several transnational non governmental groups have
participated in cooperative international networks
supporting acid rain controls. In this study, the
European Environment Bureau (EEB), the Swedish-
Norwegian NGO Secretariat on Acid Rain and the
Friends of the Earth (FOE) have been mentioned. Such
organisations have been an important force only in
the case of Great Britain.

Role of domestic regionalism

Regional strains and conflicts are present in
virtually every political system and most have roots
in cultural, social or economic reasons. In Britain,
this is evident in the Irish question in Northern
Ireland and to a much lesser extent in nationalist
groups in Scotland and Wales. These of course, are
primarily of a political dimension. There is also a
north -- south distinction in which the north, the
major geographic base of the Labour Party, views
itself as being a victim of the more prosperous and
Conservative Party dominated south. In terms of acid
rain politics, however, the regional aspect has not
been a pronounced component of the debate. The
economic debate has centered around the overall cost

of retrofit and attendant electricity rate increases rather than the economic costs to particular regions.

Canada has at least two major regional issues. One, of course has been the Quebec question and its separatist tendencies which has been largely resolved. Another regional conflict is the east -- west issue revolving around natural resources policy of the western provinces. In acid rain policy, regional distinctions exist but these have not resulted in any significant conflict. Acid rain, while gaining more recognition in the west, has not been a major environmental problem there. The eastern provinces, the source of most emissions, have accords which demonstrate general consensus on the issue. Further, in the huge Ontario and Quebec Provinces, where both source and receptor are located in the same political jurisdiction, regional conflict is mitigated.

The intense regional conflict in the US is reflected by the source -- receptor relationship of the midwest and northeast. In an economic sense, the loss of mining jobs in the midwest and Appalachia and by the cost bearing of consumers in certain regions of a control program is the source of regional conflict. This regional conflict is further reflected in Congressional policy positions and voting patterns.

Role of external forces

In each country acid rain policy has been influenced by other governments and international organisations to some extent. This is not surprising because of the transboundary nature of acid rain.

The influence of external pressures is most obvious in Britain. Britain has been criticised by the Scandinavians bilaterally and within the ECE since the early 1980's. The major reason given for the CEGB's decision to retrofit three plants was acid rain damage in Scandinavia. With the added impetus of the FRG within the EC, Britain has been subjected to a constant stream of criticism. Besides the normal diplomatic channels and EC deliberations, the critics have been invited to express their sentiments in the Select Committee's sessions and in private and professional meetings. Clearly, Britain was not stampeded into a decision to reduce emissions and accession to the compromise directive, but the weight of these external influences was significant. Britain's future environmental policies are likely to be increasingly affected by the EC, especially as national economy's move toward full integration in 1992.

Canada's stated policy for the need to reduce SO_2 emissions clearly had an American dimension, for even Canada reduced her emission drastically, the contribution of 50% of Canada's total would remain. Essentially, Canada's ability to severely cut total acid deposits on her territory is limited. Pressing for US reductions has been a major policy objective. The US has played another role in Canada's policy. Official US and private criticism of Canada's failure to take concrete actions at home while mounting pressure on the US may have played an important role in Canada's policy moves since 1984. In the international arena, Canada has accumulated important allies in her effort to pressure others for control programmes. Canada has been a leader in international efforts to curb acid rain and has hosted several significant international meetings.

In the early days of the Bush Administration it is anticipated that US legislation reducing SO_2 emissions is imminent. This prospect comes after more than a decade of pressure from Canada. It is clear that Canada has helped raise the consciousness and visibility of the issue, particularly in the Northeastern US and in the US Congress. In addition, Canadian leaders have pressed her case at the highest levels. Congress, environmental professionals and the scientific community have also been made aware of Canada's position. While no new legislation has been passed, President Reagan's appointment of a Special Envoy, his agreement to the $5 billion demonstration project, and his willingness to consider a treaty, probably would not have occurred without the insistence of Prime Minister Mulroney. In that sense, US policy has been influenced by Canadian involvement in the acid rain debate. In international organisations, particularly the ECE, the US is viewed as lagging behind for not joining the 30% club.

In each of the three countries, the movement of acid rain across national borders has led to external pressures attempting to influence national policies.

The three political systems studied are major examples of the parliamentary and presidential forms utilised in Western industrialised democracies. While the systems have in common the commitment to representative government, there are distinct differences in their structural and institutional arrangements and their policy making processes. In coping with the environmental threat posed by acid rain, structure has remained a central element in determining policy outcomes, but the transboundary nature of acid rain has subjected the structure and process of each country to extraordinary external influences and pressures. In this instance, the nature of the policy issue as well as structure, has been significant.

Bibliography

Books and Articles

Burton, T., (1972), <u>Natural Resources Policy in Canada</u>, Toronto, McClelland and Stewart Publishing Co.

Brackley, P., (1987), <u>Acid Deposition and Vehicle Emissions: European Environmental Pressures on Britain</u>, Policy Studies Institute and Royal Institute of International Affairs, Published by Gower Publishing Company, Ltd., Aldershat, England.

Caldwell, L.K., (1970), <u>Environment: A Challenge to Modern Society</u>, Garden City, N.Y., Natural History Press.

Carroll, John., (1983), Acid Rain Diplomacy: The Need for a Bilateral Resolution, <u>Alternatives</u>, v. 11, no. 2, Winter 1983.

Drewry, G., (1985), <u>The New Select Committees</u>, Oxford, Darendon Press.

Freeman, G., (1984), Do Policy Issues Determine Politics?, paper presented to the 1984 Annual Meeting of the American Political Science Association.

Gibbons, R., (1982), Regionalism in Territorial Politics, Canada and the US, Toronto, Betterworth.

Gibson, D., (1983), Constitutional Arrangements for Environmental Protection, Enhancements Under a New Constitution, in Canada and the New Constitution - the Unfinished Agenda, Vol. I, S.M. Beck and I. Bernier, (Ed), Montreal, Institute for Research on Public Policy.

Haigh, N., (1985), Developments in Europe in Environmental Policies Particularly For Air and Noise, presented to the 92nd Environmental Health Congress, The Institution of Environmental Health Officers.

_____.(1986), Desolved Responsibility and Centralization: Effects of EEC Environment Policy, Public Administration, Vol. 64, Summer 1986, Royal Institute of Public Administration.

_____.(1984), EEC Environmental Policy and Britain, London, Environmental Data Services, Ltd.

Jackson, R.J., Jackson, D., and Baxter-Moore, N., (1986), Politics In Canada, Scarborough, Ont., Prentice-Hall Canada, Inc.

Kimber, R. and Richardson, J. J., (1974) Campaigning for the Environment, London and Boston, Rutledge and Kegan Paul.

Lowe, P., and Goyder, J., (1983), Environmental Groups in Politics, London, Allen and Unwin.

Manzer, R., (1985), Public Policies and Political Development in Canada, Toronto, University of Toronto Press.

Milbrath, L., (1975), The Politics of Environmental Policy, Beverly Hills, California, SAGE Publications.

O'Riordan, T., (1981), Environmentalism, London, Pion Limited.

Pearce, F., (1987), Acid Rain, New Scientist, Nov. 1987.

Trebilcock, M.J., (Ed), (1986), Federalism and Economic Union in Canada, Toronto, Ontario Economic Council Research Studies, University of Toronto Press.

Vogel, D., (1986), National Styles of Regulation-- Environmental Policy in Great Britain and the

<u>United States</u>, Ithica, N.Y., Cornell University
Press.
Wilcher, M.E., (1986), The Acid Rain Debate in North
America - "Where You Stand Depends on Where You
Sit", <u>The Environmentalist</u>, Vol. 6, No. 4, 1986.

National Government Documents

Canada

Acid Rain; Canada-United States, <u>Canadian Embassy</u>,
Washington, undated.
Acid Rain - A National Sensitivity Assessment,
Environmental Fact Sheet 88-1, <u>Inland Waters</u>
<u>andLands Directorate, Environment Canada</u>, Ottawa,
1988.
Acid Rain, Canada-United States, The NAPAP Report,
<u>Canadian Embassy</u>, Washington, undated.
Address, The Right Honourable Brian Mulroney, Prime
Minister of Canada, Joint Session of Congress,
Wash., D.C., <u>Office of Prime Minister</u>, Ottawa,
1988.
Atmospheric Sciences and Analysis, <u>Canada - U.S.Work</u>
<u>Group II</u>, Established under Memorandum of Intent,
1980.
Canadian Environmental Protection Act(CEPA),<u>Published</u>
<u>under the authority of the Minister ofEnvironment,</u>
<u>Minister of Supply and Services</u> Canada, 1988.
Countdown Acid Rain, Ontario's Acid Gas Control
Program for 1986-1994, <u>Ministry of Environment</u>,
Toronto, 1987.
Countdown Acid Rain, Summary and Analysis of the
First Progress Reports by Ontario's Four Major
Sources of Sulphur Dioxide, <u>Ministry of the</u>
<u>Environment</u>, Toronto, 1986.
Countdown Acid Rain, Summary and Analysis of the
Third Progress Report by Ontario's Four Major
Sources of Sulphur Dioxide, <u>Ministry of the</u>
<u>Environment</u>, Toronto, 1987
Countdown Acid Rain, Summary and Analysis of the
Fourth Progress Reports by Ontario's Four Major
Sources of Sulfur Dioxide, <u>Ministry of the</u>
<u>Environment</u>, Toronto, 1988.
_____ Environmental Protection Act, <u>Government of</u>
<u>Ontario</u>, Toronto, 1987.

<u>Joint Report of the Special Envoys on Acid Rain</u>,
    Ottawa and Washington, 1986.
<u>Memorandum of Intent Between the Government of</u>Canada
    <u>and the Government of the United States of America</u>
    <u>Concerning Transboundary Air Pollution</u>, Ottawa
    and Washington, 1980.
Second Report of the U.S.-Canada Research
    Consultation Group on the Long-Range Transport of
    Air Pollutants, <u>Canadian Embassy, Public Affairs</u>
    <u>Division</u>, Washington, 1980.
Still Waters - The Chilling Reality of Acid Rain, A
    Report by the Sub-Committee on Acid Rain, <u>House of</u>
    <u>Commons, Canada</u>, Ministry of Supply and Services
    Canada, 1981.
Stopping Acid Rain, <u>Environment Canada</u>, Ottawa,
    Undated.
The Long Range Transport of Air Pollutants and Acidic
    Precipitation - A Bibliography, <u>Ministry of the</u>
    <u>Environment, Atmospheric Environment Service</u>,
    Downsview, Ont., 1980.
Time Lost - A Demand for Action on Acid Rain, A
    Report by the Sub-Committee on Acid Rain, <u>House of</u>
    <u>Commons, Canada</u>, Ottawa, 1984-85.

Federal Republic of Germany (FRG)

Forest Damage Through Air Pollution, AID 172-1985,
    <u>Food, Agriculture and Forestry (AID)</u>, Bonn, 1985.
1986 Forest Damage Survey, <u>Federal Ministry of Food,</u>
    <u>Agriculture and Forestry</u>, Bonn, 1986.

Great Britain

Acid Deposition in The United Kingdon, <u>Warren Spring</u>
    <u>Laboratory</u>, England.
Acid Rain, Background Brief, <u>Foreign and</u>
    <u>Commonwealth Office</u>, London, 1987.
Acid Rain, <u>National Coal Board Operational Research</u>
    <u>Execution</u>, London, 1985.
Acid Rain, <u>House of Commons Environment Committee,</u>
    <u>Fourth Report, Session 1983-84</u>, HC 446-1, London,
    HMSO, 1984.
Acid Rain, <u>The Government's Reply to the Fourth</u>
    <u>Report from the Environment Committee, Session</u>
    <u>1983-84, HC 446-1,</u> London, HMSO, 1984.

Acid Lakes in Scandinavia - The Evolution of
    Understanding, Dr. P. F. Chester, TPRD,Reports
    Group, Central Electricity Research Laboratories,
    1986.
Air Pollution and You, Department of the Environment,
    London, undated.
Air Pollution Control in Great Britain - Review and
    Proposals, Department of the Environment, London,
    1987.
Clean Air Legislation in the UK, Department of the
    Environment, London, undated.
Environmental Protection, Department of the
    Environment, HMSO, London, 1984.
Follow-Up to the Environment Committee on Acid Rain,
    House of Commons, Session 1985-1986, HMSO, London,
    1985.
Power News, Staff Newspaper for the CEGB, CEGB,
    Special Issue, London, 1987.
Striking a Balance, John Baker, CEGB, Department of
    Information and Public Affairs, London, 1986.

Norway

Acid Rain: International Perspective, Royal
    Norwegian Ministry of Foreign Affairs, Doc 054182,
    Eng, Oslo, 1982.
Protection of the Environment in Norway, Royal
    Norwegian Ministry of Foreign Affairs, UDA 276/82
    Eng, Oslo, 1982.
The Acid Rain Problem - An Overview, Ministry of
    Environment, Oslo, 1986.

Sweden

Acidification - A Boundless Threat To Our
    Environment, Swedish Ministry of Agriculture,
    Distributed by National Swedish Environmental
    Protection Board, Solna, 1983.
Acidification and Air Pollution, National Swedish
    Environmental Protection Board, Solna, 1987.
Air Pollution and Acidification, National Swedish
    Environmental Protection Board, Solna, 1986.
Air Pollution and Forest Damage, National Board of
    Forestry, Sweden, 1986.

United States

Acid Rain and Transported Air Pollutants-Implications for Public Policy, US Congress, Office of Technology Assessment, OTA-O-204, Washington, 1984.

Acid Rain - A Survey of Data and Current Analyses, Report for Subcommittee on Health and Environment of the U.S. House of Representatives Committee on Energy and Commerce, 98th Congress, 2d Session, Congressional Research Service, Committee Print 98-x, U.S.G.P.O., 1984.

Canada-U.S. Work-Group II - Atmospheric Sciences and Analysis. Established Under Memorandum of Intent, U.S.-Canada, 1980.

Congressional Information Service Index, U.S.G.P.O., Washington., 1975-1988.

HR 2666, To Amend the Clean Air Act to Reduce Acid Deposition, and for Other Purposes, 100th Congress, 1st Session, U.S.G.P.O., Washington, 1987.

HR 2666 and HR 3054, Committee Print, Acid Deposition Control Act of 1987, J. 81-750-0-1, U.S.G.P.O Wasghington, 1988.

HR 3400 and HR 5041, Clean Air Act Amendments, Serial 98-125, 98th Congress, 2d Session, U.S.G.P.O., Washington, 1984.

HR 4567, Acid Deposition Control Act of 1986, Serial 99-86, U.S.G.P.O., Washington, 1986.

Joint Report of the Special Envoys on Acid Rain, Ottawa and Washington, 1986.

Memorandum of Intent Between the Government of the United States and the Government of Canada Concerning Transboundary Air Pollution, Ottawa and Washington, 1980.

S.768, Clean Air Act Amendments, Senate Report 98-426, 98th Congress, 2d Session, U.S.G.P.O., Washington, 1984.

S.1894, Clean Air Standards Attainment Act of 1987, Senate Report 100-231, 100th Congress, 1st Session, U.S.G.P.O., Washington, 1987.

Convention of the Long Range Transport of Air Pollutants (LRTAP), Economic Commission of Europe, Geneva, 1979.

Draft Directive, European Community, COM (83) 704, Brussels, 1983

Document EN/111/N/1, European Parliament Directorate General for Research, 1987.

OECD Environmental Data, Compendium, OECD , Paris, 1985.

Program on the Long Range Transport of Air Pollutants – Measurements and Findings, OECD, Paris, 1977.

Protocal to 1979 Convention on the Long Range Transport of Air Pollutants, Economic Commission of Europe, Geneva, 1985.

The European Community and the Environment, European Community, European Documentation, Periodical 3 1987.

Non Governmental Organisations

Acid News, The Swedish NGO Secretariat on Acid Rain and The Stop Acid Rain Campaign, Norway, Gatebary and Oslo, 1982–1988.

Acid Rain Campaign, Friends of the Earth, London, 1985–86.

Acid Rain – The Political Challenge, Proceedings, Joint IEEP/NSCA Conference, Sponsored by the Commission of the European Communities, 1986.

Acid Rain Options, Report on the APCA International Seminar Series, Air Pollution Control Association, Pittsburgh, 1985.

Acid Rain – Research Note, The Labour Party Research Department, London, 1985.

Air Pollution and Environmental Damage, Colloquim, European Environmental Bureau, Brussels, 1985.

An Eye to the Future, Confederation of British Industry, London, C 2887, 1987.

British Industry and the Environment: CBI Statement, Confederation of British Industry, C 3980, 1980.

Clean Air Policy in Europe: A Survey of 17 Countries, International Institute for Environment and Society, IIUG, 86-9, Berlin, 1986.

Is There Scientific Consensus on Acid Rain?, Ad Hoc Committee on Acid Rain: Science and Policy, Millbrook, N.Y., 1985.

Stop Acid Rain, The Stop Acid Rain Campaign, Norway, Oslo, 1986.

The Acid Rain Contraversy, Earth Resources Research, London, Undated.

The Acid Rain Pack, Friends of the Earth, London, 1987.

The Effect of Acid Rain, Canadian Coalition on Acid Rain, Toronto, 1987.

The Environment, 1986 N.E.C. Statement to Labour Party Conference, 1986.

The Limits to Natures Tolerance, NGO Conference on Acid Rain, The Swedish NGO Secretariat on Acid Rain and The Nordic Nature Conservation Societies, Gatebary, 1986.

This Green and Pleasant Land, The Labour Party, London, 1987.

Newspapers

The Daily Telegraph, London
The Independent, London
The New York Times
The Times, London
The Toronto Globe and Mail
The Toronto Star
The Washington Post

Visits

Canada
Canadian Coalition on Acid Rain, Toronto
Environment Canada, Ottawa
Ministry of Environment, Ontario, Toronto

Great Britain
CEGB Public Affairs, London
European Parliament Office, London
Friends of the Earth, London
Institute for European Environment, London
Ministry of Environment Public Affairs, London
Royal Norwegian Embassy, London
Swedish Embassy, London

United States
Canadian Embassy, Washington
House Committee - Energy and Commerce, Washington
Senate Committee - Environment and Public Works,
Washington

Index